# ABM

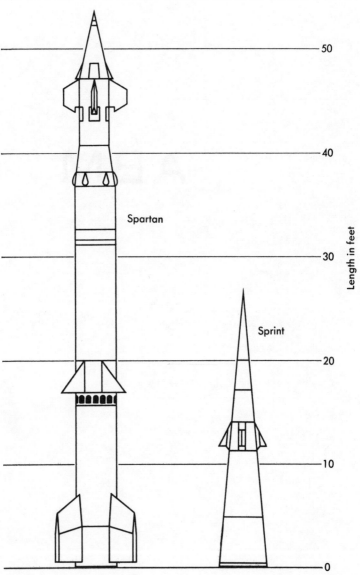

# U.S. DEFENSIVE MISSILES

Spartan

Sprint

Length in feet

60

50

40

30

20

10

0

*An Evaluation of the Decision*

*to Deploy an*

*Antiballistic Missile System*

# ABM

*An Evaluation of the Decision
to Deploy an
Antiballistic Missile System*

HARPER & ROW, PUBLISHERS

NEW YORK, EVANSTON, AND LONDON

1817

*Editors*

ABRAM CHAYES
JEROME B. WIESNER

*Introduction*

EDWARD M. KENNEDY

*Contributors*

HANS A. BETHE
ABRAM CHAYES
BERNARD T. FELD
ARTHUR J. GOLDBERG
CARL KAYSEN
J. C. R. LICKLIDER
BILL D. MOYERS
GEORGE W. RATHJENS
LEONARD S. RODBERG
MARSHALL D. SHULMAN
THEODORE C. SORENSEN
JEREMY J. STONE
STEVEN WEINBERG
ALLEN S. WHITING
JEROME B. WIESNER
MASON WILLRICH
ADAM YARMOLINSKY

ABM: AN EVALUATION OF THE DECISION TO DEPLOY AN ANTI-
BALLISTIC MISSILE SYSTEM. *Copyright © 1969 by Abram Chayes
and Jerome B. Wiesner. All rights reserved. Printed in the United
States of America. No part of this book may be used or reproduced
in any manner whatsoever without written permission except in
the case of brief quotations embodied in editorials, critical articles
and reviews. Newspapers and magazines may quote up to 2,000
words without additional permission. For information address
Harper & Row, Publishers, Incorporated, 49 East 33rd Street,
New York, N.Y. 10016.*

Library of Congress Catalog Card Number: 70–88556

F-T

# CONTENTS

vii

## V.  Arms Control: Will It Be Set Back?

## VI.  Appendix

## Illustrations

## Tables

# PREFACE

Early in February, Senator Edward Kennedy suggested to us that it might be useful, in the forthcoming Congressional debates over the decision to deploy an antiballistic missile system, if the Congress had available to it an independent, nongovernment evaluation of the ABM issue. This suggestion had great merit, we thought, both in the context of the ABM controversy itself and in the larger context of the need for closer scrutiny of defense programs and spending.

Consequently, we undertook to prepare the evaluation, and this report is the result.

Our principal conclusion is that there is no need for a decision to deploy the Sentinel/Safeguard ABM system at this time. We believe that the system, even if considerably expanded and upgraded over the years following initial deployment, cannot perform effectively the missions suggested for it.

We have developed the reasons underlying our principal conclusions in Part I of this report. It carries the signatures of George Rathjens and Steven Weinberg besides our own. Rather than report our specific conclusions and recommendations here in this Preface, we have set them out at the end of Part I in the nature of a summary.

In developing this report, we asked a number of distinguished experts from the scientific and academic worlds, and others with extensive governmental experience in these matters, to prepare papers on specialized aspects of the ABM problem, political as well as technical. They appear in Parts II through V. Each of these authors takes responsibility only for his own signed contribution. We want to take this opportunity to thank them. We also want to thank our colleagues George Kistiakowsky and Paul Doty for reading the manuscript for factual accuracy.

When he suggested the utility of a report such as this,

Senator Kennedy commented on the fact that in the past the public has heard only one side of the story—that developed by the Department of Defense—in debates on major strategic weapons systems. We have taken this as a suggestion to present the "other" side, so that Congressional and public debate would have a full complement of information as it weighed this particular issue.

We believe these questions of weapons deployments are central to our polity and perhaps to our survival. For far too long they have been made largely behind closed doors. The most important safeguard for these issues is the safeguard of an untrammeled democratic process.

We have tried, therefore, to state the problem comprehensively and in terms that can be readily understood. We have, in sum, sought to assemble a report that will serve as an authoritative handbook on the ABCs of ABM.

It has been a high honor and rewarding experience to engage in this endeavor and to have an opportunity to make a contribution to this extremely important debate. We hope it will be useful to citizen and Congressman alike.

Abram Chayes
Jerome B. Wiesner

# INTRODUCTION

## by EDWARD M. KENNEDY

There is no priority for this nation higher than that of guaranteeing our national security and safety. Without an effective military force, and without a worldwide understanding that we have the unwavering will to use this force when our national interests are in danger, we unnecessarily place our way of life in peril.

The size and composition of this military force have varied widely in the twenty-five years since World War II, largely in response to what we have seen as the shifting nature of the threats to our security. In these times of flux, we have generally shifted our strategic assumptions, adopted new defense postures and either terminated or begun major new weapons systems. Each of these shifts has had major implications for the arms race.

Today we stand at the most important crossroads in this arms race in recent memory. The two great world nuclear powers—the United States and the U.S.S.R.—possess nuclear military forces easily ample to destroy both one another and the world many times over. Three other nations possess growing nuclear military forces, and some dozen others stand within a few years of possessing them. The prospect of a world in which more than a dozen nations possess nuclear weapons, and the means of delivering them, is not comforting; fortunately, we have acted recently to forestall it. The United States Senate has ratified the Nuclear Non-Proliferation Treaty, to which the Soviet Union, Great Britain and many other nations will in all probability adhere. This treaty offers some relief to the unchecked spread of nuclear weapons forces. But it does not go to the other central problem of the nuclear age: whether the major nuclear powers will, in what has been called the "action-reaction cycle," goad each other to the development and deployment of ever-larger, ever–more sophisticated, and ever–more costly major nuclear weapons systems.

This is the crossroads at which the world stands today. Only by the conscious exercise of choice will we take one road—towards an upward spiral in the arms race—or the other road—towards some reduction in international tension and in nuclear arsenals. Albert Einstein wrote some years ago that "The unleashed power of the atom has changed everything save our modes of thinking, and thus we drift towards unparalleled catastrophe." We must not drift towards catastrophe; rather, we should set a course away from it, and should steer this course resolutely and with some confidence in its integrity.

To chart this course, we must stop depending upon concepts and information that have no true relevance to the current world situation. Yesterday's justifications for yesterday's policies should concern the historian; and while they offer lessons for today's policies, they must not determine them. We are too often too quick to accept recommendations for national defense policies without putting their justifications to a rigorous examination. There is nothing sacrosanct about the recommendations of the Department of Defense. The Congress should put them to the same scrutiny it applies to all other government programs.

The suggestion is often made that it is unpatriotic to question recommendations of the Defense Department. This, of course, is folly. Our military men, who have led our armed forces with skill, imagination and courage down through the years, are trained *how* to wage war. But it is not their job—nor is it within their competence—to weigh in the balance the diplomatic and domestic implications of deploying new strategic weapons systems. We would not ask the members of Congress or our senior diplomatic specialists for their advice on the best methods for landing Marines on a beachhead or deploying our fleet of Polaris submarines.

We are fortunate, I think, as we stand at this critical juncture, that more and more Americans are insisting that the Congress examine our defense programs with a new intensity.

When we spend nearly $80 billion a year on defense; when defense eats up 41 percent of the money Americans pay in federal taxes; when more and more waste and inefficiency come to light in defense contracts—then Americans all across the country want to know *why?* Why so many dollars for defense? Why so much waste in contracts? Why so little challenge by the Congress?

Questioning the size, cost and composition of our armed forces is not to criticize; it is not to lay fault; nor is it to be unpatriotic. Instead, it is to carry out the urgings in the farewell addresses of two of our soldier-Presidents—George Washington and Dwight Eisenhower. They warned that the protection of democracy lay in an informed citizenry, one which was wary of the influence of the military upon national policies.

Questioning of a nature and extent probably unique in recent memory currently engages the Congress and the nation over the wisdom of one particular strategic weapons system— an American antiballistic missile system. Deployment of an American ABM was first recommended in 1967 by the Administration of President Johnson. Last year, 1968, a bipartisan group of U.S. Senators mounted a nearly successful challenge to the $1.9 billion requested for initiating actual deployment of the ABM system, then called the Sentinel system. That challenge was led by Senators Mike Mansfield, John Sherman Cooper, Philip A. Hart, Gaylord Nelson, Clifford Case, Albert Gore, Jacob Javits, Charles Percy, Frank Church and Stuart Symington, with the active support of many additional Senators from both parties. In the House of Representatives, Congressmen Jeffrey Cohelan, Robert Leggett, Charles Mathias, Bradford Morse and a number of others led a similar effort.

This year, after a review of the Sentinel ABM system, the Administration of President Nixon has recommended a slight modification of Sentinel, renamed it Safeguard and requested some $1 billion in appropriations for continuing its development and deployment. Once again, a bipartisan group of Senators and Congressmen has announced its intention to oppose the funding requests for continuing deployment of this ABM system at this time.

The debate in the Congress over President Nixon's proposed Safeguard ABM system has been going on for some weeks. It has stimulated the beginnings of an informed public debate and discussion in the country at large. And it was in response to this beginning that I asked Professor Abram Chayes and Dr. Jerome Wiesner if they would organize this report, and make it available to the members of Congress and the nation alike.

Traditionally, it has been a nearly impossible task to develop a full and independent evaluation of the Defense Department requests for program funds. The sums are so large; the range of activities these funds support is so vast; the justifications are so complex and entwined in patriotism; the projects themselves are so technical; and so much of the material is classified for security reasons—that a fully developed case in opposition to a particular defense project is only rarely available.

This is particularly so in the case of the ABM.

It is to be built in response to some potential threat to the United States—but the precise nature of the threat cannot be told to the American people for security reasons.

It will cost somewhere in the neighborhood of $7 billion—but this figure does not include the billions for nuclear warheads, the billions for research and development nor the billions for customary defense contract cost underestimates.

It is the single most complex undertaking man has yet set for himself in his time on earth—but if experience with previous national defense projects teaches any lesson, it will be years late in completion and may never work at all.

It may in fact be a defensive instead of offensive weapons system, as its proponents claim—but it is virtually certain to force our potential enemies to take steps to counteract it, just as we would—and have in the past—taken steps to counteract a defensive system constructed by our enemies.

In short, there is so much so questionable about the wisdom of deploying an ABM system now, that we really do need more information on Safeguard (or whatever name it finally receives) than is available from the Pentagon. This report offers a base of comparison with the information made available by the Defense Department. To some people, the report may make a convincing case; to others, the Defense Department case may be more convincing. But for virtually the first time, we now have available to us comprehensive arguments for and against a major new strategic weapons system.

What the report points out, in summary, is that the Congress must make a number of basic judgments before it approves funds for deploying the Safeguard ABM. These judgments require answers to the following questions:

*First*, will the ABM system work? Or, will it fall victim to the fate of countless other complex weapons systems and not meet its expectations?

*Second*, does the threat against which it is designed justify its deployment? Or, are we puffing up the threat unjustifiably?

*Third*, is it the right system for the missions given it? Or, would a different system be more effective for these missions, and less costly?

*Fourth*, will it force the Soviets and other potential enemies to take steps to counter our ABM, thus escalating the arms race? Or, will they be content to let us construct an ABM without reacting?

*Fifth*, would an ABM deployment have no impact on our pursuit of an arms control agreement? Or, would it throw up a new and difficult barrier?

*Sixth*, does a commitment of these billions to an ABM further disorder our budget priorities? Or, are there other budget areas more needy of funding support?

This report suggests some answers to these questions. In general, it makes a strong case against deployment of *this* ABM system—Safeguard—at *this* time. It concludes that we should instead pursue an aggressive research and development program in ballistic missile defense systems, with a hope that we may find a system more technically sound which would give us real security, and not false security. It points out repeatedly the importance of seeking arms limitation talks with the Soviets, as the only real hope for world stability and security.

The report itself also contributes strong support to the suggestion made by Dr. James Killian, Chairman of the Board of Massachusetts Institute of Technology, when he testified on March 11, 1969, before the Senate Foreign Relations Committee. Dr. Killian urged the creation of an independent commission to evaluate our strategic weapons policies and postures, an analogy to the Gaither Commission of the mid-1950s. The Gaither Commission, in its analysis of the policies of that time, recommended among other things that the United States move immediately towards reliance upon intercontinental ballistic missiles, instead of solely upon manned bombers, for its deterrent. This recommendation, and its corollaries, has largely determined our strategic weapons policies in the intervening years. A bill to create the type of commission suggested by Dr. Killian is presently before the Senate. It deserves the most serious consideration.

We should be quick to understand that the ABM is not the sole weapons program deserving close scrutiny. A whole new generation of strategic weapons systems stands ready in the wings, waiting only to be ushered in. This new generation includes MIRVs (multiheaded missiles), new land-based ICBMs, underwater-launched ICBMs, airborne attack missiles, advanced supersonic manned bombers and a whole host of others. Many experts warn that MIRVs, for example, pose a stronger threat to world stability than does the ABM, because of the difficulty each power faces in assessing the strength of the others with MIRVs deployed. Now is an appropriate time for an independent, nongovernment, hard-headed review of our strategic weapons systems. The world is in a state of flux; we and the other nuclear powers stand ready to open a vast Pandora's box of new nuclear weapons systems. We have the time to pause and think carefully before we move to open that box, because of the overwhelming nuclear might we possess. We must think, now, and think deeply. In this context, the ABM is an important symbol showing to all of us that close questioning of defense programs can raise the most troubling implications.

As we frame our national defense policies, and, in turn, our strategic weapons systems, we must judge how best to guarantee our survival and safety in the near and foreseeable future. There is little argument with former Defense Secretary McNamara's assertion in 1968 that "the cornerstone of our strategic policy must continue to be the deterrence of a deliberate nuclear attack against either the United States or its allies." The debate, then, should focus on the kind and level of forces we need to ensure that deterrent.

Unfortunately, the relative strengths of the two great powers are often discussed in emotional terms: superiority, parity, sufficiency and so forth. President Nixon has used "sufficiency" as an appropriate measure, echoing an argument advanced by Secretary of the Air Force Donald Quarles in 1956. This seems to me a wise measure, if it means we must maintain a sufficient military force vis-à-vis the Soviets or other potential adversaries to keep our deterrent credible. That is, no nation could risk attacking the United States without incurring unacceptable damage in return. From all available evidence, we have sufficient military forces, now, to deter the Soviets or any other nation from attacking the United States. Unless the ABM would add to this deterrent there is no reason to spend the billions needed to build it.

A number of recent events have converged to make considerable information available on this ABM issue. Senator Albert Gore's Subcommittee on International Organizations and Disarmament Affairs has held a series of highly significant public hearings on the ABM. Senate Armed Services Committee Chairman John Stennis has responded to the request from Senators Cooper, Hart and Symington for open ABM hearings, and has heard both Administration and public witnesses. Senate Majority Leader Mansfield has been a steady source of reasonable and wise counsel. A number of national committees made up of private individuals, such as the one announced by Arthur Goldberg and Roswell Gilpatric, have been formed to stimulate debate and discussion all around the country. In this context, this report owes a considerable debt of gratitude to the work which has gone before; and it can be of distinct aid to Congress and the public alike in seeking to make the forthcoming decision on this vital issue a soundly based one.

The discussions in recent weeks of the ABM bring continually to mind Senator Albert Gore's phrase: that Safeguard is a "missile system in search of a mission." The fact that we have an ABM system on the drawing boards is hardly a solid justification for deploying it. And common sense dictates that we should not spend the billions for deploying it until we have a reasonable expectation that it will work. To ensure that it will work, it seems to me, we need considerably more research, development, testing and evaluation before we decide to deploy an ABM.

And in the interim we must press to reach an agreement with the Soviets on restricting the arms race, specifically including ABM systems and MIRVs. Both the Soviets and the United States have satellite reconnaissance capacities such that violation of such an agreement, as it relates to ABMs, is easily detectable. Furthermore, both the Soviets and the United States must engage in further flight testing before MIRVs are fully developed and deployed. Once again, each side has the surveillance capacity to determine if MIRV flight testing, in violation of a hypothetical agreement, were carried out by the other. We have ample evidence that the Soviets are prepared to begin such arms control talks; the best service to world peace on our part would be to suspend ABM deployment, and MIRV flight testing, for some predetermined period of time while we actively explored the contours of such talks with the Soviets. It is important, in the context of these suggestions, to recall just how overwhelming is the nuclear force we now possess, and that a suspension of ABM deployment and MIRV flight testing for some predetermined time would not in any way disadvantage our deterrent.

It is also important to put the cost of the Safeguard system beside the costs of some selected nondefense programs. The announced price tag for Safeguard is $6.6 or $7.2 billion, depending upon its size. This, it should be noted, does not include the cost of warheads (estimated to be $1.2 billion), the estimated $500 million annual operating cost nor the cost of research and development performed to date. (This latter figure dating back to the 1957 research on Nike-Zeus has been estimated at $4 billion—or twice as much as the United States spent on the Manhattan Project in World War II, which developed and constructed the atomic bombs.) Then we must, if we are to be realistic, add the average cost overruns of defense programs. The Brookings Institution has estimated the overruns to be 400 to 700 percent for advanced weapons systems programs; a study by a Bureau of the Budget official puts the figure at 200 to 300 percent. Taking a lower-range figure, 300 percent, would put the cost of Safeguard upon completion at $18 to $21 billion, excluding warheads, annual operating costs, and research and development. This $18-to-$21-billion figure does not take into account any of the "growth options" for Safeguard presently under active study and consideration by the Defense Department. It might be argued that this figure is unrealistic, insofar as Administration spokesmen have indicated their intention to review the threat and the system from time to time, particularly after the first two ABM sites are constructed. Yet the Defense Department requested the funds for Fiscal Year 1970 to purchase not two ABM sites, but twelve ABM sites.

Let us, therefore, choose $20 billion as a likely (if low) figure for the completed Safeguard system, taking $19.5 billion as the median between $18 to $21 billion, and adding only $500 million for the other costs. What could this $20 billion mean for the advancement of security and justice here

in the United States? How many young people could be saved
who now go into the streets to commit violence? How many
health centers could be built for those who now suffer from
disease? Could we not, with this sum, clean up all our rivers
and the air above all our cities? Could we not raise an entire
generation of children with the advantages of a Headstart
program?

Could we not, in sum, use the savings to offer new hope to
those who have lost hope in the America of our dreams?

When our country is under attack, all of these expenditures
give way to the protection of the national security. But when,
as today, the debate is over a weapons system whose addition
to our security is questionable, this money should be used
for programs of security and progress here at home.

We in the Congress have a number of obligations as we
vote on the Administration's request for funds to deploy Safeguard. We have obligations to our national security and
safety; to world peace and stability; and to the shape of the
world we pass to the next generation. We must also seek to
avoid the horror of nuclear war; to reduce waste in the use
of federal funds; and to establish a sound set of priorities for
available federal funds. It is against all these standards that
we must place the request for funds to deploy the Safeguard
ABM system. It is our responsibility to see that the people we
represent are not deprived of their tax money and of the
opportunity to meet their own pressing problems, in order to
purchase a defense capability they do not need.

The material in this report indicates that the wise choice
would be a deferral of a decision to deploy Safeguard at this
particular time. Such a decision would not lay us open,
defenseless, to an attack by an enemy. Our nuclear forces are
so large, and so sophisticated, that they would deter an
enemy from attacking us while we sought an arms limitation
agreement with the Soviets over some predetermined period,
just as they have deterred our enemies over all the years of
the nuclear age. If we determined, after some serious and
candid attempts, that our adversaries were simply not interested in an arms limitation agreement, then we would perhaps
know more about an ABM system's effectiveness and would
still have ample time and opportunity to react appropriately.

I would like to say a final word about defense in the
nuclear age. In the past, nations preparing for war or siege
have relied upon a combination of defense and offense to

protect themselves. Thus, the castles of the feudal barons were joined with a force of horse and foot soldiers. The Maginot Line was coupled with a partially mechanized army. The defenses at Normandy were backed up by a mobile army and an air force. Those in the Pacific Islands in World War II were backed up by an entrenched land force and naval and air units. None of these defenses, down through the years, withstood attack by a determined, powerful, sophisticated aggressor.

The real question in the nuclear age, however, is whether a defense force is real security, or only false security. The Soviets' limited ABM system has not affected our confidence in our own deterrent; it is difficult to understand how an American ABM system, which will not be operational for at least four years from now and is based upon a technology of questionable reliability, will be any serious obstacle to the Soviets. It is well to remind ourselves that the Soviets have very sophisticated technological abilities. We may well be lulling ourselves into a sense of false security by believing that our Safeguard ABM system will provide us any true defensive capability, and thus prove a serious challenge to the Soviets and consequently be useful in any bargaining with them.

This report was prepared by some of the nation's most respected scholars, scientists and statesmen, and I commend it to all citizens concerned and perplexed about questions of security in a nuclear age. As I view it, the truth about the ABM is that it is probably unworkable and potentially very costly. The consequence, as I view it, is another spiral in the arms race and a setback for arms control. Accordingly, until convincing evidence is available to answer the troublesome technical, strategic and diplomatic questions raised by this report, I intend to work with that group of United States Senators opposed to deploying this ABM system at this cross-roads in the arms race. The implications these questions raise for the world our children will inherit are too serious to let them remain unanswered.

# I

## ABM DEPLOYMENT:
## WHAT'S WRONG WITH IT?

*History is littered with Maginot Lines.*
—Dr. Herbert York, before the Senate Armed
Services Committee, April 22, 1969

# AN OVERVIEW

by **ABRAM CHAYES, JEROME B. WIESNER, GEORGE W. RATHJENS and STEVEN WEINBERG***

SERIOUS CONCERN IN the United States Government about antiballistic missiles stretches back over the last decade and a half to 1954. In that year we began to shift the emphasis in our strategic weapons program from manned bombers to ballistic missiles. At the same time, we initiated an intensive program of research and development into missile defenses. The reasons were twofold: first, to be able to defend our own country, if that was possible; and, second, to gain knowledge of the barriers an adversary could raise against United States offensive missiles.

Since that time the United States has continuously engaged in large-scale research and development on antiballistic missiles. Total expenditures for this purpose to date are approaching $10 billion. On a number of occasions, proposals for procurement and deployment of an ABM system were pressed within the Department of Defense. In 1959 the issue reached the Presidential level, but President Dwight D. Eisenhower vetoed the deployment of the system developed

* Abram Chayes is Professor of Law, Harvard University; he was The Legal Adviser to the Department of State, 1961–1964. Jerome B. Wiesner is Provost, Massachusetts Institute of Technology; he was Science Adviser to the President, 1961–1964. George W. Rathjens is Visiting Professor of Political Science, Massachusetts Institute of Technology. Steven Weinberg is Professor of Physics, Massachusetts Institute of Technology and Consultant, Institute for Defense Analyses.

3

at that time, the Nike-Zeus. A principal objection was that its radar system, which depended on mechanically rotated antennas, was simply too slow to cope with the problems of missile attack. This decision was reaffirmed by President Kennedy in 1962.

Research and development work continued, however. Prototype missiles were developed and test intercepts attempted, a number successfully, at the Kwajalein missile range in the Pacific Ocean. Work went forward on a new concept, the phased-array radar, that gave promise of avoiding some of the difficulties of the mechanical system. Again, in late 1966, the issue went to the White House, and again the President decided against deployment. This time, the proposed system was the Nike-X, with a proposed deployment designed to defend the fifty-two largest United States cities against a massive nuclear attack, or, as an alternative, a scaled-down version for about half as many cities. Then, in September, 1967, Secretary of Defense Robert McNamara announced the decision to deploy a "thin" ABM system, the Sentinel, oriented primarily toward defending the United States population against a potential Chinese missile attack in the mid-1970s.

That proposal has itself been modified by the present Administration. In its place, President Richard Nixon proposed, on March 14, 1969, the Safeguard system, involving a somewhat different arrangement of the parts of the Sentinel system and a different stated primary mission: to protect some Minuteman intercontinental missiles, some Strategic Air Command bases and the National Command Center in Washington, D.C., against a possible first-strike attack by the Soviet Union. Population defense against a Chinese attack was retained as a secondary mission.

This analysis is occasioned by these two recent decisions to go ahead with ABM deployment, and particularly by the Administration's decision of March 14, 1969. It has necessitated a broad-gauge review of the general problems associated with antiballistic missile defense.

## I. *The Antiballistic Missile System: Its Theory*

An ABM missile is a missile armed with a nuclear warhead, designed to intercept and destroy an incoming missile and prevent it from reaching its target. United States ABM systems have been planned primarily to respond to attacks by intercontinental ballistic missiles (ICBMs), although they might be used to some extent in case of attack by shorter-range missiles.

ICBMs are rockets sending nuclear warheads from launchers several thousand miles to the final target. Normally an ICBM consists of several rocket stages. The large first stage is known as the booster. The last stage carries one or more re-entry vehicles (RVs) containing nuclear warheads. After a short period of powered and guided flight immediately after launch, the re-entry vehicle follows a fixed path or trajectory very much as a cannon ball does. The trajectory is thousands of miles long and extends at its highest point nearly one thousand miles above the earth, well into outer space. The missile travels at enormous speed—some two miles a second. The total time elapsed from launch to target is hardly more than one-half hour. Today only the United States and the Soviet Union have ICBMs. China is expected to have one or a few operational by 1972 at the earliest, and probably somewhat later.

An ABM system is made up of three main subsystems—radars, computers and missiles—plus interconnecting communications and controls. A word about each is in order, with emphasis on the elements planned for the Sentinel/Safeguard system.

*Radars:* A radar is a device that sends out pulses of electromagnetic radiation. The pulses are reflected back to the radar from any objects they hit. The radar system detects these echoes and this permits accurate measurement of the distance to the object and its velocity, and gives some indication of the direction to the object. If the object is on a ballistic trajectory, like a cannon ball, then this information is sufficient for a computer to calculate the trajectory, and thus determine with considerable accuracy the likely point of impact on the earth.

The Sentinel/Safeguard system uses two kinds of radars. The first is called Perimeter Acquisition Radar (PAR). This is a long-range radar, using recently developed technology to pick up the incoming ICBM while it is still several thousand miles from its target—near the Arctic Circle, for example, assuming an attack from Siberia or central China over the polar regions. At this point a period of about ten minutes at most would remain before the incoming missile would reach its target.[1]

The PAR would have to follow the incoming missile with its radar beams, so that its trajectory could be computed and the anticipated intercept set in motion. At this point, the second radar—the Missile Site Radar (MSR)—would come into play. This radar takes over the tracking of the incoming missile from the PAR, and then on computer command seeks to guide the defending missiles to the point of intercept. The MSR has been designed to handle a large number of missiles and interceptors simultaneously.

*Computers:* The computers involved in ABM systems would be the largest and most complex ever built. The proposed system would include up to twenty data-processing units and have a capacity equivalent to one hundred large commercial computers. The instructions for the computer—the program—would also have to be more sophisticated and complex than any accomplished so far. The computer has to perform many tasks at the same time—interpreting the radar signals, identifying potential targets, tracking incoming objects, predicting trajectories, distinguishing between warheads and decoys, eliminating false targets, rejecting signals from earlier nuclear explosions, correcting for blackout effects, allocating and guiding interceptor missiles, and arming and firing them if they get within range of a target. All this must be done continuously and with split-second precision during the short period—ten minutes at most—between the time the attacking missiles first appear to the radar and the moment of impact. In addition, the computer must check its own performance for errors and defects. Perhaps 10 to 15 percent of the computer capacity would be assigned to this self-corrective function; this computer operation is simply too rapid and complicated to rely on human monitors.

The computer programing would employ the "time-shared" approach, still being developed by data-processing theorists. A central, governing unit would be used to oversee a group of subordinate computers. It would broadly outline the solution of individual problems, determine the amount of computer time and storage space to be devoted to each problem in light

---

[1] The existing Ballistic Missile Early Warning System (BMEWS) would provide a warning perhaps ten minutes earlier for most ICBM attacks from the north, but would not supply very useful trajectory data.

of its importance, and assign the problems among the subordinate computers for detailed analysis.

*Missiles:* Sentinel/Safeguard contemplates the use of two
different kinds of missiles. The Spartan is a missile operating
at relatively long range—up to several hundred miles. It is
armed with a rather large warhead. The exact yield is secret,
but it is known to be in the megaton range.[2] It is designed to
intercept while the incoming missile is still in outer space, far
from its target. At these altitudes, there would be no nuclear
radiation, fallout, or heat or blast effects on the surface of the
earth below the explosion, either from the Spartan warhead
itself or from the attacking missile if it should detonate. It has
been suggested, however, that people below looking in the
direction of the explosion might sustain severe, possibly
permanent, eye damage.

The second missile is the Sprint, and is a weapon of much
shorter range—about twenty-five miles. It is designed to take
care of incoming warheads which get past the Spartan. The
Sprint is a high-acceleration missile, rising the first mile in a
very few seconds. It is designed to intercept at altitudes of up
to twenty miles, but most intercepts would probably take
place at five to ten miles. At this point the warhead is only
seconds from its target. Because the intercept will take place
so close to the target, the Sprint carries a much smaller nuclear warhead—a few kilotons—and must come correspondingly closer to the incoming warhead to be able to destroy it.
The Sprint explosions would be high enough, however, and
the weapons small enough so that there would be little or no
direct effects of radiation, fallout, blast or heat on the area
immediately below.

The destruction of the incoming warhead would be accomplished primarily by radiation from the explosion of the defending missile's nuclear warhead: X-rays for the Spartans in
space and neutrons for the Sprints in the atmosphere. Various
devices are available to the attacker to shield his warheads
against these effects, but the protection afforded is uncertain,
and the devices can be used only by taking up some of the
space and weight that would otherwise be devoted to the
nuclear warhead.

It is assumed that both Sprints and Spartans would be so

[2] 1 megaton = 1,000 kilotons of TNT. 1 kiloton = 1,000 tons of
TNT. The Hiroshima bomb was about 20 kilotons.

designed as to prevent their warheads from exploding while on the ground or even after launch, unless an intercept actually took place.[3] Similar devices have worked effectively thus far to prevent accidental explosions of our nuclear weapons, including at least three incidents involving unanticipated damage to nuclear warheads.[4] However, it is possible that if an unexploded warhead fell to earth from the altitudes involved, a certain amount of radioactive material would be released locally even without an explosion. This occurred in the crash of a B-52 carrying nuclear warheads near Palomares, Spain, in January, 1966.

An ABM site in either the Sentinel or the Safeguard system, then, might consist of a PAR, an MSR, the necessary computer installation and a battery of on the order of 40 Spartans and perhaps 10 to 75 Sprints. We assume that the radars and computers could handle additional missiles if they should be installed at the site. There would also be the necessary command-and-control structures, and housing for the troops manning the battery.

Although the original Sentinel and the proposed Safeguard systems are essentially similar, there are certain marginal differences between the two systems, which should be noted.

The fully deployed Sentinel system called for fifteen sites in the continental United States, plus one each for Hawaii and Alaska, with the possibility of adding three or four more. The fully deployed Safeguard system, as now described, would include twelve sites in the continental United States. One in Hawaii and one in Alaska might possibly be added later.

At the outset, it was not specified where, exactly, the Sentinel sites would be located, but it was subsequently decided that the sites would be in suburban areas adjacent to major cities. This decision was reversed in the Safeguard plan, and the intention now is to place the sites at some distance from population centers, although some of those defending Strategic Air Command bases would still be in the vicinity of major cities. All the large cities in the country,

[3] The Defense Department has announced that the ABM missiles would not contain "fail-safe" or "destruct" devices. It is our understanding, however, that the weapon will not detonate except on positive instructions from the computer, given when intercept range is achieved.

[4] In the crash of a B-52 outside Goldsboro, N.C., on January 24, 1961, although four of the six fail-safe devices on one of the warheads were triggered in the crash, the last two prevented an explosion.

except possibly New Orleans and Phoenix, would continue to be within range of a Spartan battery under the announced Safeguard deployment.

The shift in site location makes it somewhat more expensive, though by no means impossible, to alter the system at a later date in an attempt to provide defense of population against heavy attack. In the Sentinel pattern, this could have been accomplished for the fifteen cities involved simply by the addition of Sprints at all ABM sites. These would have been controlled by the missile site radar already at the site to handle the Spartans. With the Safeguard location pattern, it would be necessary to deploy the additional Sprints and also to supply radar services, either by using a nearby MSR, if there were one, or by building an additional MSR.

Because of the very extensive range of the perimeter acquisition radars (PARs), they are not needed at every site. The Sentinel configuration called for these radars at only five of the contemplated sites in the continental United States; the Safeguard at seven. In addition, some Safeguard PARs would have two faces, permitting them to scan in two directions. The MSRs would have four faces, to cover the full 360 degrees of the horizon. In the Sentinel system only the ABM radars and perhaps some Minutemen were to be defended with Sprint as well as Spartan missiles. This was because the radars, as the nerve centers of the whole system, were considered primary targets thought to require close-in protection against incoming missiles which might get through the Spartans. In the Safeguard plan all sites are to be equipped with both Sprints and Spartans, since all sites are to be located at places where an effort at close-in defense is said to be appropriate.

*Costs:* The costs for the components of the system were stated by the Pentagon to be: Sprints, $1.1 million; Spartans, $1.5 million; one-faced PARs, $130 million; two-faced PARs, $160 million; MSRs, $165 million. The quoted missile costs do not include warheads. The total budgeted cost of Sentinel was $5.5 billion. Deputy Defense Secretary Packard has put the full cost of the Safeguard variant at $6.6 billion for the twelve sites in the continental United States, and $7.2 billion if Alaska and Hawaii are added. The additional cost is represented by the additional Sprints, increased missile costs over the earlier estimates and by the additional faces per radar. However, the new deployment schedule proposed by President Nixon means that the appropriations for Safeguard would be just under $1 billion for Fiscal Year 1970, about $900 million less than President Johnson had budgeted for Sentinel.

Costs for complicated weapons systems have characteristically turned out very much higher than the originally budgeted figures. It is unlikely that the Sentinel/Safeguard system will prove an exception. Estimates of missile costs may prove fairly reliable, although recent reports have suggested that the $1.5 million price tag per Spartan missile may rise to the order of $3 million. Cost estimates have been particularly unreliable with respect to electronic and computer elements, which make up the major portion of Sentinel/Safeguard expense. On complex weapons systems in recent years, these costs have exceeded original budget estimates by at least 200 to 300 percent.

Nevertheless, we do not feel justified in predicting what the final costs of the Sentinel/Safeguard system might finally total. In addition to cost overruns on the system as originally designed, in the event of deployment there will surely be very large and unpredictable expenditures on modifications needed to meet the system's known shortcomings, technological developments and the changing nature of the offensive capability the system will face.

Table 1 gives the details that have been made public of the proposed deployment of the Sentinel and Safeguard systems, for comparative purposes.

## II. *The ABM System: Its Reliability*

Can the antiballistic missile system be counted on to function at the times and places desired? A very substantial portion of the scientific and technical community has taken the position that it will not—at least, not with the degree of confidence necessary if we are to place substantial reliance on the system's defensive capability.

It is necessary to be clear about the kind of question here involved. Some people have thought it analogous to the technical issues surrounding the decision to go forward with the development of the hydrogen bomb. In that instance, it is pointed out, a substantial and respected portion of the scientific community opposed a high-priority effort to develop the H-bomb. But in the hydrogen bomb controversy the scientific issue was whether a specific design concept could *in principle*

**Table 1.** Sentinel/Safeguard Deployment, Excluding Alaska and Hawaii: A Comparison

|                          | Sentinel                   | Safeguard                                        |
| ------------------------ | -------------------------- | ------------------------------------------------ |
| Spartan sites (each with MSR) | 15                    | 12                                               |
| MSR faces                | 34                         | 48                                               |
| Locations                | Mainly near cities         | 4 Minuteman bases, 7 SAC bases, Washington       |
| PARs                     | 5                          | 7                                                |
| Faces                    | 5                          | 11                                               |
| Locations                | Some at Spartan sites      | All at Spartan sites                             |
| ABMs                     |                            |                                                  |
| Sprints                  | Several hundred            | Several hundred (more than Sentinel)             |
| Spartans                 | Several hundred            | Several hundred                                  |
| Budgeted costs           | $5.5 billion               | $6.6 billion                                     |

ever be developed into a workable weapon. That question could be and was resolved by additional theoretical calculations; and in fact, though this is not generally appreciated, the original concept was demonstrated to be unworkable. As a result of this subsequent analysis, a new approach was developed which was found to be feasible, first by theoretical and laboratory studies and ultimately by test explosions. The program for production and deployment of hydrogen weapons, about which there was little scientific controversy, did not go forward until these theoretical issues had been resolved.

In the ABM case the issues are not theoretical but practical and technological. There is no dispute that in theory a defending missile can be brought into close enough proximity to an incoming ICBM warhead to destroy it with a nuclear explosion. In fact, limited test intercepts have been successfully performed on the missile range at Kwajalein, where unarmed ABMs have been fired and achieved the necessary proximity to offensive missiles fired in the test. The problem is to meet the many rigorous and interacting requirements for an actual operational system: The apparatus itself is highly complex in all its components—missiles, radars and computers. Each separate part must function well not only by itself but in intricate coordination with the others. To develop adequately this extremely complex computer program, which is the real control and coordinating element, in time to meet the deployment schedule may well be beyond today's capabilities. The attack pattern against which the system is deployed is uncertain and will shift over time. The reaction time is extremely short. And with all this, there will be no opportunity to test the system as a whole, manned by operating military personnel, in anything approaching the operating conditions which would exist in a massive nuclear attack.

Given all these conditions, the question is whether the system can be counted on to function in combat with a high degree of confidence that most or many of the ABMs deployed will in fact intercept incoming missiles. We believe there is no basis for such confidence, for the following reasons:

1. *There is no possibility for testing the system.*

From the combat infantryman's side arm on up, the United States has not in modern times put any weapons system into service without a program of rigorous and prolonged testing under conditions approximating or even more difficult than those to be faced in operations. Even then there have been frequent defects and bugs that could only be worked out over time after experience in combat. The M-16 rifle and the F-111 (previously known as the TFX) are recent and well-known examples of weapons that, despite extensive predeployment testing, failed to work satisfactorily when first put into the field.

At least three considerations prevent realistic testing of the Sentinel/Safeguard ABM system and will continue to do so: First, the system would be called upon to react on short notice against a significant number of incoming objects—at least twenty-five to thirty in the case of an assumed Chinese attack and many more in the case of a Soviet attack—in sophisticated and deceptive patterns, probably including efforts to black out or confuse the radars. A number of ABM missile sites will have to respond in an interconnected and coordinated fashion. These conditions cannot be created on a test range or simulated after the missiles are emplaced. Thus the most that can be hoped for is the testing of limited numbers of unarmed weapons, under conditions where all are aware that a test is in progress and where the necessity for multiple coordinated response is, at best, simulated.

Second, we cannot know what attack patterns and countermeasures an adversary might use. Thus we could not simulate them in the test activity. The best we could do would be to test the defensive system and its computer program against attacks designed by our own offensive planners and thus dominated by our own notions of tactical doctrine. But there is no great probability that the kind of attack the system would have to face in actual combat would be designed along those lines.

Finally, the system will have to operate in an environment involving many nearly simultaneous nuclear explosions in space or in the atmosphere. Such an environment is not well understood and could not be simulated even in the absence of the Nuclear Test Ban Treaty.

The need for testing, we think, is especially strong with ABM systems because of the high degree of sophistication of the various components and the extraordinary degree of quasi-instantaneous coordination required.

2. *Past experience with similar sophisticated systems.*

Work on defense against manned-bomber attack was begun in 1952. Like ABM defense, the SAGE (Semiautomatic Ground Environment) air-defense system depends on radar sensing of incoming planes and computer analysis of course and target information. The reaction time is, of course, much slower than for antimissile defense, being measured in hours rather than minutes. Simulation of manned-aircraft attack is feasible, and the bomber defense has been repeatedly tested against such attacks and improved and tightened up on the basis of the results. Still, after fifteen years, and the expenditure of more than $20 billion, it is generally conceded that we do not have a significant capability to defend against a well-planned air attack. The Soviet Union, after an even greater effort, has probably not done much better.

A second way of approaching the problem is to look at analyses of the reliability of projected offensive missiles. To begin with, the offense problem is simpler than that of defense, because ICBMs are pretargeted, and they do not have to be aimed within a few moments of launch on the basis of recently acquired target data. Moreover, the timing of the launch is not critical with offensive weapons, unlike the ABM, which must be able to respond on call against a target approaching at seventy-two hundred miles per hour.

In a recent article written by Dr. Daniel Fink, shortly after his resignation as Deputy Director of Defense Research and Engineering, four separate operational factors were set forth as relevant in determining the reliability of the United States offensive missile force.[5] The four factors are:

1. Missiles available.
2. Readiness reliability.
3. Launch reliability.
4. In-flight reliability.

Dr. Fink applied two different discounts at each stage, one of 90 percent labeled "nominal" and "synthesized from public statements to Congressional committees"; and one labeled "conservative," at 80 percent. By applying those discounts to each of the four key stages, Dr. Fink found a 65 percent reliability for offensive missiles on the "nominal" basis, and 41 percent reliability on the "conservative" basis. Offensive planning, according to Dr. Fink, must be carried forward on the assumption that at best two-thirds, and possibly only two-fifths, of our offensive missiles will function reliably.[6] If this is true for offensive planning, it would be folly to rate the reliability of defensive missiles any higher.[7] Moreover, in the defensive system the missiles are not the only components subject to failure. Radars and computers can also malfunction, and unlike missile failures these might be such as to immobilize the whole system until they were discovered and repaired.

[5] "Strategic Warfare," *Science and Technology*, October, 1968, p. 54.

[6] In the same calculation, Dr. Fink assumes that 75 percent of our missiles arriving over target would penetrate a 1972 Soviet ABM defense —67 percent on a "conservative" basis. Thus he is willing to concede to the Soviet defenses the ability to knock down only one in four—and one in three on the "conservative" basis—of our offensive ICBMs.

[7] To cite one other example of the widespread recognition of ICBM unreliability: In hearings before the Preparedness Investigating Subcommittee of the Armed Services Committee, U.S. Senate, April 26, 1968, its Chief Counsel noted: "I know the growing pains we went through with Atlas. . . . We were predicting something like 80 percent reliability. It went off the board at something like 4 percent. I know the growing pains we went through with Minuteman accuracy, and the problems we had in that [deleted]."

A further aspect of our recent experience with sophisticated weapons systems is applicable. Richard A. Stubbing, a senior officer of the Bureau of the Budget with responsibility in that agency for advanced weapons systems, has analyzed in detail the performance experience of major weapons systems developed since World War II.[8] He focused his analysis on the computer and radar elements. Stubbing found that of the thirteen systems analyzed, only four performed up to specifications. Of the others, five achieved less than 75 percent of specified performance, two were phased out for low reliability and two were canceled.

The picture is even grimmer when attention is confined to weapons systems with radar and computer components that have been classified as "high-risk." A system falls within this classification if "at least one major component of the system must be redesigned" before it could work successfully. By these standards Sentinel/Safeguard is a high-risk system. Among this group, amounting to eleven major systems designed between 1960 and 1967, only two met performance specifications, and only one achieved as high as 75 percent of planned performance. Two met a 50 percent standard and six rose only to 25 percent of planned performance. In a number of these cases, large-scale redesign and redevelopment of electronic and computer elements of the system after extensive in-service testing failed to result in materially improved performance.

There is little reason to suppose that the Sentinel/Safeguard system will better the average of these other systems, and some grounds for thinking it may be even worse. It has all the characteristics that made these systems vulnerable to performance failures. In addition, it presents more difficulties in computer programing and more possibility for computer failure than any previous system, with the possible exception of SAGE. Design, development and contracting procedures for proposed ABM systems exemplify the weaknesses Stubbing found in the systems he analyzed. And in this case the absence of opportunity for realistic testing means that it will be difficult to identify performance deficiencies in advance and work to correct them.

[8] For security reasons, the systems were not identified by popular name, but by neutral labels. Mr. Stubbing's article, entitled "Improving the Acquisition Process for High Risk Electronics Systems," is reprinted at page S 1450 of the *Congressional Record* for February 7, 1969.

It goes without saying that unreliability of anything approaching the magnitudes suggested by the experience reviewed above would be wholly unacceptable for a defensive missile system with any kind of a population-defense mission, even without taking account of countermeasures employed by the attacker. Some proponents of the system have suggested that Spartans could successfully defend and prevent all but a very few ICBMs or possibly all from reaching their targets. To our knowledge, none of these proponents has suggested plausible reasons for attributing such high reliability to the Sentinel/Safeguard ABM system, in the light of the experience with similar systems reviewed above.

3. *Specific sources of failure in ABM systems.*

The least troublesome sources of failure are those that can be anticipated now. Some of these are:

*Missile failures:* No missile is perfect, and defense planners are accustomed to take into account the possibility that a missile will not be available or will fail in its function. We have quoted the study of Dr. Fink, which gives the probability of failure as 34 to 59 percent for ICBMs. The Spartan missile, like a Minuteman, has three stages and is not very much smaller in size, cost or payload, so it probably has a similar probability of failure. The Sprint is smaller and has only two stages, but its acceleration is unprecedented, so it too is likely to have an appreciable probability of failure. It would take 3 missiles with 30 percent failure probability to destroy an incoming warhead with 97 percent certainty. Some such requirement must be incorporated into the firing doctrine for any ABM defense of cities, radars or bomber bases, and this uses up defensive missiles at a fearsome rate.

*Radar and computer failures:* Although the ABM radars may to some extent be netted together, the failure of any one MSR or its associated computer will eliminate the local Sprint defense and will reduce the area defended by the Spartans. Assuming a radar availability rate of 90 percent, there is, therefore, a 72 percent chance that one or more radars will actually be out of service at any particular time in a system of twelve MSRs.

It is also possible that the ABM system may turn out to be partially or totally ineffective and be known to be so after deployment but before any attack. One way this can happen is:

*Programing failures:* We have already described the complexity of the task that the computer programer faces. It has been authoritatively suggested that it just may be impossible during the next few years to write a computer program for dealing with the various forms of attack that can be anticipated. There is one small consolation in that some program deficiencies could, at least, be discovered in advance by testing how the computer reacted to simulated radar signals.

Most worrisome of all is the possibility that the ABM system will unexpectedly fail during an attack. Obviously no one can predict how this might happen, but we can guess at some areas that may give trouble:

*False assumptions:* We cannot know exactly what a real attack, involving nuclear blackout, booster fragments, chaff, decoys and so forth, would actually be like. False assumptions here would lead to errors in programing the defense which would only be discovered during an attack.

*Electromagnetic pulses:* Nuclear explosions produce electromagnetic pulses which can interfere with radars, computers and communications. We cannot know the effect this will have on a full-scale ABM system in a major nuclear attack. The prospect of a breakdown in communications combined with a command-and-control crisis is particularly disquieting.

## III. *The ABM Operation: Its Countermeasures*

The final effectiveness of an ABM system is determined not only by its intrinsic reliability but by the attacker's ability to evade, neutralize or overcome the system. A wide range of such countermeasures exist.

1. *Decoys and multiple warheads:* An attacker can, and probably will, launch other objects along with the actual warheads to confuse and complicate the picture for the defense. These objects are known as decoys. An attack with decoys presents two different problems to the defender:

First, the long-range radar, although very sophisticated, has little capability of discriminating and identifying different kinds of objects that it picks up. Unless the defense can be sure that the observed object is not a warhead (or unless the object is not on target) an ABM must be sent up to try to intercept. Thus the limited supply of defensive missiles can be used up against cheap, harmless objects.

Second, the use of decoys opens the possibility of filling the

sky with so many objects that the data-handling capacity of
the computer would be insufficient, even if it could distinguish individual decoys from actual warheads.

In the simplest case, fragments of the rocket that launched
the nuclear warhead will be traveling through space on the
same trajectory with the warhead. The radar may not be able
to tell which among this cluster of objects is the warhead and
which are rocket fragments. If the attacker had made no positive effort to separate these objects, they might be close
enough together so that a single interceptor explosion could
destroy all of them. But the attacker could ensure in any one
of several ways that they were spread farther apart.

Beyond this rather primitive expedient lies the possibility
of launching objects designed to appear very much like warheads to the radar. Dr. Hans A. Bethe describes one such
device that is relatively simple and inexpensive. Balloons with
thin metallic skins can be carried by the missile along with
the warhead. They would be inflated and dispersed above the
atmosphere but before the ICBM had come within range of
the PAR. The balloons could be given a shape much like that
of an actual warhead, and the radar would then have great
difficulty in telling which was the warhead and which was
not. The principal clue would be that some of the objects
would be on trajectories that did not lead to any logical
target. But many of the decoys would not sort out on this
basis, and ABMs would have to be fired at any object if its
path looked plausible. Assuming that there are about fifty
interceptors to a battery, one or two missiles might well carry
enough decoys to use up all the long-range ABMs at a single
defensive site. In fact, an attack can be planned so that the
first wave is all decoys, perhaps several thousand of them. All
the Spartans in the system might have to be used against
these objects. The real warheads would then follow in a
second missile volley, and no defensive missiles would be
available.

There are, of course, possibilities for countering decoy
attacks, but they are very complicated. The difficulty is
compounded because reaction time is short and the defender
does not know the kinds and patterns of decoys an attacker
might use. The computer would have to be programed for a
wide range of possibilities, with no assurance that the offensive tactic actually used would be among them.

Thus it is not at all difficult for decoys to exhaust the

Spartan part of the Sentinel/Safeguard system. Dr. Bethe says:

> The Chinese will probably build even their first operational intercontinental ballistic missiles so that they will have a chance to penetrate. Moreover, we believe it is well within China's capabilities to do a good job at this without intensive testing or tremendous sacrifice in payload.

and further:

> The key point is that since the putative Chinese intercontinental ballistic missile force is still in the early research and development stage, it can and will be designed to deal with the Sentinel [now Safeguard] system, whose interceptors and sensors are nearing production and are rather well publicized. It is much easier to design a missile force to counter a defense that is already being deployed than to design one for any of the possible systems that might or might not be deployed sometime in the future.

The United States technical literature is replete with discussions of decoy problems and technology.

Once the incoming objects reach the atmosphere, the lighter balloons and fragments will be slowed down drastically. Thus simple decoys of the kind described above are not effective against missiles that are designed to intercept in the atmosphere. Here the attacker would have to use weighted decoys that would behave much like warheads in the atmosphere. To do so would involve the sacrifice of much of the energy of the offensive missile to carrying dummy warheads. A more expensive alternative would be to have a single missile carry a number of live warheads. In an attack on a large city, any one of these might be effective, and the ABM system would have to try to destroy all of them.

In an attack on a hard-point target, such as a missile silo or command center, decoys' usefulness is more limited. The defender can wait before deciding to commit an intercepting missile until the incoming objects reach very low altitudes, where the atmosphere will have filtered out most of the decoys. Moreover, the object may be disregarded completely by the defense unless it is going to land within a very short distance of a point to be defended. The necessary accuracy could not be attained by multiple warheads launched from the same missile unless each could be separately and very precisely targeted. Such a weapon is known as a Multiple Independently Targetable Re-entry Vehicle (MIRV). Neither the United States nor the U.S.S.R. has these in operational form, although the U.S., and probably the U.S.S.R., is working on the problem.

2. *Radar neutralization:* The attacker has a number of ways to interfere with or limit the radars' ability to perceive incoming objects. A simple method is to equip the offensive warheads or decoys with electronic jamming devices. This would be effective at the high altitudes of Spartan intercepts, but might be costly in payload sacrificed.

A simpler method of interfering with the radars is for the attacker to spread "chaff"—small metal wires—in the path of the incoming missiles. The chaff would reflect the radar waves emitted from the PAR. It would appear to the radar as a large obscure volume, many miles across, moving on a ballistic trajectory. The computer could not be sure whether or not there were warheads in this large cloud and would have to commit a number of interceptors to ensure the destruction of any that might be there.

The explosion of specially designed nuclear weapons in outer space in advance of the attacking warhead would give rise to even greater uncertainty through radar blackout and distortion. A nuclear explosion creates a fireball and also, through its beta radiation, produces a sheet of ionized air at about forty-five miles altitude. Both effects cause reflection or absorption of radar waves for a ten-minute period, screening the incoming missiles from the defending radar.

The explosion can be designed to create beta-effect blackout over an area of more than ten thousand square miles. If well placed, this blackout could prevent the PAR from observing the missile except for a few moments, just as it was clearing the horizon—too short a time to plot the trajectory accurately.

The fireball blackout rises from the point of explosion, and thus the obscured portion of sky gets smaller over time. However, even after the ten-minute period of complete blackout, the lingering presence of the fireball will bend the radar waves so that objects will appear to the radar to be in places different from where they really are, much the way a stick appears to be bent when it is partly under water. Again, the

PAR will have difficulty locating the incoming missile with the necessary accuracy.

In addition to planned blackout by the attacking force, the explosions of the intercepting nuclear warheads themselves may have significant blackout effects. The weapons and the altitudes of intercept can and will be designed to minimize these effects, but the problem cannot be eliminated completely. Thus it is possible that the group of defensive missiles fired at the first incoming objects—perhaps only decoys—would themselves make it impossible for their own radar to pick up subsequent volleys.

None of these approaches—jamming, chaff or blackout—is particularly effective for intercepts in the atmosphere. In that case, the effort to blind the system must concentrate on attacking the radars. These structures are necessarily rather vulnerable targets and can be destroyed by offensive weapons of relatively low yield and accuracy. A warhead can be devised to home on the defensive radar. If the radar is destroyed, and there is no back up, all the defensive missiles controlled by it are out of action for the rest of the attack.

3. *Evasion:* A ballistic missile trajectory normally arches a thousand miles above the earth. Thus it appears above the horizon to the PAR while still many miles from the target. This is the key to the ABM system's ability to pick up the incoming missile in time to make the necessary calculations and launch a long-range defensive interceptor. The incoming missile can be launched on a much lower orbiting trajectory, however, so as not to become visible to the radar until about three minutes before impact. This is too late for the Spartan, and would give very little time for a Sprint interception as well. The low trajectory can be achieved by a "fractional orbit" launch (FOBS). This requires more energy, so that the nuclear warhead of the incoming missile would be correspondingly smaller. Missiles launched from submarines would also have a lower trajectory than ICBMs and would get closer to the target before being discovered by the PAR. Neither fractional orbit nor submarine-launched missiles have yet achieved the accuracy necessary to attack hard-point targets.

A second tactic, salvage fusing, would be effective against ABMs providing close-in defense of bomber bases or cities. An attacking missile could be fused to explode when a defensive ABM begins to get within striking range or even in the

# PATHS OF ATTACK

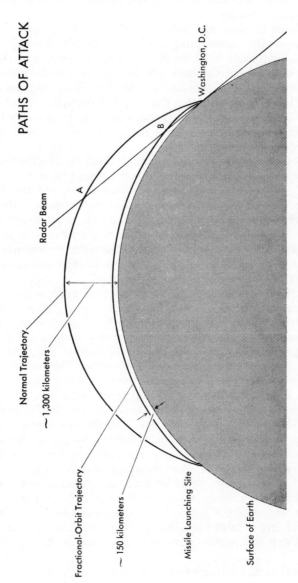

ABM radars begin to track an enemy warhead in normal trajectory at point A. But in a fractional orbit trajectory, they first see it at point B, giving much less reaction time. (Courtesy *Scientific American*)

first instant of the interceptor's explosion, to "salvage" its usefulness to an attacker. In the case of the Sprint this altitude would normally be between five and ten miles. At these heights, the effect of an explosion of the offensive weapon could be devastating to unprotected objects on the earth below. For instance a 5-megaton bomb exploding at a height of ten miles would set fire to the clothing of people standing in the open and to wooden structures over a 400-square-mile area. A fire storm is a serious likelihood. A 30-megaton warhead detonated at ten miles altitude would ignite an area of 2,500 square miles. The attacker could achieve similar effects by exploding the incoming warhead at a pre-set altitude just above the intercept height.

Alternatively, since the Sprint range is limited to about twenty-five miles, it would be easy for the attacker to explode his weapons just out of range of the ABM, in a place where the wind would blow the fallout over the target city.

4. *"Cost exchange"*: Any ABM system can be overwhelmed simply by attacking the target with more offensive missiles than there are defensive missiles available to respond. This approach may be more expensive than those already discussed, but we believe it is still considerably cheaper than the deployment of the defensive system itself. That is to say, an attacker can increase his offensive capability enough to overcome completely an ABM defense for less than it would cost the defender to build the system as proposed. Some years ago, it was generally agreed that the advantage held by the offense was ten to one or even more. The exact ratio, however, will depend on the character of the defense, the nature of the attack, the kind of mission and the degree of effectiveness required.

For example, in an attack on a valuable soft target like a city, bomber base or radar, the attacker might use ICBMs carrying four to ten RVs (not necessarily independently targeted), and the defense would typically have to commit three to five Sprints to each RV. If the attacking ICBMs cost the same as four Sprints, the exchange ratio is between three to one and twelve to one.

A system specially designed for the hard-point defense mission could do considerably better in this respect.

5. *The penetrability of the Sentinel/Safeguard system:* The net conclusions we draw from this analysis are as follows:

*First:* The Spartan defense can be easily penetrated. It cannot effectively discriminate decoys, it is sensitive to blackout, and it can be evaded by a variety of tactics. It has been said that this element of the system will "complicate" the problem of the attacker. Perhaps so, but certainly not to a degree that will be difficult for the attacker to overcome.

*Second:* The Sprint, too, is vulnerable to skillful offensive tactics and, particularly in any city-defense mission, to evasive tactics.

*Third:* Countermeasures are more difficult against ABMs defending hard-point targets. The Sentinel/Safeguard system, however, is vulnerable because it has extremely soft radars. Moreover, the cost to the offense of overwhelming the system is significantly less than the cost of deploying it. The margin is increased in Sentinel/Safeguard because the radars and missiles are more complex and expensive than is necessary for the hard-point defense mission.

## IV. *The ABM Missions: Their Obstacles*

Thus far, we have discussed in general terms the reliability of ABM systems, like those being proposed for deployment, and the countermeasures which might be used against them. But the effectiveness of defensive systems cannot be considered in the abstract. It must be judged in relation to the specific mission a system is called upon to perform. Four different and rather clearly defined missions have been frequently cited:

1. Defense of population against heavy attack.
2. Defense of population against light attack.
3. Defense of the strategic deterrent.
4. Defense against missiles launched by accident or through failure of command and control.

We usually think of the effectiveness of a defensive system in terms of how well it could be expected to perform if actually called upon to meet an attack—how many lives would be saved, how much damage prevented, how many of our own bombers or deterrent missiles defended. Our evaluation above of the reliability of proposed systems suggests that their effectiveness in this sense for any of the four missions is dubious at best.

But effectiveness can also be judged in the absence of

attack. It is generally agreed that any defensive system can be offset if the attacker is willing to pay enough to do so. Thus it can be said that a system is not effective unless it can impose on the attacker additional costs large enough to prevent or discourage him from taking the measures necessary to offset the system and to restore his capability for delivering the particular type of attack involved. This approach means, in the first place, a careful analysis of the requirements of each defensive mission: what will a system deployed for that mission have to do and with what degree of efficiency in order to impose significant additional costs on the adversary? Second, we must weigh the importance of the particular capability to the opponent. He will be prepared to pay a heavy price to maintain a capability he feels is essential. Finally, even if the defense is effective in some absolute sense for a particular mission, we must consider what alternative courses are available—including the alternative of doing nothing—and try to estimate the costs and risks of these alternatives compared to those of ABM deployment.

We turn now to the application of these lines of analysis to each of the proposed missions.

1. *Defense of population against heavy attack:* Both this Administration and the last have concluded that this mission cannot be performed by ABM systems using components like those under consideration. In his announcement on September 18, 1967, Defense Secretary McNamara warned:

> There is no point whatever in our responding [to a failure in arms limitation agreements] by going to a massive ABM deployment to protect our population, when such a system would be ineffective against a sophisticated Soviet offense.

And President Nixon, on March 14, 1969, explained that

> Although every instinct motivates me to provide the American people with complete protection against a major nuclear attack, it is not now within our power to do so. The heaviest defense system we considered, one designed to protect our major cities, still could not prevent a catastrophic level of U.S. fatalities from a deliberate all-out Soviet attack.

Substantially all informed technical opinion agrees.

Despite this near-unanimity of view, we thought it important to consider the mission of city defense against heavy attack. This is not only so that the report will be comprehensive. This mission, if it could be accomplished, would obviously be the most important that could be assigned to an ABM system. It is often argued in favor of ABM deployment for other missions that, as a by-product, we will gain valuable experience that can be applied to a heavy defense sometime in the future. If we accept the conclusion that it is inherently impossible to defend our cities by means of ABMs of the present mode against a massive retaliatory strike, it follows that the experience of simpler ABM deployments will be of only illusory value.

About three-quarters of the population of the United States are now concentrated in two hundred urban areas, occupying less than 1 percent of our land mass. A thousand megatons in weapons of 1- and 5-megaton yields properly mixed and targeted would wreak total destruction or heavy damage throughout this area. The fatalities from blast, incineration and direct radiation would be of the order of 100 million. This figure would grow to 120 million or more as death from fallout, injury, disease, starvation and exposure took its toll. Not only has the Soviet Union the capability to deliver an attack of at least this size and complexity; it will be able to deliver an attack several times as large a few years hence. And we have, and will continue to have, the capability to reciprocate and more. An attack in the range of 5,000 megatons would kill essentially all the inhabitants of either country. Nor is this all. The stockpiles of nuclear warheads in the Soviet Union and the United States are now measured in many thousands of megatons. And almost limitless expansion beyond this level is possible with presently available supplies of nuclear material. Hence, beyond what is quickly deliverable by missile, lies enough, if used, to end most human life on this planet.

The enormous scale of the potential for nuclear destruction puts the problem of providing city defense in its proper perspective. We now rely on mutual deterrence to prevent all-out nuclear war. Secretary McNamara estimated direct fatalities from a second-strike attack on the United States in the mid-seventies at more than 100 million, and this would be true even if the United States struck first at Soviet military targets.[9]

[9] Secretary McNamara gave no estimate for casualties from indirect effects and the destruction caused by the attack.

No defense could be effective in protecting city population against the maximum strike of which the Soviets are presently capable. Even if an ABM system were 90 percent successful, several hundred megatons would be delivered on the United States—meaning virtual destruction of a comparable number of target cities and perhaps fifty million people.

We do not believe 90 percent success is anything like a realistic figure against a determined and sophisticated attack on soft urban targets. But if United States ABM defense began to approach or even appeared to be approaching a significant degree of effectiveness, the ineluctable logic of mutual deterrence would take over. The Soviet Union would have to take measures to offset these defenses to whatever extent it felt necessary to maintain a secure deterrent. Still more of its essentially inexhaustible nuclear stockpile would be put on the firing line.

Interaction between offense and defense is inevitable in a city-defense mission. If we deploy defenses of cities against the present Soviet capability, they will respond. The response may take two forms. Either they will increase the level of their capability by adding to their arsenal of offensive missiles, or they may provide additional penetration aids to the present force. In practice, they are likely to do some of both. The deployments would introduce great uncertainty into the situation on both sides, and so each would be led to overcompensate in its response to the moves made by the other.

Others have argued that the ABM city defense will be effective in that it will force the offense to multiply the warheads carried by a single missile. This, they say, would mean "smaller" warheads with less destructive capability. But the offensive will not necessarily follow this course. It may simply deploy more missiles. Even if it does multiply warheads, the destructive capacity of its missiles may not be reduced and may be increased. The Soviet SS-11 carries warheads of about 1 megaton. Even if these were to be reduced to 50 kilotons—that is by a factor of 20—the warhead would be two and a half times as large as the Hiroshima bomb. A cluster of these might be more efficient than a single 1-megaton warhead. Finally, the offense could use larger missiles capable of carrying multiple warheads in the megaton range. The Soviet SS-9 may be such a missile.

The point, of course, is not that the offense would avoid incurring additional costs. But these costs would be significantly less than the costs of deploying the defense. And in any case, the other side would consider it essential to accept the additional costs to the extent necessary to ensure that it continued to have undoubted retaliatory power.

We in turn would reconfigure and try to improve our ABM system in response to our changing perceptions of how their offensive system was developing. But ABM defense is much more complicated and highly integrated than offensive missile systems. It is intrinsically less flexible than the offense and cannot be altered rapidly to accommodate new threats. Thus it will be easier and cheaper for them to adapt their offense to the changing situation than for us to adapt our defense.

These considerations are particularly relevant to the city-defense mission because cities are vulnerable to a wide range of different attack strategies. We list a few. An ABM system with the mission of population defense against heavy attack would have to be prepared to cope with all of these and more:

a. Very large warheads, in the range of 25–100 megatons, exploded at altitudes of ten to thirty miles; the largest of such bursts could burn out an area the size of Connecticut.

b. Salvage fusing.

c. Showers of small bombs ranging from Hiroshima size to perhaps 100 kilotons, carried by a relatively few offensive missiles, to overload the data-handling capacity and exhaust the missiles of the ABM system.

d. Maneuverable warheads designed to evade interception.

e. Bombs carried by boost-glide re-entry vehicles, which permit pull-ups, turns, dives and other evasive maneuvers.

f. Fallout attacks, with large, dirty bombs targeted at a considerable distance upwind from population centers; long-lived fallout can be maximized by use of cobalt bombs, so that fallout shelters would not be much help.

g. Large weapons delivered by FOBS (Fractional Orbital Bombardment Systems) or other systems that may give only a short warning, in the range of a few minutes.

h. Large weapons exploded in the waters off shore from major cities, including the Great Lakes and largest rivers, causing tidal waves that might engulf the cities.

In addition the offense would doubtless apply the penetration strategies discussed in Section III above: decoys of great variety interspersed with the warheads; blackout or other measures to confuse the radars; and attacks on the radars by homing missiles or cheap, large warheads.

These are but a part of the arsenal available to a determined adversary intent on maintaining a reliable deterrent. And his ingenuity would be further stimulated if he knew he were faced with a major attempt at city defense on our side. Thus, population defense against heavy attack would require an enormous system reactive in a very short time to a great number and variety of attack options and attack weapons.

It is perhaps possible to design and build in five years' time a defense against a known delivery system, with predictable characteristics and numbers of warheads. Even then, there is the question of reliability: whether it would perform as designed. But the offensive delivery system would *not* remain unchanged for five years, when the defensive system might be installed and operational. And to design a system that would deal with the whole range of unknown and unknowable attack patterns available to the offense, and with their shifts over time, is simply not now in the cards.

Even the attempt to develop such a system might have significant adverse consequences. There might be an effort, for instance, to improve the ratio of incoming missiles destroyed, by seeking to intercept at lower altitudes. Below five miles the intercepting warheads themselves, as well as salvage-fused and airburst offensive weapons, would have radiation, blast and fallout effects on the defended area beneath. Proponents of heavy population defense have drawn the necessary conclusions and advocated a nationwide heavy shelter program as one component. But this would involve sums that no responsible official has been willing to contemplate, to say nothing of the psychological atmosphere of a garrison state.

We should state categorically that simply "thickening" Sentinel/Safeguard by deploying missiles around cities and increasing the number at each site would not be even a first approximation to the task of designing a city defense against heavy attack. A thicker system is, of course, more costly for the attacker to overcome by simply exhausting the ABMs than a thinner one. Even then, it seems clear that the cost advantage is with the attacker. But the simple expedient of thickening does not begin to address the problems presented by possible variations in the tactics of the attack such as those discussed just above.

As a result, we conclude that, because of the vulnerability

of our cities and population to even a small fraction of the
megatons the Soviets can deliver, the problem of defending
the population against a heavy attack by using antiballistic
missiles is essentially insoluble with the technology presently
available or likely to be available in the foreseeable future.
Research and development on this problem should concentrate
on different lines of approach.

2. *Defense of population against light attack:* The key
element in planning for ABM defense against a light attack is
the possibility that a single ABM battery could defend a very
large region, rather than the relatively small area around the
target at which the battery is emplaced. If, for example,
defensive missiles had no more than the twenty-five-mile
range of the Sprint, it would be necessary to defend each city
target with its own ABM battery. A light attack, by definition, would not attack all cities, and would, in fact, very
likely be concentrated on one or a few. Thus most of the short-
range missiles deployed would never get into action. The cost
of such a defense would be very high indeed, compared to
the costs required for the attacker to offset it.

By contrast, the Spartan missile is designed to make its
intercept at a range of several hundred miles, when the
ICBM is still above the atmosphere. Thus an area of some
250,000 square miles is within range of a single Spartan
battery, and a dozen or so properly placed could cover the
entire land area of the United States. See pages 43 and 45 for
maps of Spartan deployments. In addition, there would be the
obvious advantage that engagements would be fought far
from the ground so that the effects of the nuclear explosions
would be negligible.

But these advantages carry with them their own severe
defects. The system, as noted, is especially vulnerable to
countermeasures. Let us recall a few of them:

a. The ABM system can be confused by decoys because it
cannot depend on the atmosphere to sort out light decoys
from the heavier warheads.

b. Chaff, blackout and radar jamming are most effective at
the altitudes of planned intercept for this system.

c. Attacking missiles can be programed to execute evasive
maneuvers in the intercept range.

d. Cruise missiles, FOBS or other low-trajectory launches

would probably not be detected soon enough for interception by a relatively long-range missile.

It will be recalled that most of these tactics are available not only to the U.S.S.R. The technology and cost are thought to be within reach of China also, and for its first generation of ICBMs.

Each of these countermeasures in area-defense systems can be offset to some extent. The Pentagon has made generally reassuring statements on this matter, but there has been little public discussion of the specific techniques planned for the Sentinel/Safeguard system and no basis for judging their effectiveness. In the absence of more detailed analysis, it is hard to be very sanguine. Each of the attack options listed above is formidable in itself. It seems unlikely that their use in skillful combination could be countered by any currently foreseeable defense.

Penetrability is not the only hazard for area defense. It is by nature a thin defense—let us assume about forty long-range missiles to a site.[10] What protection can these forty missiles provide to the population of an area of 250,000 square miles, even if the attacking side does not use penetration aids? The answer has to be "not much."

An attack, even though characterized as "light," would not be spread evenly over the country as is the defense. The attacker could, and doubtless would, concentrate his few missiles on one or a very few areas. Thus he has a very good chance of exhausting or overwhelming even a 100 percent reliable ABM defense. At the 50 to 70 percent interceptor reliabilities we must count on, attacking missiles would get through in 25 to 58 percent of the cases, even if only three are successfully launched at each target city and two interceptors are committed to each incoming missile.

Against an attack with as many as a dozen missiles equipped with even primitive penetration aids—the kind that China may be able to deploy in the 1970s—the chances for successfully defending a city target must be rated extremely low.

It is argued that if any missiles are intercepted by the system, many lives will be saved. Moreover, even forcing the attacker to concentrate his forces will have that effect, since

[10] A figure in this range is consistent with the descriptions given of the Sentinel/Safeguard.

missiles that could otherwise have been aimed against other cities will now have to be used to beef up the main attack. This may be granted. But it does not amount to the capability to prevent virtually any damage in a light attack, a capability that has been claimed for an area-defense system. A concentrated attack against even one heavily populated area—say, New York—would almost certainly result in casualties of several millions.

We should, of course, be willing to pay a good deal to save lives if there were no disadvantages to deploying the defense and if the contingency against which we were defending were a real one. But neither of these conditions holds.

If we run some risk by not deploying, that must be weighed against the risk that deployment will upset the strategic balance between the United States and the U.S.S.R.

In any case, the risk is small.

A careful analysis of Chinese use of force since the Communists came to power in 1949 shows that, despite stridency and bluster, Peking has kept its forces on a tight rein, not committing them in support of an adventurous foreign policy, but only when what appeared to be vital interests close to China's own borders were at stake. Except for Vietnam, Red China has not even given significant support to so-called "wars of national liberation."

It is almost inconceivable that China, or any other infant nuclear power that had expended the vast resources and the many years of purposeful effort required to develop a modern nuclear capability, would squander it in an attack that could achieve no useful end, and would bring on its own annihilation under the full force of the United States retaliatory nuclear arsenal. Why should we assume that the deterrence which has prevented nuclear war during two decades in which the Soviets have had nuclear arms will not operate equally against the Chinese? That a "thin" area defense, which addresses itself to a microscopic part of the spectrum of nuclear threat, at a cost comparable to that of the entire Minuteman or Polaris force, can be seriously considered is itself a kind of irrationality.

There is one possible situation in which a Chinese-oriented ABM system will perform a function—not essentially defensive but offensive. With an ABM system in being, it might seem to some that the United States could make a first strike against China on the assumption that our own territory would be safe from retaliation. We have already argued that the assumption would be false. And certainly the notion of the United States making a deliberate first strike against any country is repugnant to most Americans. Nevertheless, it is likely that this is the motive the Chinese would see behind any Chinese-oriented ABM system. In that sense, its result would be to prolong the period of intransigence and hostility between us and mainland China.

3. *Defense of the deterrent:* The United States nuclear deterrent comprises primarily three strategic offensive forces:

*Polaris nuclear submarines.* At present, the Polaris fleet consists of 41 ships carrying 16 intermediate-range missiles each, for a total of 656 nuclear missiles. Thirty-one of these submarines are being refitted with Poseidon missiles, which have a longer range than Polaris and are able to carry about 10 warheads each. Thus, when the program is completed, the submarine fleet will be able to deliver about 5,000 nuclear warheads.

*ICBMs of two varieties.* There are 1,000 Minutemen carrying 1-megaton warheads, and 54 Titans with larger warheads. Some of the Minutemen are also about to be refitted with multiple warheads.

*Strategic Air Command bombers.* There are 650 intercontinental bombers, carrying an average of about 4 weapons each, and capable of reaching the Soviet Union from bases in the United States, delivering their bomb loads and returning home.

In all then, we presently have about 4,200 strategic nuclear weapons (to be more than doubled in the next few years), plus some thousands of additional warheads in carrier and tactical aircraft stationed abroad within range of the Soviet Union. These weapons systems, or any one of them, are capable of launching a devastating attack within a few minutes' notice on any conceivable enemy.

Only the U.S.S.R. has a nuclear arsenal of anything like these dimensions. Our present intelligence on Soviet strategic forces shows an ICBM force of about 1,000. (It may be that some 200 more are in the process of deployment.) About 600 of these are SS-11s, comparable to our Minuteman; about 230 are SS-9s, capable of carrying considerably larger payloads. The remainder are of other models. The bulk of this force has been deployed in the last three years. In addition, the Soviets have 150 intercontinental bombers, a few nuclear submarines

# UNITED STATES OFFENSIVE MISSILES

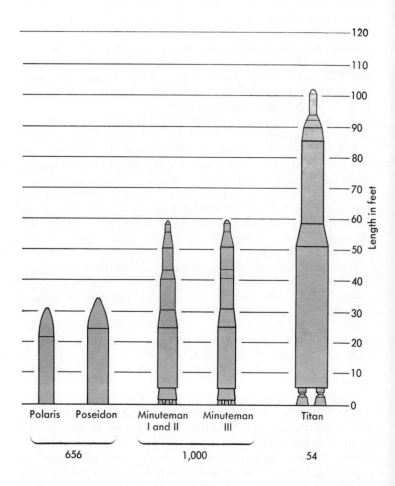

The Minuteman and Titan missiles (land-based) and the Polaris and Poseidon missiles (sea-based) make up only part of the U.S. strategic deterrent. The 650 Strategic Air Command bombers (B-52s and B-58s) carry some 2,600 nuclear bombs. The Navy's carrier-based aircraft and the medium and intermediate range missiles in Europe all carry nuclear weapons and confront any potential adversary. As the United States adds multiple warheads to its missiles, the number of deliverable *strategic* (long-range) nuclear warheads will rise sharply from the 4,200 figure given in October, 1968. (Courtesy *Scientific American*)

and large numbers of intermediate-range missiles and planes that could be used to attack targets in Europe or in the bordering oceans.

These two formidable forces are kept at bay by the operation of mutual deterrence. This means that each side knows the other can absorb an all-out attack and still be able to inflict "unacceptable damage" on the attacker in retaliation. If each side knows this, it will not attack first. Nuclear stalemate is the result. The essence of this relationship is the maintenance of an "invulnerable deterrent" or "assured destruction capability"[11]—a retaliatory force secure at all times against being knocked out by a surprise attack.

There is no doubt that the U.S. retaliatory force is secure in this sense today. It is worth analyzing what it would take for an adversary to achieve a first-strike capability. The attack would have to destroy simultaneously close to 100 percent of each of the three strategic forces and the tactical aircraft described above. The offense would not only have to be able to accomplish this feat, but be quite certain it could. Otherwise it could not rationally attack.

With our Minutemen in hardened silos, it would take at least two attacking ICBMs to be reasonably sure of destroying one Minuteman. Since this report was delivered to the Senate, Dr. John Foster, Director of Defense Research and Engineering, has argued that the two-to-one ratio in favor of the attacker is unnecessary, if the attacker uses a two-volley attack pattern. The second volley would be aimed at the particular Minutemen that had survived through malfunction of attacking missiles in the first volley. The possibility of such an attack pattern depends on the addition of a complex and not-yet-invented reporting and feedback component in the Russian missiles. It is subject to other objections; for example, it as-

[11] All these terms are used more or less interchangeably. In 1968 Secretary McNamara defined "unacceptable damage" as 20 to 25 percent of a country's population and a higher percentage of its industrial economy after absorbing a heavy first strike. But it is overprecise to try to talk in such quantitative terms. There are not very many political objectives for which political leaders would take substantial risks of even one or a few million casualties. The same problem arises in the discussion of first-strike capability. The number of weapons required to give high confidence of destroying an opposing missile force can be calculated with fair accuracy. But decisions in the real world are not made by counting missiles. Indeed, the danger is that moments of political crisis may obscure the horrifying truth behind these dry calculations.

sumes an extraordinarily high kill probability once the missile is successfully launched. But the overriding defect in the argument is this: In order to use the two-volley pattern, the attacker has to be sure, not only that the defense will not fire on warning when the first volley appears on the radar (a point on which we comment below), but also that the defense would wait passively for the second volley after a large number of his missiles were actually destroyed in the first wave. Perhaps the defense would be that obliging in the event of an actual attack, but surely the first-strike attacker could not rely on this. He must plan to knock out substantially all U.S. Minutemen in his first blow, and to do so, he must go back to the two-to-one ratio.

Bombers would start leaving the ground within five minutes of warning. Half can be airborne in fifteen minutes and a larger fraction if they have been put on alert status. This is too much for Soviet air defenses to cope with now, or in the foreseeable future. Thus the bomber bases would have to be attacked by a method giving extremely short warning. Even this would not help if a substantial portion of the SAC bombers were on airborne alert.

Every Polaris submarine would have to be destroyed virtually at the same time, probably by a separate vessel assigned for the attack.

In addition, the European bases and carriers would have to be taken out.

All this would have to be coordinated so that no part of the attack gave adequate warning time to any substantial element of the retaliatory force. Thus, for example, only ICBMs are accurate and powerful enough to destroy hardened missile sites. Our BMEWS radar will give a twenty-minute warning of a missile attack against Minutemen, and the other warning systems—as by satellite—may give somewhat more. Thus the bombers will be alerted and will be able to take off. But if the opposing missiles are held back to permit a short-warning attack against the bomber bases, the destruction of those bases will be the signal for the launch of the Minutemen, before an ICBM attack can reach them.

There is another major difficulty with any first-strike plan —the possibility of early launch of the ICBMs under attack. U.S. firing doctrine for ICBMs has always stressed that they will not be launched on warning, but only after hostile nuclear weapons have actually landed on friendly territory. This is a salutary rule for itchy trigger fingers. Still, no matter how often we recite this rule, the attacker cannot be certain that, in case of massive attack, we would not decide that the best way to ensure that the Minutemen performed their retaliatory mission would be to fire them before the hostile ICBMs arrived at their silos.

It is thus apparent that a successful first strike against United States retaliatory forces is today an impossibility. Secretary of Defense Laird has said, however, that he believes the Soviet Union may be seeking such a capability in the future. He cites the rapid deployment of the 25-megaton-warhead[12] SS-9 resumed in December, 1968, after a period of quiescence.

Secretary Laird argues that the Soviets *may* continue SS-9 deployment at the recent rate for the next several years, that they *may* equip each of these missiles with three or more warheads, and that they *may* achieve the capability to aim each warhead separately with sufficient accuracy to be useful in an attack on Minutemen silos. He also cites Russian expansion of its nuclear submarine fleet and development of FOBS. Both weapons systems are capable of attacking soft targets, such as bomber bases, on very short warning. He speaks of Soviet progress in antisubmarine warfare, though without adducing any evidence to offset the repeated claims that have been made for the invulnerability of the Polaris fleet. Finally, the Soviet ABM deployment around Moscow, it is said, may be designed to limit the damage that would be done by U.S. retaliation. It is important to understand that these assertions by Secretary Laird are not based on any intelli-

[12] The 25-megaton warhead is not a much more serious threat than a 5-megaton warhead. Delivery of a 5-megaton weapon with an accuracy of one-half mile would give about a 65 percent probability of a Minuteman silo's being destroyed, according to information recently made available by Deputy Secretary of Defense Packard. Assuming a 70 percent reliability for Soviet ICBMs, approximately four would have to be targeted on each of our Minuteman sites to achieve a 90 percent probability of destruction. Even if Soviet weapons had yields of 25 megatons and accuracy considerably better than one-half mile, about two would have to be targeted on each Minuteman to achieve the same probability of destruction. Thus, as long as the number of accurately targetable Soviet warheads does not exceed approximately double the number of our own launchers, a substantial number of our ICBMs would survive a pre-emptive attack—probably enough so that, even neglecting completely the other components of our strategic forces, we would have an adequate retaliatory capability.

gence about new Soviet weapons systems. They represent his interpretation of facts that have, in the main, been known for some time, but have not been viewed heretofore by the responsible officials as signaling a Soviet attempt to attain a first-strike capability.

The Soviet developments noted are subject to a variety of explanations. Indeed, we have been engaged in similar activities ourselves, although we do not have a policy of seeking a first-strike capacity. The Soviet missile build-up in recent years can be seen as a response to our increase from about 200 to 1,000 ICBMs in the early 1960s. SS-9s and submarine-launched missiles are effective anti-city—that is, second-strike—weapons. The deployment of FOBS, which can perform the same mission, may represent a hedge against a U.S. area antimissile defense system. Accurate targeting of MIRVs is still a considerable time in the future for the U.S.S.R. There is no reason to suppose that their ASW effort, though stepped up, will be any more successful than it has been heretofore; or than our very intensive one has, for that matter. The Soviet ABM deployment is very small and has, in any case, been an on-again, off-again effort.

For our part, we agree with a less threatening interpretation of the intelligence data. It corresponds to Soviet behavior in the past, when they failed to take advantage of what we thought were opportunities to gain a first-strike capability against us. The nonexistent bomber gap of the early fifties, and a similar missile gap of the early sixties—and the vast armaments we built to fill them—are earlier monuments to our propensity for exaggerating Soviet capabilities and intentions.

Nevertheless these are matters on which it is hard to be certain, and prudence has always dictated protective measures for the deterrent force. The Polaris has relied on its silence, range and maneuverability to provide what has been thought impregnable concealment. For the bombers, we have also depended on mobility and quick reaction—the ability to get a substantial portion of the force off the ground on very short alert. And for ICBMs, we have employed hardening and dispersal techniques so that only a very accurate attack by a fairly large weapon could destroy even one.

We believe that nothing more by way of defensive measures need be taken now. This is not only because we do not accept Secretary Laird's interpretation of the intelligence. Even if his predictions about future Soviet developments and deployments turn out to be correct, there will be ample time to take any necessary measures after a year or two, when further observation will have clarified the uncertainties in the present picture. At the present rate of SS-9 deployment—even assuming spectacularly rapid MIRV development—it would take eight years for the Soviet Union to acquire the minimum two-to-one superiority over our Minuteman force, if our force remained at its present level. United States intelligence would certainly know of any such large build-up, to say nothing of developments in air defense and effective ASW methods, that would be necessary for any first strike.

From the technical standpoint alone, it is desirable to delay defensive measures as long as possible, because it will be more difficult for the opponent to adapt an offensive force already in place to the particular form of response chosen; and it will be easier to plan a response for the offense already deployed when its characteristics are known.

But even if further assurances for this deterrent were needed now, the question remains whether it should take the form of an ABM system. The Polaris fleet is not vulnerable to missile attack, so that ABM defense is irrelevant for that portion of the deterrent force. We now examine the possibilities of ABM systems for defending bomber bases and ICBMs.

a. *Strategic bomber bases:* Bombers are soft targets, like cities. Their protection presents similar problems. For a particular base, anything less than a 100 percent successful defense must be counted a failure. A 5-megaton explosion within five miles of a bomber would create an overpressure exceeding 5 pounds per square inch and would destroy the bomber. Thus the whole base, even if very extensive, is at risk from a single explosion.

As we have seen, there are other ways to protect bombers. In the event of a developing crisis, they can be dispersed individually to other locations, and, as we have seen, they can respond very quickly to warning. Thus removing the bombers from the target area will continue to represent a much better strategy than attempting to provide a perfect ABM defense.

An attack on bombers is necessarily an attack on short warning. This, as we have seen, is not easy to carry out. But if it could be accomplished, area defense would be bypassed.

The ABM defense would then have to rely on the close-in, short-range missiles. These would be exhausted easily, for in defense of a soft target, requiring virtually 100 percent effectiveness, at least three interceptors must be committed to each incoming missile.

b. *Missile bases:* Any attack against our Minutemen would almost certainly be a heavy one, with the full array of decoys and penetration aids. Long-range area defense is, therefore, irrelevant. Only shorter-range interceptors, deployed close to the target, will have any chance of defending the hardened ICBM site.

We recognize that this defense does not face many of the problems of ABM systems in population-defense missions. Because the heights of intercept can be very much lower, light decoys, chaff, blackout and other devices to neutralize the radars are relatively ineffective. Simpler and cheaper interceptors can be used, and also cheaper radars. Most important of all, the defense need not be virtually 100 percent effective. Not all targets need be defended; not all those defended need be saved. The object is to preserve a significant part of the missile force against heavy attack, and this can be done even if many attacking warheads get through.

There is one great weakness in the ABM defense, however. If a radar is knocked out, all the associated interceptor missiles are useless. ABM radars are large structures with enclosures that must be transparent to radar waves. Consequently, the possibilities for hardening them are limited. It seems reasonable that resistance to pressures of 20–30 pounds per square inch is about the maximum that could be achieved. A 1-megaton burst creates this overpressure out to about $1\frac{1}{2}$ miles. Hence the radar is an easy target. Any ICBM with present-day guidance, including relatively inaccurate ones, like the Soviet SS-11, could destroy it. The attacker's strategy would be to go after the radars. Only a mythical 100 percent effectiveness in dealing with such an attack would permit the ABM battery to continue to function.

One alternative to defending existing missiles is to deploy additional ones. It is argued that such a move is provocative, but in fact we are moving to increase our offensive warheads already by installing MIRVs on Minuteman IIIs. In any case, the problem of "provocation" would not arise in a situation where the Soviets were approaching a substantial superiority in ICBMs.

In simplest terms, the cost of defending a U.S. ICBM must not be more than a few times greater than the cost of building or super-hardening another. We might accept a certain additional cost to avoid "provocation." But if the cost of defense is many times that of the missiles protected, the pressures to increase the offensive force will be hard to deny. Because of the necessity of defending the radar, we are clear that this economic requirement is not met by ABM systems with presently planned radars.

4. *Defense against accidental launch:* A single missile launched by accident or failure of command and control could take a high toll of lives and property. Perhaps more important, an accidental launch, misinterpreted, might itself be the trigger for a large-scale nuclear war. Thus it is self-evidently desirable to be able to intercept and destroy such missiles.

The range of possible but improbable firings is so great, however, that only a fraction of them could be anticipated in the program of an ABM system. The area defense might provide some protection against the most frequently mentioned kind of accident: a single missile fired by error. But if the malfunction is in the other side's control mechanisms, it might result in salvo firing, complete with decoys and penetration aids, so that the ABM system would have the same vulnerabilities as against a real attack.

It should be noted that in order to be effective against accident, the system and its personnel would have to be operating at a high state of alert at all times. It is doubtful whether such a degree of alert can be maintained for long periods. In any case, the effort to keep the ABM system continuously in a state of extreme readiness in itself adds to the likelihood of an accidental launch of a *defensive* missile. It is unlikely, as we have said, that such an accident would result in a nuclear explosion, but in the area where the missile fell to earth, in the United States or Canada, the consequences might be considerable. It would be ironic if, in our pursuit of absolute security against missiles accidentally launched from abroad, we increased the hazards created by our own missiles at home.

Fortunately, the major nuclear powers have been keenly aware of the possible consequences of accidental launch. They have made intensive efforts to ensure that it will not occur. This self-interest will continue to be the major force operating to prevent accidents in the future, as it has in the past. The maintenance of ready communication between the nuclear powers is perhaps the most practical insurance against misinterpretation in the event that an accidental launch does occur. In this situation, the time is approaching when it will be important to include China in the "hot line" network. Possibly, too, nuclear powers could be persuaded to mount devices in ICBMs that would permit destruction of missiles fired by accident.

We conclude that an ABM system, if it performed reliably, could provide some protection against some kinds of accidental missile launches. Nobody, however, has argued that the costs of ABM deployment could be justified on the basis of its performance in this mission alone.

## V. *Sentinel/Safeguard: Its Tasks*

When the F-111 (nee TFX) was in its early stages of development, it was cast as the all-purpose fighter-bomber. The temptation to assign a series of tasks to a single weapons system is indeed understandable, given the time, cost and complexity associated with any such large-scale defense project. The job description of the Sentinel/Safeguard has, in this respect, been instructive. It was, in its Sentinel period, characterized by Secretary McNamara as a defense of the population "against the Chinese threat," as well as a protection against the accidental launch of a few ICBMs. Under Secretary Laird, its name was changed—to Safeguard—and its duties were effectively enlarged. This, of course, poses the concrete question: How well can the ABM that is on the drawing boards perform its assigned tasks?

As outlined by Secretary Laird in testimony before the Senate Armed Services Committee on March 19, 1969, the purposes of Safeguard were four in number:

a. A local defense of the Minuteman missile silos.

b. Early warning and area defense of our bomber bases and command-and-control system.

c. A defense of the continental United States against the kind of attack which the Chinese Communists may be able to launch in the mid-1970s.

d. Protection against an accidental or small attack from any source.

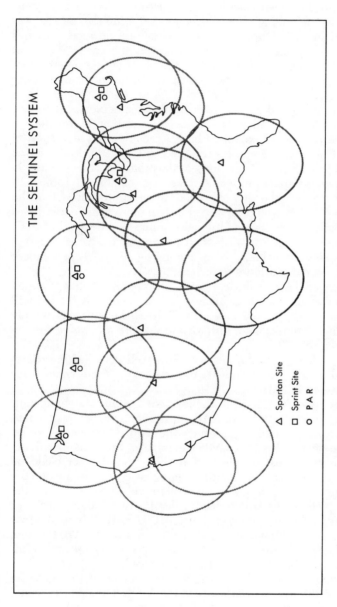

THE SENTINEL SYSTEM

△ Spartan Site

□ Sprint Site

O P A R

The oval "footprints" show the U.S. area covered by the now-discarded Sentinel system, using both Sprint and Spartan missiles. (Courtesy *Scientific American*)

There has been a widespread misconception that the mission of defending U.S. cities against Chinese attack was abandoned by the new Administration. Secretary Laird's testimony makes clear that this is not the case. The point deserves emphasis, because it is the effort at city defense that tends to upset the strategic balance between major nuclear powers.

The Safeguard system is scheduled for deployment in two distinct phases, allowing for some variation in mission in response to developments. Phase 1 includes only two sites, at the Minuteman complexes centered on Grand Forks Air Force Base in North Dakota, and Malmstrom Air Force Base in Montana. Expansion would take one of several forms: In Phase 2A, if the ICBMs need more protection from the U.S.S.R., sites would be added at two more Minuteman bases with all sites getting additional Sprints. In Phases 2B or 2C, the system would be expanded to the full twelve sites either in response to a threat to our bombers (2B) or if the Chinese ICBM threat continues to increase (2C).

Our analysis will deal with all phases of the planned deployment, since it is likely that the conditions for 2C will be met, and, in any case, the Defense Department is now seeking Congressional authority to acquire all twelve sites in Fiscal 1969–70.

a. *Defense of the deterrent:* How well does Sentinel/Safeguard meet the technical and economic requirements for defense of ICBMs?

The two-site Phase 1 deployment, within the budgetary limits announced by the Administration, would have about 150 Sprint missiles guarding the two Minuteman wings. There would also be a smaller number of Spartans, but these, as we saw, must be discounted. Thus the attacker could be sure to exhaust the Sentinel/Safeguard defense by simply adding 150 warheads to his offensive force to offset the Sprints. Since he would need at least a two-to-one margin, or 2,100 warheads, to attack the 1,050 U.S. ICBMs in the first place, the additional cost imposed on him by the ABM system would be at most 7 percent. This is not a "significant" additional cost, but it could be further reduced.

The attacker could exploit the importance of the radar by aiming the first 50 warheads at the MSR. The defense would have to commit at least 3 Sprints per incoming warhead to be sure to save the radar, so the 150 Sprints would be exhausted

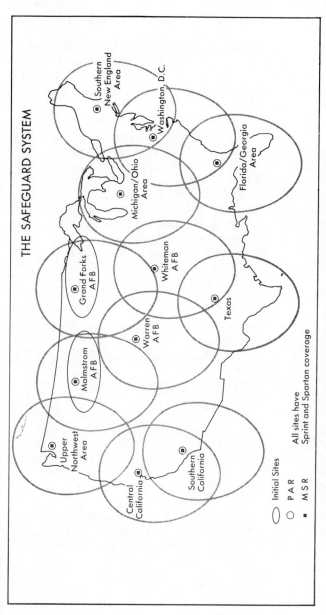

# THE SAFEGUARD SYSTEM

| | |
|---|---|
| ○ Initial Sites | All sites have |
| ◎ PAR | Sprint and Spartan coverage |
| ■ MSR | |

Labels on map: Southern New England Area; Washington D.C.; Florida/Georgia Area; Michigan/Ohio Area; Grand Forks AFB; Whiteman AFB; Texas; Warren AFB; Malmstrom AFB; Upper Northwest Area; Central California; Southern California

The "footprints" for the Safeguard system reveal that the area of the United States to be covered by Sprint and Spartan missiles is very nearly the same as that in the Sentinel system. (Courtesy *Scientific American*)

by the first 50 warheads, even if the radar were not destroyed earlier. The additional cost would be less than 2.5 percent of the total.

He could exploit the softness of the radar by firing at it with large but inaccurate weapons not good enough to use against hardened silos. The Soviet SS-11 is such a weapon. In that event the cost of the attacking force is not increased at all.

Even without attacking the radar he could exhaust the Sprints at a rapid rate by delivering a mixed attack including many light warheads and heavy decoys at low altitudes.

If the Phase 1 deployment by itself is useless, what of Phase 2A, in which four Minuteman bases are defended with a greater number of Sprints? The answer depends in part on how many more Sprints. To be very conservative, suppose that for every three Sprints we add, we force the attacker to add one warhead. At some point the cost to him could become so great that he would refuse to accept it and would abandon his goal of a first-strike capacity. We cannot say exactly when this would happen. But on this analysis, he would have to double the size of the 2,100 warhead force originally required, if we deployed a Phase 2A with 6,000 Sprints at a cost of some $10 billion. But we could accomplish the same thing by increasing our Minuteman force at a cost of perhaps $4 billion, a ratio of almost four to one in favor of the latter alternative.

Finally, what about the full twelve-site deployment of Phase 2B or 2C? This would include, in addition to the four Minuteman wings, seven bomber bases and the National Command Center at Washington. The bomber bases are soft targets that can be destroyed by a single warhead. As we have seen, their defense against heavy attack poses insuperable problems for an ABM system with the reliability and penetrability of Sentinel/Safeguard. The bombers must continue to rely on mobility and alert.

b. *Defense of the population:* We have already said that no system could successfully defend cities against heavy attack. Sentinel/Safeguard cannot, and it is not intended to do so. It is, however, intended to provide thin, nationwide defense against a Chinese or other light attack and also against accidental launch. The latter alone, as we said, would not justify the system, but it might be worth deploying an ABM that could reliably protect against light attack by China or some other new nuclear power. Our analysis raises serious doubts that any presently designable ABM system could provide such protection. Sentinel/Safeguard almost certainly could not.

It relies for the defense of cities almost entirely on the high-altitude intercepts by Spartan missiles. The Chinese are still developing their ICBMs. They can include a number of simple penetration aids that can rather easily negate the high-altitude defense. As we have seen, they would concentrate their attack on one or a few great population centers. The duel would be between a few dozen Chinese ICBMs and a single Spartan battery. The concentration would also enhance the effectiveness of chaff and blackout in confusing the defending radars. There seems no reason to doubt that at least a few warheads would get through, with deaths running into the millions.

We should reiterate that our conclusion directly contradicts the claim of Dr. John S. Foster, Jr., the Pentagon's Director of Defense Research and Engineering, that the Sentinel/Safeguard system would prevent any significant damage from a light Chinese attack. The Department of Defense has not revealed the assumptions that underlie such claims for Sentinel/Safeguard's effectiveness. Until they do, those claims must be treated with the greatest skepticism.

We believe the issue could be illuminated by running computer simulations of the system's response to various possible Chinese attacks. Security considerations have prevented us from doing so for this report. No doubt the results of such studies could be produced in appropriately classified Congressional hearings.

A population defense would have value even if it only reduced the number of casualties. But before committing upwards of $7 billion to this end, we must consider the likelihood of the contingency to be guarded against and the other negative effects deployment might have. We have rated the probability of a light Chinese attack in the decade of the seventies as extremely small. And we think deployment of a city defense with any significant damage-limiting capability, even if it was said to be aimed only at China, would set in train a response in the Soviet Union that would seriously worsen our over-all national security. We return to this issue in Section VI below.

c. *Sentinel/Safeguard as a first step:* A common argument for immediate ABM deployment is that, despite the flaws in the system, it at least makes a start toward an effective defense. But this argument breaks down upon analysis, particularly in relation to the specific missions involved.

We have already seen that Sentinel/Safeguard is not an effective defense of ICBM and bomber bases *and probably could never become cost-effective no matter how many Sprints were added*. This conclusion is hardly surprising since the system uses for these purposes the same missiles and the same radars in much the same numbers as the original Sentinel system. But that system was designed for a wholly different purpose—population defense against light attack. It may be possible to make a silk purse out of a sow's ear, but not simply by changing its name.

To see how far from the mark Sentinel/Safeguard is, consider the elements of a well-conceived deterrent defense:

(1) It would be concentrated on the number of ICBMs sufficient for assured retaliatory capability—say, two wings. It would certainly not try to defend the soft bomber bases.

(2) It would not use long-range missiles or radars like the Spartans and PARs, which are useless against a heavy and sophisticated attack.

(3) It would not use Sprints for terminal defense, but would use a simpler, cheaper weapon to permit deployment in great numbers. This would be feasible because defense of hardened ICBM silos does not require the range or the altitude of intercept of the Sprints, which were designed to protect soft PARs and cities.

(4) It would use cheaper, harder radars and more of them at each missile site. This, too, is feasible because the shorter-range lower-altitude intercepts require less sophistication and power in the radar to control them.

(5) Finally, the computer programing could be simpler. The tactics available to the attacker are limited. Decoys, chaff, blackout and other penetration tactics are less effective at lower altitudes. And evasive maneuvers could well be inconsistent with the accuracy required to knock out a hardened silo.

Deploying Sentinel/Safeguard, then, would not make a start toward developing a deterrent defense with the characteristics required for effectiveness. Rather, it would raise political and economic obstacles to the design of an effective system, which would have to proceed almost from scratch.

If the Sentinel/Safeguard is a first step toward anything, it looks much more like a first step towards a system to defend the population from a Chinese first strike, or possibly a Soviet second strike. Indeed, considerably more than half of the cost of the proposed deployment is attributable to city-defense elements. Secretary McNamara, in his 1968 Posture Statement, described what an expanded system would look like. It would be based on the Spartan area defense, but would have MSRs and Sprints at fifty-two cities at a total cost of $22 to $40 billion. Sentinel/Safeguard could provide the necessary tooling plus some testing and evaluation for such an expanded system. And all the costs of the Sentinel or Safeguard deployment could be written off against the cost of the final system.

We have demonstrated above that to search for an effective ABM city-defense system against heavy attack is to chase a will-o'-the-wisp. The experience with smaller deployments is valueless, because the goal is essentially unattainable. And the terrible logic of the arms race would force the other side to move to offset anything that began to look like a potential defense against a second strike.

Secretary Laird accepted this analysis in his March 19 testimony. He said that one of the reasons the Administration rejected Sentinel was that it could be interpreted by the Russians as a first step toward a heavy city defense. If this was true of Sentinel, it is almost equally true of Safeguard. And the same perilous consequences for the strategic balance would follow from its deployment. We now turn to a closer examination of those consequences.

## VI. *National Security: Its Fragility*

### 1. *The ABM and the Arms Race*

Questions about the wisdom of deploying the ABM extend beyond its technical effectiveness and its capability to perform various missions. They reach to the broader issue of its impact on national security. The crux of the matter is the effect of ABM on the strategic balance between the nuclear powers, on which we depend for the maintenance of peace— or at least the avoidance of nuclear war.

We have discussed at some length the concept of mutual deterrence, the central organizing principle of each side's strategy for survival and independence in the nuclear age. In time, one may hope for an acceptance of self-discipline, agreements or reciprocal acts that will lower the force levels of each side, and we must continue to work to this end. But for the near future there is no visible escape from the common dependence on the strategy of mutual deterrence.

In the 1950s the quest of each side for a secure second-strike capability was marked by repeated and reciprocal new deployments on both sides, either in the hope of gaining a temporary advantage, to repair a vulnerability, or simply in anticipation of an escalatory move from the other side. This process evolved by the early 1960s into a strategic balance—a plateau in the arms race. In this period, on both sides, new deployments, and especially the introduction of new weapons systems, slowed markedly.

The strategic balance thus achieved consists not so much in a symmetrical matching of deliverable megatonnage or numbers of launchers as in the preservation of a secure deterrent: the certainty of being able to deliver a crippling retaliatory blow. This means that either side can add or withdraw even a substantial number of offensive missiles without disturbing the balance.

The key to this stability is, in the first place, the immense power of any single strategic weapon against urban targets. Beyond this is the near-invulnerability of the deterrent force, which arises from the diversity of weapons systems, each requiring a different kind of attack to destroy it and each protected in a different way. It is not alone the size of the retaliatory force, but its several elements and their configuration in space and time that make it secure.

Because the strategic balance has this inherent stability over a fairly wide range of increases or changes on one side or the other, neither side is compelled to introduce at once all imaginable new weapons or to increase its numbers of existing ones indefinitely. There is enough lead time for either side to compensate if it seems apparent that the other is mounting a serious attempt to upset the over-all balance.

These features are illustrated in the history of strategic weapons deployments over the past decade. Both sides have developed many new weapons that have not been manufactured and deployed. The Soviet Union has had an inferior position in numbers of weapons during most of this period, and neither we nor they have thought that the security of their deterrent was compromised. We have kept our own number of deliverable warheads constant at about 4,200 over the last four years despite a Soviet build-up that still continues.

This broad stability of mutual deterrence has its limits, however. We now face the likelihood that the era of strategic balance is coming to an end, to be replaced by a situation of much greater uncertainty, in which neither side will know whether it or the other does have a secure deterrent. There are three main reasons for this disturbing change in the strategic picture: (a) the continuing deployment of Soviet ICBMs together with certain other strategic weapons; (b) the move on both sides for ABM deployment; and (c) the development, in the U.S. and probably in the U.S.S.R. as well, of Multiple Independently Targetable Re-entry Vehicles (MIRVs).

The first of these factors by itself would give no serious cause for concern at this time. As we have seen, the strategic balance is not sensitive to increases in one side's ICBMs, at least until one force begins to approach a two-to-one advantage over the other. Nevertheless, the growth of the Soviet force is troubling.

The second and third factors are very serious. It is important to understand that they are closely connected. Each reinforces the other.

An ABM system that guards population destabilizes the strategic balance. It reduces the confidence of either side that its own retaliatory force will get through to its targets. The same is true of a system that can be adapted for city defense. As we have argued, the effectiveness of any ABM system in actual combat is likely to be small. Nevertheless, the military planner confronting it will make his estimate along very conservative lines. Thus, the use of such systems, or even, sometimes, the anticipation that they may be deployed, tends to disturb the balance regardless of actual effectiveness in a real attack.

For example, several times in the mid-1960s the Soviet Union constructed something that appeared to be an ABM system. None of these, on any reading, was large enough to intercept much of our deterrent force. Further intelligence has downgraded the earlier evidence, so that now only the Galosh system of about seventy missiles[13] around Moscow is credited with an ABM capability.

---

[13] We stress that at present the Galosh system contains on the order of seventy *missile launchers,* not *missile sites* as has sometimes been said.

What was our reaction to this modest system? First, it would seem reasonable to conclude that U.S. retaliatory planners have targeted more missiles on Moscow. If, as would be likely, the Galosh systems should perform poorly in action, the Moscow area would be much more severely devastated than if the system had never been deployed.[14] Second, and much more important, the Moscow ABM system furnished the main argument for those in the United States Government who were urging that we should equip our offensive missiles with MIRVs. Indeed, it appears to have been one of the crucial factors in the United States decision to develop and then begin deploying MIRVs.

MIRV-equipped offensive weapons themselves would destabilize the strategic balance. They multiply the number of available warheads by three to ten times, a large enough factor so that the other side is likely to consider that its retaliatory force is threatened. If it does, it will necessarily take action to preserve its deterrent, such as by increasing its ICBM force.

MIRV deployment by both sides will not restore the balance. A rough equality between the opposing forces is stable only if the attacker has to use two or more missiles to take out one of his opponent's. But with MIRVs, one booster, with, say, four warheads—if they were accurate enough—might take out two opposing missiles. Thus, if two forces of 1,000 MIRV missiles faced each other, the side that struck first might destroy the entire opposing force with only 500 of its missiles, saving the other half for use against cities. Thus equivalent MIRV deployments on both sides would lead to even further offensive deployments on both sides—more submarines, mobile land-based missiles mounted on trucks or railway cars, air-launched missiles, underwater-launched ICBMs and other systems that are not yet on the drawing board.

The availability of all these weapons systems would introduce new and very large uncertainties into strategic planning. Unilateral intelligence capabilities available to each side are now good enough to identify and count the opposing missile silos with great accuracy. But there would be no way of

---

[14] The identical analysis cautions against a special ABM site to defend Washington, D.C.

telling whether the missile in the silo was equipped with a MIRV, and if so how many warheads it carried. Similarly, it would be very difficult to keep track of mobile land-based missiles. This uncertainty alone might be enough to induce new offensive deployments on the other side.

The interaction between defensive and offensive systems—ABM and MIRV—thus portends another anxious and costly round of the arms race, with, at the end, not more security but at best a restoration of the strategic balance at a higher and more dangerous level.

The Administration contends that the Safeguard deployment is not "provocative," that it will not induce a Soviet response large enough to upset the strategic balance and lead to renewal of an intensive arms race. The argument is that Safeguard is primarily a defense of strategic forces, not cities. Moreover, it is said, the Soviets have their own ABM system; and the initial Soviet reaction to our deployment plans has not been severely critical.

In the end, however, Soviet actions will depend on how they judge their self-interest to be affected. On this basis a rather different answer can be predicted for the long run.

First, the full Sentinel/Safeguard system would contain at least ten times as many ABM missiles as the Galosh system being installed around Moscow. Considering the reaction and overreaction on our side to their Galosh system, it is unrealistic to suppose that they would not in time react vigorously to a system ten times as large.

Second, Sentinel/Safeguard is not restricted to defense of strategic forces. As we have seen, it presumes to offer light area protection to practically all of continental United States, and terminal defense of Washington, D.C. We calculate that about $4 billion of the $6.6 budgeted cost of the system is allocable to components used essentially for population defense. The deployment of Sentinel/Safeguard would provide a base for relatively cheap, fast expansion into a "thick" city defense system that the Soviets would have to treat as though it were effective.

Looking at the question in reverse, it is clear that if the Soviet Union deployed an ABM system at a level ten times greater than that now under way, with major portions protecting urban areas, we would also find it impossible not to respond so as to maintain our secure deterrent. Thus an ABM system of the size and configuration contemplated for Sentinel/Safeguard must be considered escalatory and is almost certain to provoke a Soviet reaction as deployment proceeds.

The result would be that both sides would be in a state of greater uncertainty than they are now as to what constituted a sufficient force to ensure a secure deterrent. The conditions for an intensified arms race would be established. And, because of the complications that ABM systems introduce into the arms control problem, the race would be very difficult to stop.

If the arms race should refuel, some will advocate expanding the ABM system further. But this course will have to face the hard logic of the cost-effectiveness analysis reviewed above. For missile defense, the cost of ABMs must be measured in tens of billions of dollars, while the cost of duplicating the *entire* ICBM force or the *entire* Polaris fleet is on the order of $5 billion. For city defense, ABM has to reckon with the problem of blast and fallout effects from the warheads that everyone admits would get through or be targeted around the city. A program of shelters, stockpiling and hardening of facilities, even at enormous cost, economic and psychological, could not in the end be relied on to protect against these factors.

We conclude that the deployment of Sentinel/Safeguard would not enhance the national security but would lessen it. The reaction reasonably to be expected from the Soviet Union would lead to a serious disturbance of the present strategic balance, and a resumption of intensive competition in strategic arms between ourselves and the Soviet Union.

## 2. *ABM and Arms Control*

The Administration has said that it does not believe that the Sentinel/Safeguard deployment will be an impediment to negotiations with the Soviet Union to curtail the strategic arms race. This judgment is difficult to accept, particularly if by Safeguard we mean the full twelve-site nationwide deployment. The difficulty is in defining the capabilities of a permissible ABM system in an agreement to limit strategic weapons.

Under any arms agreement in the near future both sides will retain high levels of nuclear armament. Thus both sides will continue to rely on their retaliatory forces to avoid nuclear war. Unless ABMs were also limited, their expansion and improvement by one side might, at some point, call into question the ability of the other's ICBMs to get through in a retaliatory strike. Concern with a first strike will be very real in any case if we proceed, as we intend, to develop high-accuracy MIRVs. The problem is that the Soviet Union must have *very high confidence* that a U.S. ABM system will not be effective against Soviet retaliatory capability (and we, of course, would have to have very high confidence that any Soviet system did not compromise *our* deterrent).

Because of the great intrinsic uncertainty in ABM performance, only a very feeble system or one designed specifically and unambiguously for ICBM defense would permit the adversary to have the necessary high confidence that it will not blunt his deterrent. The problem of confidence will be exacerbated greatly if the full details of the ABM system cannot be disclosed to the adversary. It will be further complicated if the system must be constantly improved to meet an evolving third-party threat, or even to do the job for which it was initially built.

The Sentinel/Safeguard deployment will unfortunately raise all these problems. Obviously, a nationwide Soviet ABM system would pose the same kind of problems for us.

What will an agreement limiting ABM be like, and how much information must each side have if it is to be confident that its deterrent will not be compromised? Limitations on the numbers of interceptor missiles come first to mind as perhaps the preferred means of control. Could we, though, really have confidence in our ability to determine whether such limitations were being complied with, particularly if the defense included large numbers of small missiles—even smaller than our Sprint—which might be stored on mobile launchers until needed? Or could we be confident that adversary interceptor missiles did not have multiple warheads, now that that possibility has been broached by a responsible U.S. spokesman?[15]

When one considers these problems, or, perhaps worse yet, the difficulty of limiting radar performance, computer capacity or computer programs, it becomes apparent that if nationwide ABM systems are to be deployed under an arms control agreement, the requirement for verification arrangements will be radically more intrusive than those that would be adequate if neither side had ABMs. The difficulties are heightened when it is realized that each side must have confidence not only that an adversary ABM system is not effec-

[15] General A. W. Betts, Chief of Army Research and Development.

tive against its deterrent force, but that it cannot be made effective in a short period of time in the event of abrogation of the agreement.

We have already had a foretaste of these problems with the Soviet Tallinn air-defense system. Having to rely only on unilateral intelligence collection, we were for years unsure about whether that system might have an ABM capability, or might be upgraded to have one. The difficulties will be far worse with systems designed for ABM defense. Indeed, negotiation of mutually acceptable arrangements for verification of compliance will probably prove impossible.

One might ask whether we would not be confronted with the same difficulties with the Moscow ABM system, which has already been partially deployed. Probably not, for that system is already obsolete.

Even a limited initial U.S. deployment of an up-to-date ABM, however, may interfere with the successful conclusion of an agreement to limit strategic systems. The lead time for a nationwide ABM deployment will have been reduced, since in Sentinel/Safeguard the same components are used for ICBM defense and population defense. The production lines that will be needed will have been established for the initial deployment. This difficulty would not arise, or would at least be greatly attenuated, if defenses for Minuteman sites were designed specifically for that purpose. Such defenses, as we have seen, would almost certainly not use components that would be readily adaptable to defense of population.

Aside from the very serious problems of definition and verification of "thinness," there is another difficulty that ABM deployment may cause in an arms control context. With such systems deployed, the incentives to develop and deploy MIRVs will be enhanced, since MIRVs are believed to provide very high confidence of penetrating ABM systems. While it may be very difficult anyway, and perhaps impossible, to control MIRV development and deployment by agreement, ABMs will certainly make the problem more difficult.

Finally, in any consideration of ABM and arms control there is the question of whether a U.S. deployment would strengthen our hand in negotiations with the U.S.S.R. Implicit here is the idea that since the Soviet Union has a limited ABM system with which it will enter any negotiations, we should too.

If we feel we may be entering such negotiations from a position of weakness, this would seem a strange way indeed of strengthening our hand. In buying an ABM system, particularly one specifically designed so that it will not be effective against a U.S.S.R. retaliatory strike, we will be buying an almost worthless card for which we will be paying a heavy price, both in dollars and in its complicating effects on the problem of reaching agreement in negotiations.

More fundamentally, there is no particular reason why we should want to enter negotiations from a position of symmetry with the U.S.S.R. The U.S. has a strategic bomber force and a sea-launch ballistic missile force, each of which is greatly superior to those of the U.S.S.R. Indeed, the superiority in the Polaris force alone offsets many times over whatever small plus the U.S.S.R. may have in its very modest ABM system. It would seem the height of folly for the U.S. to give the Soviet Union the opportunity to argue that it should be permitted to close the gap in submarine-launched missile capabilities and further increase its ICBMs. The U.S. would be better off if all strategic force deployment, both offensive and defensive, on both sides could be terminated at the earliest possible date. Thus to think of starting ABM deployment first and then entering into arms control negotiations is to invert the priorities.

Indeed, early negotiations to curtail the arms race are, we believe, strongly in the U.S. interest from every point of view. Now we are in the best bargaining position. If a successful negotiation could be accomplished, any concern there may be about the possible future vulnerability of our deterrent force would be minimized. And the hands of those in the Soviet leadership who would be most likely to move toward accommodation with us on other issues would be strengthened.

## VII. *Conclusion: ABM's Drawbacks*

Our conclusion, based on the foregoing analysis, is that the Sentinel/Safeguard antiballistic missile system should not be deployed at this time.

1. *Reliability:* The system is one of the most, if not the most, complicated ever attempted. Each of its elements—missiles, computers, radars—is at the extreme of sophistication for its type. Extraordinary coordination is required among these elements, within a reaction time which cannot

be more than twenty minutes from first warning to time of anticipated intercept. The computer programing, in particular, presents problems not yet solved even on the theoretical level. The environment of multiple nuclear explosions, in which the system must function, is not well understood. Past experience with highly complex military systems is not encouraging, even after extensive testing and correction. In this case, despite all the uncertainties about performance, there will be no possibility for realistic testing of the system as a whole in the setting in which it will be called upon to operate.

• *We conclude that the system is unlikely to perform according to specifications in the event of nuclear attack.*

2. *Penetration:* A variety of tactics to penetrate, evade or overwhelm the system are available to the attacker. Decoys and measures to blind the radars, such as blackout, chaff and jamming, are particularly effective at the high altitudes at which the Spartan intercepts are designed to take place. These penetration devices should be available to the Chinese at an early stage in their ICBM program, and of course are now available to the Soviets. At lower altitudes, effective evasive tactics by incoming missiles are not difficult, especially against cities and other unprotected, soft targets. Since the ABM system's radars themselves are soft, the Sentinal/Safeguard ABM can be overwhelmed at relatively low cost to the aggressor.

• *We conclude that the system is highly susceptible to penetration.*

3. *Performance of missions:* There is almost unanimous agreement that the Sentinel/Safeguard system, whether in its proposed deployment or in some other and expanded configuration, could not defend U.S. urban population against a heavy attack of the kind which could readily be mounted from the Soviet Union.

Nor could it prevent substantial casualties, running into the millions, from a comparatively light attack of perhaps twenty-five to seventy-five missiles, such as Red China might mount in the mid-1970s. In any case, the possibility of such an attack, in view of the enormous and resilient U.S. retaliatory capability, must be regarded as extremely remote.

The system, if it were maintained at a sufficient degree of alert, and if it functioned at all, might provide protection against some kinds of accidentally launched missiles, but this alone is not thought by any of its proponents to justify the system.

The only mission for which an ABM system might have significant capability, if it worked at all, is defense of the U.S. retaliatory ICBM force. There is no threat to our deterrent now, and no foreseeable threat in the next five to seven years. We find the evidence that the U.S.S.R. is seeking a first-strike capability against the U.S. to be thin and unpersuasive. In the remote contingency that further intelligence should belie this conclusion, there would be ample time to take a variety of countermeasures. Even if the threat should develop, it is by no means clear that an ABM system would be the right answer, and it is almost certain that the Sentinel/Safeguard —or any other system using its components—would not.

• *We conclude that Sentinel/Safeguard is not well adapted to perform the missions assigned to it by either the previous Administration or the present one.*

4. *The arms race and arms control:* A major part of the Sentinel/Safeguard ABM system is devoted solely to area defense, and still other elements have population-defense functions. As such, it is almost certain to evoke an effort by the Soviets to maintain the effectiveness of their own retaliatory force. The response is likely to take the form, in whole or in part, of further offensive deployments, and these in turn will call for a response on our part. The stage will be set for another action-reaction cycle, another lap in the arms race, another period of uncertainty and instability in the strategic posture of the two powers—to end, if at all, only in another plateau of mutual deterrence, but at a much higher level of armament and expenditure on both sides.

The deployment of an ABM by the United States—certainly if it led to an action-reaction response as described above—would enormously complicate the task of the forthcoming U.S-U.S.S.R. talks in negotiating an effective agreement to limit strategic weapons.

• *We conclude that deployment of Sentinel/Safeguard now would probably start a new round in the arms race, and would seriously impede the conclusion of an arms control agreement.*

5. *Recommendation:* We fully support continued research and development on ABM and other defensive techniques. The arms limitation talks may fail. The Russian or Chinese threat may grow far beyond what now seems possible. In that

case, there might be justification for Sentinel/Safeguard deployments, and we should have a broad choice of defensive techniques—including ABM—to choose from.

* * *

It is hard to understand why a system with so many such obvious defects, both inherent and in relation to its assigned missions, should command continuing support from military leaders, and in the last few years from political leaders as well. It is not easy to answer such a question, and even to begin to do so requires a hard, and even skeptical, look at the processes by which decisions on major weapons systems are made.

Until this controversy over the ABM, these decisions were not subject to the ordinary public scrutiny and debate that mark the rest of our political process. This is one of the rare occasions in the postwar period when the Senate Armed Services Committee has held public hearings on a major weapons system—with opportunity for opponents as well as proponents to testify.

We are all conscious, as we must be, of the dangers of failing to take the necessary steps or to spend the necessary funds to ensure the safety of the United States. But there are other risks of nuclear disaster, of which we are often not so conscious. They lie in the never-ending spiral of nuclear armament stockpiling, in a quest for what is ultimately a will-o'-the-wisp—absolute security. In this quest lie very profound dangers.

Between too little and too much is what President Nixon has called a "sufficiency." To choose the way between too little and too much is the task of statesmanship.

We are now at a point where it can be said that both sides have a sufficiency, a moment of rare and precarious strategic balance. That is why this moment seems so hopeful for the conclusion of some kind of strategic arms limitation agreement, in which, as almost everyone agrees, the best hope for ultimate security lies.

If there are risks in deferring deployment for a time, we believe they are small. There are also risks in going forward now, because if this moment is lost, one like it will not come soon again.

As we weigh the risks and the gains on both sides, the balance points unmistakably in the direction of deferring the deployment of the Sentinel/Safeguard system at this time.

# II

## MINUTEMAN DEFENSE: WILL IT HELP?

*Is there a compelling strategic reason for deploying an ABM system at this time?*

# DEFENSE OF
# THE DETERRENT

### by CARL KAYSEN

*Director, Institute for Advanced Study*
*Deputy Special Assistant to the President for*
*National Security Affairs, 1961–1963*

THE BASIC FACTS in the ABM controversy are quite straight-forward. They can be quickly recounted. The Administration has recommended the deployment of an antiballistic missile system to defend our own missile forces and strategic bomber bases against Soviet missile attack. In this mode, it has changed the name of the system, formerly Sentinel, to Safe-guard, thus emphasizing that it has a new purpose and rationale—the third since the first announcement by the previous Administration of its decision to proceed with an ABM system. The proposed initial deployment is paced modestly: two Minuteman bases containing 300 of our more than 1,000 land-based launchers are to be protected by the end of 1973. The Administration has characterized this decision as neces-sary to maintain our security in the next five to seven years.

And the key question facing the country is equally straight-forward: Is it really necessary to deploy an ABM system at this time?

An approach to this central question must start with the observation that deployment of antiballistic missiles is, in general, perfectly consistent with the principle of deterrence. This is the strategic concept that has formed the basis of our nuclear defense policy for at least the past decade. Deter-rence has rested on the capability of our offensive forces to survive an effectively launched surprise strike. This has meant that the United States would respond with such devastating strength as to rule out a rational decision to attack by any possible opponent. What has come to be called our second-strike capability has, in turn, imposed a variety of requirements on our offensive force in terms of numbers, location, concealment, hardness, communications, etc. All of these, of course, have to be evaluated in terms of the capabilities, existing and potential, of our adversaries; in concrete terms, those of the long-range striking forces of the Soviet Union.

Active defense, if technically effective, could certainly play a part in adding to the ability of our striking force to survive an attack. Further, like hardening of launch sites and dispersion and concealment of weapons, it can do so without directly threatening the security of the other side. Thus, in theory, an ABM system designed to defend missile sites and bomber bases may not directly call for a response from an adversary whose own strategic doctrine is also based on deterrence. The other side may feel that its own second-strike capability is unimpaired. Insofar as it conforms to this purpose, the proposed initial Safeguard deployment is preferable to the deployment of the Sentinel system previously proposed. In theory, if not in practice, the latest rationale for the ABM is to protect U.S. offensive weapons, not cities. Hence, it theoretically is less likely to frighten the other side into calculating that the United States is starting to build a first-strike capability.

Even so, this general proposition does not meet the central issue, whether the present decision is *necessary* for our security, not just less undesirable than programs previously recommended. This, in turn, raises two rather different questions. The first, primarily a question of technology and economics, is how effectively will the proposed system function, both on its own terms, and compared with alternative ways of protecting our striking forces? The second is a more complex and wider-ranging question, and also a more fundamental one; namely, is the increase in the prospective Soviet threat such as to require new measures to ensure the continued security of our deterrent force?

The fundamental question of ABM reliability is fully examined in the next section of this book. So only two observations on the effectiveness of Safeguard need to be made at the outset. First, the present system was conceived and designed for a quite different task than the defense of missile sites and airfields. It is unlikely that, given the tasks set out for Safeguard, our weapons designers would prescribe the present system as a solution. It is, therefore, quite likely that both a more effective and a cheaper system for performing the task could be created. This would be the case even if the designers were limited to using already available elements in the way of radars and defensive missiles; that is, provided they had some time to reexamine the problem, rather than adapting to the new task the array conceived for the defense of cities. Second, if the purpose of the system is to increase the survivability of our offensive forces, it should be evaluated in cost-effectiveness terms against alternatives, such as further hardening of existing missile sites, increasing the proportion of the B-52 force on air alert and other possible measures. There is no evidence that a careful evaluation of these logical—and probably less expensive—alternatives has been made.

## Intelligence Estimates: Another "Gap"?

The second and more fundamental question is whether there is a newly increased threat in evidence or in prospect, which makes clear the need, now, to increase the capability of our strategic striking forces to withstand a surprise attack.

Secretary of Defense Melvin R. Laird, in his presentation to the Armed Services Committee of the Senate, has argued precisely that there is such evidence. He has subsequently reiterated his assertion that the Soviet Union is engaged in expanding its entire weapons arsenal. He has particularly emphasized his projections of the rate of build-up of Soviet offensive weapons, especially of SS-9 missiles, capable of carrying large warheads or multiple warheads. The facts on which this argument rests, so far as can be determined, are essentially the same facts from which the two preceding Secretaries of Defense drew quite different conclusions. These show a rapid growth of Soviet land-based intercontinental missile forces: from some 250 launchers in total in mid-1966; 570 in mid-1967; to some 1,000 by early 1969. Of these, some 200 to 250 are of the SS-9 type, all of which were added since 1966. In additon, the Soviet Union is building a missile-launching submarine force which now has some 50 to 100 missiles and is similar to our Polaris fleet. Secretary of De-

fense Clark Clifford, in describing the situation of the Soviet
land-based missile force, said late in 1968: "The rate of increase over the past year has been somewhat greater than
estimated a year ago. However, we believe the rate of increase will be considerably smaller over the next two or three
years. Beyond that point, our estimates become less firm."
The belief referred to is, of course, based on intelligence, not
speculation, and involves the rate at which construction of
new launching sites is going forward. Thus the Soviets in a
year or two can be expected to have at least 1,200 or 1,300
land-based ICBMs compared to our present 1,054; at that
point, they will still have less than half our present number,
656, of submarine-launched ballistic missiles. In both cate-
gories they may or may not be continuing to expand their
force further; we simply do not and cannot know now.

To use these estimates of current and immediate-future
Soviet strength—which are neither revised nor disputed—to
justify a threat in 1973 or 1974, Administration spokesmen
have simply projected continued growth in numbers of Soviet
missiles, especially of the SS-9, at a high rate. Further, they
have probably assumed, without explicitly so stating, that a
substantial fraction of these would carry multiple, independently aimable warheads; and also assumed, without any
indication of supporting evidence, that these would be significantly more accurate than we now believe Soviet missiles
to be. On the basis of these projections and assumptions, the
Soviets are credited with a capability of achieving a successful first strike against our land-based missiles, and even the
intention of seeking to do so.

This is a curious, and—unfortunately—not a novel type of
argument. Even in its own terms, it contains a glaring omis-
sion. The Administration case has included no attempt to
explain how a first strike which attacked only our land-based
missiles could make sense, in the face of our mobile and
concealed seaborne force that alone could launch at least 600
1-megaton warheads—not to mention, by that time, five or
six times that number of smaller weight. There was, to be
sure, a passing reference by Secretary Laird to the possibility
that developments in antisubmarine warfare might reduce
the invulnerability of the Polaris force, a conclusion supported
by neither evidence nor argument, and inconsistent with
known expert judgment in this field. Nor, in the alternative,
are the Soviets deploying the kind of large ABM system for

the defense of cities that would also be required by a serious effort to achieve a first-strike capability. But without a lively possibility of success with the first and evidence of the second, the notion that the Soviets are specifically seeking a first-strike capability is absurd.

More fundamental, however, is the weakness and danger of "worst-case" arguments of the sort Secretary Laird has set forth. These proceed by projecting the assumed maximum capabilities of the other side as the measure of the threat. Such were the arguments that produced the "bomber defense gap" of the early fifties, and the "missile gap" of 1960. The large and rapid increase in missile deployments made in response to the "missile gap" was in turn an important factor in stimulating the build-up of Soviet offensive forces. And now we appear about to rediscover another "missile gap"! To be sure, we cannot say with assurance that a build-up of Soviet offensive forces at the rate projected cannot or will not take place. But what we can say with assurance is that we can safely wait to find out whether it is occurring, before deploying a defensive system to protect our missiles against its possibility.

Our safety in waiting rests on two factors. First is our fleet of nuclear submarines. Second is our general ability to react in a variety of ways in the next several years, should the alleged Soviet build-up persist and give quantitative and qualitative evidence that a response to it is indeed required. These include increased hardening of our existing missile sites; increased use of airborne alerts for our bomber force; beginning deployments of defensive missiles, on a larger scale and at a faster pace; and, if necessary, increasing our offensive force. None of these is offered as a presently desirable course of action, but only as a response that could be made in a timely way to an increased Soviet threat and so avoid a dangerous situation for us should it develop. It points up the fact that the ABM is not necessarily the best—or cheapest—response the U.S. could make.

In assessing the dangers of a continued rapid Soviet build-up, it is well to remember that for some years, U.S. missile and bomber forces outnumbered corresponding Soviet forces by factors of from three-to-one to five-to-one, but this numerical superiority was not translatable into usable political power. The crux of deterrence, as we have noted, is that a credible second strike exists. We still have that capacity. The temptation to engage in a numbers game should not be allowed to confuse the "sufficiency" (in President Nixon's terminology) of the U.S. deterrent. To the question, "how much is enough?" it can be answered that the United States has more than enough for the present.

Thus we can afford to defer decision, rather than now moving ahead with the initial steps toward deployment of an ABM system to defend our missile sites. In view of the huge costs of any large new military system, and the astonishing difficulty of reversing direction once deployment has started, this in itself is a powerful reason for waiting. In an age of pressing national needs, if a large new military expenditure is not strictly necessary, it is unnecessary.

## Deferred Decision: The Gains

But the case for deferring decision goes further. It rests on our strong interest in seeking strategic arms limitation agreements with the Soviets in the present, relatively simple and stable milieu of mutual deterrence. We are now in a situation in which we understand each other's deployments in both a quantitative and a qualitative sense. Deterrence is at bottom a political and psychological concept. It rests on the perception and interpretation of the military situation by political decision-makers. It is as much open to influence by changes in their perceptions as by changes in the hard technical facts. This inevitably marks it with a certain elusiveness—and requires sensitivity and sensibility on the part of its practitioners. It is clear that constant, or slowly changing, force structures, whose technical performance characteristics are reasonably well understood—subject, of course, to the important fundamental limitation that no one has experienced their use in war—provide a much more stable basis for mutual reliance on and acceptance of deterrence than a rapidly moving process of qualitative and quantitative competition. And it is just such acceleration that the ABM promises to bring to the strategic balance.

Current technical developments in weaponry could thus significantly diminish the stability of deterrence. The natural response to our ABM deployments will be to hasten Soviet MIRV development, and possibly deployment. This was our response to the initiation of a quite-small Soviet deployment of a defensive system around Moscow; one which we now believe to be of limited effectiveness. Whatever we say about the purposes of our own ABM and the limited scale on which we propose to deploy it, we cannot simply assume there will be no Soviet response. In turn this will stimulate our own efforts in this direction, and both sides will then look to the next logical step of deploying land-mobile missiles. The result may well be a situation of great strategic instability and uncertainty, in which neither the numbers nor the character-istics of the weapons of each side are well known to the other. This is in contrast to the relatively secure position in which both sides now find themselves. In such a situation, arms control negotiations will become much more difficult.

The decision to begin our ABM deployment is not simply a small step that is necessary to maintain the current balance. The necessity of an ABM system has not been established. Safeguard thus looms as the first step toward a much more frightening and unstable strategic environment—one which we should defer as long as possible, while we actively seek ways to make it unnecessary.

*Does it make sense for the Soviets to consider a
first strike against the United States?*

# SOME FIRST-STRIKE
# SCENARIOS

## by JEROME B. WIESNER

*Provost, Massachusetts Institute of Technology
Science Adviser to the President, 1961–1964
Member, President's Science Advisory
Committee*

THE UNEASY PEACE between the Soviet Union and the United States has been preserved by the clearly recognized ability of each country to cause unacceptable devastation to the other's land and people by means of nuclear weapons. For this reason, planners and technicians on both sides have been particularly alert to the danger of a successful surprise attack, after which the victim's retaliatory response would be so feeble that the aggressor would be prepared to pay the price in deaths and destruction of his own population and property in order to eliminate the threat posed by the victim. The consequences of a successful surprise attack are so overwhelming that eliminating the chance that one could occur has been a dominant factor in the design of U.S. strategic nuclear forces. It is clear from the writings of the military analysts in the Soviet Union that fear of a surprise attack has been an ever-present consideration in their planning as well.

The specter of a surprise attack has haunted United States leaders ever since the Soviet Union developed thermonuclear weapons and intercontinental bombers. Several times in the intervening period, the U.S. leaders have feared that developments in Soviet strategic forces might lead to their having a first-strike capability, with bombers in the 1950s and with missiles in the early 1960s. Now the United States is being told by the Secretary of Defense and other spokesmen for the Nixon Administration that the trend of Soviet missile developments may leave the U.S. vulnerable to a successful surprise attack in the mid-to-late 1970s. This view is obviously different from the picture presented by Defense Secretary Clark Clifford just a few months ago (in his 1969 Defense Posture Statement). It is based on recent intelligence observations showing that the U.S.S.R. has resumed the deployment of SS-9 missiles and an estimate of the capability that the continuation of the program would create in the 1975 period.

In this chapter we will explore the various elements that must be included in an evaluation of the strategic balance, with particular attention to the situation as it might look during the 1975–80 period, and then demonstrate that even if the Soviets achieve the predicted posture, it will not be possible for them to achieve a first-strike capability.

A strategic force could have a number of purposes: (1) to provide a credible deterrent; (2) to provide a damage-limiting capability if a war actually occurs; or (3) to make possible a first strike on a potential opponent's strategic forces if nuclear war appears to be inevitable. It is obviously much more difficult to do the last than the first. In fact, it is highly unlikely that either the United States or the U.S.S.R. could achieve a first-strike capability which would preclude major damage in a retaliatory response. Since the possibility of a successful Soviet surprise attack has been raised, we will examine that possibility in some detail, looking first at a variety of conceivable technical developments and associated deployments which might increase the Soviet capability to launch a surprise attack, and then at a number of U.S. responses.

This is a very complicated problem, depending not only on the properties of the weapons and delivery systems—missiles, aircraft and submarines—but upon warning systems, antisubmarine warfare systems, command-and-control structures, firing doctrines for missiles, the interplay between offense and defense, and finally, the degree of destruction of his homeland that an aggressor is prepared to risk.

A thorough discussion of these issues requires an examination of much highly classified information and is beyond the scope of this discussion, but with the facts available and some common sense, a reasonable analysis can be made which is not sensitive to classified information and the conclusions arrived at will *not* be significantly different from those of a study with full access to classified material.

The U.S. deterrent forces are made up of a number of quite different components; approximately 650 B-52 bombers, each carrying 4 thermonuclear weapons; 1,000 Minuteman missiles and approximately 50 Titan II missiles in hardened silos; and 41 Polaris submarines each carrying 16 intermediate-range missiles. There are plans to replace both the Minuteman force and the Polaris fleet with new missiles capable of carrying several warheads each. Also, there are available in Europe and in the fleet large numbers of tactical bombers that could be used to deliver megaton-range nuclear weapons to many targets in the Soviet Union. While these tactical aircraft are not normally considered to be part of the U.S. strategic force, they are available for such use if they should be needed, and the Soviets undoubtedly consider them in their own evaluation.

The Soviet Union is estimated to have available to attack this diversified force approximately 600 SS-11 missiles of a Minuteman type, 230 SS-9s capable of carrying very large payloads, a small number of earlier model missiles, about 150 intercontinental bombers, approximately 1,000 intermediate-range ballistic missiles (IRBMs) which could be used against targets in Europe and a large fleet of medium- and short-range fighter-bombers that could also be used against European and naval targets near the Soviet borders. They are also believed to be building a fractional orbital bomb capability (FOBS) and developing the ability to fire their ICBMs at low angles to avoid BMEWS detection. To carry out a surprise attack these forces would have to eliminate, simultaneously, all but a trivial number of the total U.S. forces.

At the present time they clearly could not do this. The various early-warning systems, such as the over-the-horizon radar and the BMEWS missile warning systems, etc., would provide substantial (twenty-to-thirty-minute) warning against a missile attack (including the FOBS and low-angle attacks) and the DEW line would provide even longer warning against a bomber attack. These warnings would allow our strategic bombers to become airborne and safe. They would also provide time for key leaders to get to safe quarters and to decide on the scale of the U.S. response. We can count on the ability of the major portion of our forces to ride out the heaviest attack that can be launched against them today. The

230 SS-9s would at best destroy only one Minuteman each. (It would more likely require two SS-9s per target to have a 90 percent probability of destroying a 300 psi [pounds per square inch] hard Minuteman silo, and even more for a 1,000 psi silo.) The long-range bombers and Polaris submarines cannot be effectively attacked.

Now let us look at Secretary Laird's 1975 situation. He projects a continued deployment of SS-9s at the present rate (possibly with high-accuracy multiple warheads), enough Soviet Polaris-type submarines to make all the B-52 bases vulnerable to a surprise attack, and sufficient advances in Soviet antisubmarine warfare capabilities to make the U.S. Polaris deterrent force unreliable. We believe this is an unjustifiably pessimistic picture (as we shall show). Nonetheless, having carefully examined this situation, we believe that even in the extremely unlikely event that all of these developments occur and the United States makes no compensating moves, it will still retain a thoroughly convincing deterrent posture. In the following analysis we shall simply examine each component of the deterrent system to see how it will fare in the surprise attack Secretary Laird has imagined for us.

## *Land-based Missiles: Could They Retaliate?*

Assume that 250 to 300 more SS-9s, making a total of approximately 500, are built, and that each one can deliver 3 MIRVs against the present Minuteman with the MIRV guidance accuracy estimated by Secretary Laird. If the SS-9s are targeted solely against U.S. missiles and control centers (for a total of 1,100 targets), the Titans and approximately 350 Minutemen will have 2 MIRVs directed at them, the remaining 650 Minutemen only one. Approximately 230 of the single-targeted Minutemen will survive, as well as 40 of the doubly-targeted Titans and Minutemen. This would leave a total of 270 U.S. attack missiles—a very convincing retaliatory force all by itself.

In these calculations we have assumed an accurate MIRV and a highly reliable missile system. Prudence would require a Soviet planner to be somewhat more pessimistic. By today's standards, a retaliatory force of 200 missiles may seem small, but we can regain perspective by recalling that 200 missiles *total* was the ICBM force level that President Eisenhower planned in 1960.

The Soviets could also use the SS-11 force to attack Minuteman missile sites, but because of their low-yield warheads and current poor accuracy, they are not good counterforce weapons. Assuming an over-all kill probability of 0.3 for an SS-11 against a hardened Minuteman, the total SS-11 force would only reduce the surviving U.S. force to about 200 missiles. It could also be argued that the SS-11s might be withheld to threaten U.S. cities in an attempt to forestall retaliation for a first strike aimed only at U.S. strategic forces. In this chapter we will not examine the endless strategies of this sort that professional planners must examine.

This scenario requires the U.S. missile force to ride out the attack. This is regarded as desirable so that the President may be "deliberate" in his response. However, if one is truly worried about a full-scale SS-9 attack, it is possible to launch the Minuteman and Titan missiles after unequivocal warning of a large attack is received but before the attacking missiles have hit. The missile warning could be associated with other knowledge, such as information about attacks on bomber bases, Polaris submarines, etc., in order to provide confirmation that an attack is really under way.[1] It is possible to fire a Minuteman quickly—in about sixty seconds—so that the response can be withheld until the very last moment. The limiting factor will be the time required for the missiles, which themselves are vulnerable, to get beyond the destructive range of the attacking bombs. This option will be discussed more fully in a later section.

### Long-range Bombers: Would Some Survive?

The bomber problem is more complicated, for aircraft are about as vulnerable as cities to nuclear attack. Five psi (pounds per square inch) overpressure will cause major damage to large bombers. For this reason, the U.S. bomber force has been stationed on a quick-reaction alert which will allow most of the ready bombers to be off the ground and safe within fifteen minutes of an attack. More warning time than is needed to flush the bomber force is available in the case of either an ICBM or a bomber attack. However, if one assumes

---

[1] Furthermore, by means of satellite reconnaissance and other intelligence sources, we would almost certainly have a clear warning at least thirty minutes in advance should the Soviets launch a massive first strike.

that the Soviet Union will have a substantial fleet of Polaris-type submarines by 1975, that it would be willing to use them for an attack upon the U.S. bomber bases, that the U.S. antisubmarine warfare capability is so poor that a large fleet of hostile submarines can come into position close to U.S. shores without being challenged and that their navigation and command-and-control capabilities are such that they could carry out such an attack—a farfetched set of assumptions—then certainly many bombers will be destroyed on the ground. But not all of them. The location of the airfields is such that some planes will get airborne before the attack arrives, allowing a substantial number of the aircraft to survive even the most skillfully planned and executed attack. (Note that such an attack would occur before attacking ICBMs launched at the same time would reach their targets and that this could provide the basis for firing the U.S. missile force.)

Some sample calculations will show that it is impossible for a submarine-launched missile attack to destroy the entire long-range bomber force if the warning system operates and the quick-reaction deployment responds as planned. To show the sensitivity to warning, reaction time and base location we will examine several different situations.

For the first example we will assume that 5 minutes is required to get the first aircraft airborne and that subsequent planes will take off at 30-second intervals. We also will assume that the missile-launching submarines are 300 miles from the appropriate coast and that all of the missiles fired at airbases are launched simultaneously. Assuming that 540 available aircraft are distributed uniformly to the existing SAC bases, approximately 200 of them will be able to take off before the bases are destroyed.

If the reaction time of the bombers were actually 2 minutes rather than 5 minutes, approximately 290 aircraft would survive. If in the latter case the missile firings were distributed uniformly over a 3-minute interval—a not unlikely situation—approximately 330 bombers would escape the attack.

Additionally, if the most vulnerable aircraft, those near the coasts, were moved to inland bases, approximately 480 would survive in the 2-minute response case.

Alternatively, if an attack upon the bomber force became a serious concern, an air alert similar to that which operated in the 1950s could be reactivated, keeping a part of the B-52 force safely in the air. Here it would be wise to put the aircraft from the most vulnerable coastal bases on air alert. With this precaution the surviving retaliatory bomber force could easily number more than 450 aircraft.

## The Polaris Fleet: Could It Be Destroyed?

At the present time the United States has 41 Polaris fleet ballistic missile submarines, each carrying 16 missiles. The Navy has plans to refit 31 of these with Poseidon missiles, which will extend the range and payload of the individual missiles and make it possible for each one to carry 10 separate warheads or a mixture of warheads and penetration aids. Thus each submarine might be capable of delivering 100–160 separate nuclear bombs. The bomb load of a single submarine would be a substantial deterrent by itself. For reasons which the author has not been able to determine, Secretary Laird fears that the antisubmarine warfare (ASW) capability of the Soviet Union might become so effective that the Polaris fleet would be neutralized. While it is known that the Soviets have a large research and development program in this field, just as the United States does, there is no evidence that it is markedly better than ours. Strangely, in considering the possibility of a Soviet Polaris-type attack on the U.S., it is assumed that our antisubmarine forces will be ineffective. Yet the still-developing Soviet ASW capabilities seem to be very similar to those of the United States, employing sonars, ASW ships and hunter-killer submarines. Their development of the latter seems to be lagging substantially behind the U.S. effort.

The tactical problem of attacking and destroying Polaris submarines on command is extremely difficult. For an aggressor to be in a position to do this he must track them in the wide ocean reaches. He also exposes himself to detection by our system of underwater microphones and other sensors. If the Polaris submarines are attacked prematurely, this also will provide warning; if they are allowed to survive for just a short time after the firing command is given, they will be able to launch their missiles. Antisubmarine warfare just does not operate on such short-time scales and with such high confidence in destroying the target. But let us assume that it does, and that with half of the fleet—20 submarines—at sea, only 6 survive to fire their missiles, thus launching 96 Polaris missiles. If these submarines are equipped with MIRVs, which they might be in 1975, this surviving naval force might launch several hundred warheads.

## *Fighter-Bombers: Could They Contribute?*

Both the U.S. Navy and Air Force have a large force of fighter-bombers capable of carrying megaton-range nuclear weapons and able to fly moderately long distances. There are more than 4,000 of these aircraft altogether, and at any given moment a substantial number could serve as retaliation bombers. To attack these planes would require a large, coordinated effort which would also provide warning. If we assume that only 5 percent survive and are available when needed, 200 fighter-bombers could participate in a retaliatory raid.

## *Quick-Response Strategy: Would There Be Time?*

In arriving at the number of Minutemen that would survive an imagined Soviet first strike, we calculated the number of U.S. missiles that might survive assuming that they were forced to ride out the attack. Another option is available. Given an attack of the scope and magnitude postulated by Secretary Laird, and examined earlier in this chapter, the optimum timing, from the attacker's point of view, would launch the land-based ICBMs after the sea-launched missiles had been detected by the victim. If, as should be the case, all missile launchings, sea- or land-based, can be detected, there will be no opportunity for clever timings, and all missiles used in a surprise attack would probably be launched at once. There would then be a half-hour's warning of the ICBM attack and 10-to-20-minute warning before the short-range missiles hit, depending upon the location of the launching submarines and the targets. In this short space of time it would be necessary to ascertain that the warning was valid and decide upon a course of action.

There would be at least 10 minutes, and possibly 15, before the first bomb impacted and 30 minutes before the ICBMs arrived. During that period the President would have to decide upon a response. He could wait until the attack was over, as was assumed in the previous analysis, or he could decide to launch the retaliatory attack after the first bomb had exploded on U.S. territory. Or, given several independent warning sources, which he could have, he might well retaliate before any enemy bombs had landed. Assuming that it could take 5 minutes after the first bomb arrived to get the word to the President, and 10 minutes for him to arrive at a decision, 10 to 15 minutes would still be available to fire the retaliatory missiles. In this case all of the missiles that were operational could be launched. Again, the President might choose to withhold the Polaris missiles and even part of the bomber forces for his "hand" in the poststrike bargaining.

In any event, in this case all of the land-based missile force and a part of the Polaris fleet would be available for the retaliatory strike. It might also be possible to target some portion of the Minuteman force against the unused Soviet missiles in a damage-limiting attack if sufficient information were available.

This strategy has a number of advantages. In particular, it ensures that all U.S. ICBMs are used rather than destroyed. It prevents an attempt to halt a U.S. retaliatory strike by a threat to destroy U.S. cities, and in all probability it discourages an early attack on the bomber bases from the sea. In fact, by ensuring the use of the Minuteman and Titan forces, the strategy would undoubtedly be most effective in deterring a surprise attack.

If the bomber bases were not attacked, the decision to launch before the main attack would be more complicated. It would have to depend upon assessment of warning information and possibly the first detonations on U.S. missile sites. But the entire bomber force would then be available.

## Safeguard: Would It Help?

If the Safeguard system currently proposed to protect two Minuteman bases were operational, the situation would not be much different. In fact, the analysis in this section provides a dramatic example of the ease with which a missile defense can be overcome by someone having access to sophisticated missile technology and nuclear weapons capabilities. In this section we have assumed only that an ABM deployment by the United States was followed by a Soviet addition of penetration aids to their SS-9 missile force. In the calculations made to support our arguments in this chapter we explored two possibilities, the use of heavy decoys and the substitution of many medium-sized nuclear weapons for the large weapons which might otherwise be on the SS-9 missiles. Our calculations showed that either tactic would overwhelm the Safeguard system and, for that matter, a much heavier deployment of Sprints, which we also explored. A designer might indeed prefer to use heavy decoys as the way to penetrate an ABM system least expensively; but we were concerned that a claim could be made that the computer program was "sophisticated enough" to tell decoys from the real warheads. By postulating that all re-entry vehicles carry nuclear warheads we avoid that argument. In all likelihood, the optimum attack would contain a mixture of warheads and heavy decoys. The actual situation would depend upon many specific characteristics of the offensive and defensive systems and would always be unknown to us.

In the case of the Safeguard system, the SS-9s would have to carry only enough decoys to penetrate the Spartan defenses and enough multiple-warhead decoys to exhaust the Sprint inventory. We will examine the case in which multiple warheads are employed. Assume that the defense includes 300 Sprints—more than currently planned—plus 70 Spartan defensive missiles; that the payloads of 10 SS-9s were required to provide decoys to defeat the Spartan defense; and that the single twenty-five-megaton warhead of the SS-9 was replaced by 15 one-half-megaton weapons each having 0.2 kill probability against a hardened base. That is, instead of 3 five-megaton MIRVs each SS-9 is assumed to carry 15 one-half-megaton MIRVs. We will use the same operational characteristics employed earlier for the SS-9 missiles and make the highly optimistic assumption that a Sprint defense missile has a 0.75 possibility of making a successful interception. We assume further that the Safeguard system is deployed to protect 300 Minutemen; that 2 SS-9 five-megaton warheads were previously targeted at each of them; and the same total payload will be used in this case. If we assume that the overall SS-9 and MIRV reliabilities are 0.8, there will be approximately 2,400 incoming warheads for the Sprints to attack. Two hundred and twenty-five of them will be intercepted. Without the Safeguard system, approximately 23 of the defended Minutemen would have survived, and with the defense about 60 will. Two hundred and ninety of the undefended missiles would also survive, leaving a total of 350 Minuteman and Titan missiles after the attack, compared to 270 in the case without any active defense. This was not an optimum attack, for too much attention was given to the defended force compared to the undefended component. In these calculations we have assumed that the Safeguard system would function perfectly; that only appropriate MIRVs—not blackout, heavy decoys or jamming—would be used to help penetration of the Sprint defense; and that the individual kill probability of a Sprint would be 0.75. These are highly optimistic assumptions made to show the possible value of the system if it could be made to work well.

The case of a heavy defense, employing 2,000 Sprints, matched by a large-scale Soviet MIRV deployment, was also examined. Using the same assumptions made in the limited-deployment situation, i.e., 15 one-half-megaton weapons per SS-9, but scaling the defense to protect the entire Minuteman and Titan force—using 2,000 Sprints—we found that approximately 420 missiles would survive, considerably less than half of the original force. It is striking to note that in this case we are little better off than with the limited Safeguard system and hardly much better than with no defense at all. In fact, 316 U.S. missiles would survive this attack without any defense. These cases illustrate how obviously straightforward offensive responses, which are relatively easy to make compared to building an ABM system, can totally neutralize such a system. This analysis is sensitive to the underlying assumptions. However, except for the assumption regarding many medium-weight warheads it favors the Safeguard system. For example, the over-all effectiveness of 0.75 for Sprint mentioned previously is probably much too high judging by past experience, where an over-all effectiveness nearer 0.1 to 0.3 has been usual. Also, more smaller warheads would further exhaust the Sprint defense without seriously degrading the offensive potential. Also, no advantage was taken of the serious vulnerability of the Safeguard system radars to blast, though a well-organized attack would make them a prime target. In fact, there is reason to question whether or not they would survive the enemy attack.

## Summary: The Survivors

The results of the preceding analysis are summarized in Table 1, page 82 for the five cases examined. Column I shows that a major U.S. retaliatory force would survive a first-strike attack by the Soviet Union even if they continued to build SS-9 missiles at a fast rate; equipped these missiles with highly accurate and reliable multiple warheads (MIRVs); developed antisubmarine warfare far beyond anything now available, thus overcoming the Polaris fleet; and developed a large and sophisticated submarine-borne missile fleet which the United States could not neutralize.

Column II shows how the situation would be improved by a two-base Safeguard defense system employing 300 Sprints (more than in the present plan). Approximately 350 Minutemen would survive instead of 270 in the undefended case.

Column III shows the value of firing before the attacking bombs have been detonated. Here the full missile force is available. Note, too, if a potential aggressor has reason to believe that this might be the strategy, he is powerless to develop a tactic which prevents damage to his country.

Column IV shows the situation if one assumes the same intense Soviet build-up and attack as in Column I, but makes less gloomy assumptions regarding Polaris survival and U.S. anti-submarine warfare capability. This chart also includes other options available to the United States in the period under consideration, such as the development of MIRVs.

Column V shows the situation under the assumption of 500 SS-9 missiles using one-half-megaton MIRVs if a large-scale Safeguard system were deployed to protect the Minutemen. This analysis, which is clearly optimistic, shows that the entire investment will increase the number of surviving U.S. missiles from 270 in Case I to 420.

## *Conclusions: Safeguard—A Nonresponse to a Nonneed*

1. This analysis shows that even in the worst case postulated for 1975 by Defense Secretary Laird the United States would have over 300 megatons (the equivalent of 15,000 Hiroshima bombs) on missiles, plus an even greater amount on aircraft, for a retaliatory blow.

2. The analysis also shows that the Safeguard system contributes very little to the survivability of the U.S. forces against a "Laird" type attack.

3. Finally it demonstrates clearly that there is no urgency to safeguard our deterrent now. But if the Soviet Union were to develop an even greater-than-"Laird" threat (i.e., more ICBMs, high-accuracy MIRVs, good antisubmarine capabilities and an effective ABM of its own), then we should examine a variety of responses including a proper hard-point defense to decide upon the best response. Nike-X components, designed for city defense and hooked together to make a hard-point defense, are not likely to provide an adequate basis for an effective system.

Table 1. U.S. Strategic Forces Available for Response in Event of a First-Strike Surprise Attack: 1975–80

| | I | II | III | IV | V |
|---|---|---|---|---|---|
| WEAPON SYSTEM | Current Pentagon "scare" analysis. No U.S. effort to avoid damage or use available resources | Same as I, but adding Safeguard defense to 2 Minuteman bases | No change in posture, but firing Minuteman after first damage or unequivocal warning | Same Soviet build-up as in I, but with realistic assumptions regarding Polaris and ASW and showing effects of adding MIRV | Large-scale Safeguard system. Soviet MIRV response. Other assumptions the same as I. |
| LAND-BASED MISSILES | 270 missiles (270 megatons) | 350 missiles (350 megatons) | more than 1,000 missiles (more than 1,000 megatons) | Choices: 1. ride out attack—270 missiles 2. add MIRVs—750 warheads 3. fire on warning—1,000 missiles; with MIRV 3,000 warheads | 420 missiles (approx. 316 would survive without any defense) |
| LONG-RANGE BOMBERS | 200–450 B-52s, depending upon air alert and nature of attack (greater than 2,000 megatons) | 200–450 B-52s, depending upon air alert and nature of attack (more than 2,000 megatons) | 200–450 B-52s, depending upon air alert and nature of attack (more than 2,000 megatons) | more than 500 B-52s (more than 5,000 megatons) | 200–450 B-52s (more than 2,000 megatons) |

| MISSILES ON POLARIS SUBMARINES | AIR FORCE AND NAVY TACTICAL BOMBERS | TOTAL MEGATONS AVAILABLE |
|---|---|---|
| 96 missiles (approx. 60 megatons) | more than 200 aircraft (200 megatons) | more than 2,500 |
| 96 missiles (approx. 60 megatons) | more than 200 aircraft (200 megatons) | more than 2,500 |
| 96 missiles (approx. 60 megatons) | more than 200 aircraft (200 megatons) | more than 3,600 |
| 1. 300 Polaris missiles 2. 1,000–3,000 Poseidon missiles, if desired | 200–500 aircraft, depending upon effort (200–500 megatons) | 5,000–7,500 |
| 96 missiles | more than 200 aircraft | more than 2,600 |

*How well, in a technical sense, will*
*Safeguard protect the U.S. deterrent?*

# WHAT DOES SAFEGUARD
# SAFEGUARD?

## by STEVEN WEINBERG

*Professor of Physics, Massachusetts*
*Institute of Technology*
*Consultant, Institute for Defense Analyses*
*and Brookhaven National Laboratory*

THE ADMINISTRATION HAS recently decided to deploy an ABM system, called Safeguard, in place of the Sentinel ABM system announced by Defense Secretary McNamara in 1967.

The Sentinel system was to have provided a "thin" protection of the U.S. population from attack by the Chinese or other nuclear powers and from a possible accidental ICBM launch. According to Defense Secretary Laird, the Sentinel system was rejected by the present Administration "because it would not provide sufficient protection against the emerging Soviet threat to our strategic offensive forces" and because "the original Sentinel plan could be misinterpreted as . . . and could in fact have been . . . a first step toward the construction of a heavy system for the defense of our cities."[1]

This apparent shift in defense policy raises questions of great importance for the ABM debate. First, of course, is whether or not there is an "emerging Soviet threat to our strategic offensive forces" which necessitates an immediate ABM deployment. I do not agree that such a threat exists, for reasons discussed in detail in the chapters by Carl Kaysen and Jerome Wiesner.

But what if we had received really convincing evidence that the U.S.S.R. has begun an extraordinary improvement in the numbers, yield and accuracy of their ICBM war-

[1] Statement by Secretary of Defense Melvin R. Laird before the Senate Armed Services Committee, March 19, 1969.

heads, as well as in their air-defense, antisubmarine warfare (ASW) and ABM capabilities? In this unlikely event, we would consider an ABM deployment as one of a number of possible ways of preserving the arsenal of offensive weapons that forms our strategic deterrent. However, any proposed ABM defense of our deterrent would have to meet the following common-sense criteria:

1. The ABM deterrent-defense system would have to be effective. That is, it would have to protect our deterrent sufficiently well so that the cost to the attacker of destroying our deterrent rises to an unacceptable level.

2. The ABM deterrent-defense system would have to be reasonably economical in comparison with other equally effective expedients, such as a superhardening of Minuteman silos or simply an increase in the number of our ICBMs. (This requirement is important here because an effective ABM defense would cost a good fraction of our defense budget.)

3. The ABM deterrent-defense system should to the greatest degree possible avoid the appearance of being a city-defense system because any such system, however "thin," will raise Soviet doubts about their own ability to retaliate after a U.S. first strike. The Russians would then have to increase their offensive forces to preserve their own strategic deterrent. Also, if there actually is a faction in the Kremlin advocating a first strike on the U.S., any doubts about the second-strike abilities of the U.S.S.R. would only strengthen that group's hand. For the same reasons, it is even more important that the proposed ABM system not appear as a first step toward a *thick* city-defense system. The statement of Secretary Laird quoted above gives this as one of the reasons that the Administration decided to replace Sentinel with Safeguard.

In this chapter I will examine the Safeguard system, to see how well it meets these criteria. My conclusions are

1. Safeguard is ineffective as a defense of our deterrent, because an attacker could overwhelm it by increasing his forces by a few percent.

2. If expanded sufficiently to become effective, Safeguard would be grossly uneconomical in comparison with alternative expedients.

3. The Safeguard system would destabilize the arms race, because it is primarily a "thin" population-defense system, like Sentinel. And, like Sentinel, Safeguard could be misinterpreted as, and could in fact be, "a first step toward the construction of a heavy system for the defense of our cities."

To put these conclusions another way: the criticism of the Sentinel system by Secretary Laird applies equally well to the Safeguard system, because the Safeguard system does not substantially differ from the Sentinel system in any important respect. Let us explore these basic conclusions in greater detail.

## Minuteman Defense: Effectiveness and Cost

We will assume here for the sake of argument that the U.S.S.R. is able to mount the kind of enormous first strike which could destroy our deterrent if it were not defended. The United States has about 1,050 ICBM silos. Thus we must suppose that Moscow can deliver at least 2,100 re-entry vehicles (RVs) with megaton yield and high accuracy, two for each of our ICBM silos. (Even with two Soviet RVs targeted on each U.S. ICBM, and assuming that each RV had an 80 percent chance[2] of destroying a hardened silo, 42 ICBMs would still be left, and these could destroy a sizable fraction of Soviet industry.) We must also assume that they have nearly perfect antisubmarine and air-defense systems to negate our Polaris submarines and SAC bombers.

Suppose we deploy an ABM system to meet this hypothetical threat. The U.S.S.R. would not be likely to launch a first strike without first improving its offensive forces to restore their previous effectiveness. If this improvement raises the cost of their force by only 10 percent, we must assume that

[2] In testimony before the Senate Armed Services Committee on March 20, 1969, Deputy Secretary Packard stated that an ICBM with a CEP of 0.6 to 0.8 miles would have to carry a 20 MT warhead if it is to have an 80% chance of destroying a hardened Minuteman silo. This kill probability does not incorporate the readiness, launch, and in-flight reliabilities of Soviet ICBMs. Instead of attempting to take these unknown reliabilities into account explicitly, I will throughout only quote figures for the number of Soviet RVs which actually arrive near the target. Thus, if the over-all Soviet ICBM reliability is 50%, then the actual Soviet ICBM deployments must be at twice the levels quoted here.

they will pay this price, and our defense is then ineffective in preventing an attack. However, if our defense pushes the cost of a Soviet first strike up by 100 percent, then we may hope that they will give up the idea of an attack on our deterrent, and we might regard this defense as effective.

One way to apply this proposed standard of effectiveness is to assume that the U.S.S.R. would simply exhaust the ABM defense, by adding one RV to their forces for each of our Sprints and Spartans. For instance, in the proposed Phase 1 Safeguard deployment we will defend two Minuteman bases with roughly 150 Sprints and 65 Spartans.[3] The U.S.S.R. can exhaust this defense by adding 215 RVs. But this would add less than 10 percent to the cost of the Soviet attack because, as we have seen, they would not have dared to attack us in the first place without 2,100 RVs and expensive air-defense and antisubmarine warfare establishments. Thus the Phase 1 Safeguard deployment is not an effective defense.

To do a more realistic calculation, we must consider the many tactics that an attacker can use to make any such ABM defense even less effective:

a. High-altitude penetration aids.

The Spartan warhead is designed to destroy an incoming missile by means of thermal X-rays. Such radiation is strongly absorbed in air, so Spartans must intercept their targets above an altitude of about fifty miles.

Any such high-altitude defense is susceptible to a great many penetration tactics. The Spartans can be exhausted with decoys or chaff clouds, which need not survive re-entry into the atmosphere and can therefore be very light and cheap to deliver. The radar can be confused by active jamming; the power required decreases with the inverse square of the distance between the jammer and the radar. The defense radars, and particularly the perimeter acquisition

[3] The numbers of Sprints and Spartans in the Safeguard system are classified. However, on March 2, 1969, the press carried reports that the Pentagon was seeking to deploy a modified Sentinel system having 300 Sprints and 700 Spartans. This number of Spartans sounds too high, so throughout this paper I will assume that Safeguard has 400 Sprints and 400 Spartans. According to Laird's statement all 12 Safeguard sites would have Sprints and Spartans. The Spartans are presumably spread evenly among all the sites. The Sprints have to do most of the work of defending our ICBMs, and they would be rapidly exhausted by a heavy attack, so I have put 75 Sprints at each of the four Minuteman bases in the full deployment, and have spread 100 Sprints evenly throughout the rest of the country.

radar (PAR), can be blacked out with precursor nuclear explosions which produce huge fireballs at high altitude and ionize the D-layer at about forty miles' altitude. (For more details, see the chapter by Hans Bethe.) In a heavy, well-timed attack the radars could even be blacked out by the defense's own nuclear explosions.

It has been hotly contested whether the Chinese would be able to develop such penetration tactics in the next few years. However, there has never been much doubt that the U.S.S.R. would find this an easy task. I therefore conclude that our Spartan missiles can be negated by the U.S.S.R. at a negligible cost.

b. Attacks on the missile site radar (MSR).

The missile site radar is very much softer than a Minuteman silo, so a single offensive warhead, with sufficient yield and accuracy to have a fair chance of destroying a Minuteman silo, will surely destroy the MSR. If this happens, then all Sprints (and Spartans) controlled by the destroyed radar become useless.

Suppose the attacker directs his first wave of weapons at the MSR. The defense must commit enough Sprints to each incoming RV aimed at the radar to prevent the tracking system from being destroyed before all his Sprints are fired.[4] Let us assume that the kill probability $P_k$ for each Sprint is 0.7. The number of Sprints required to give the MSR a 10 percent chance of surviving an attack of N RVs is shown in Table 1.

For example, a battery of 75 Sprints can be exhausted with 33 RVs because if the defense does not use up all his Sprints defending the radar it will surely be destroyed, leaving the remaining Sprints useless. (In this case, if the defense tries to save 9 Sprints by committing only 2 to each RV, the chance of his MSR surviving is only 4.5 percent. If only one Sprint is committed to each RV, the chance of its surviving is 0.000008.)

It has been suggested by George W. Rathjens before the Senate Foreign Relations Committee that the radar is so soft that it could be attacked with lighter RVs that might weigh

---

[4] I am not taking into account here the fact that some Sprints will not be successfully launched, since this problem can to some extent be dealt with by immediate reprograming of the Sprints. I am also not taking into account the fact that a whole number of Sprints must be committed to each RV. Both of these approximations will lead to *underestimates* of the number of Sprints required.

Table 1.  NUMBER OF SPRINTS NEEDED TO MAKE THE PROB-
ABILITY OF THE MSRs SURVIVING THE ATTACK
EQUAL TO 0.1

| RVs ATTACKING MSR (N) | AVERAGE SPRINTS COMMITTED PER RV (n) | TOTAL SPRINTS NEEDED (Nn) |
|---|---|---|
| 10 | 1.3 | 13 |
| 30 | 2.2 | 66 |
| 100 | 3.1 | 310 |
| 300 | 4.0 | 1,200 |
| 1,000 | 5.0 | 5,000 |
| 1,500 | 5.4 | 8,100 |

only one-third as much as an RV capable of destroying a
Minuteman silo. In this case, the cost to the U.S.S.R. of exhausting a given Sprint battery is one-third the cost of the
required number of silo-killing RVs. (Rathjens also points out
that the U.S.S.R. might even use SS-11s to attack the radars.
They already have great numbers of these missiles, and since
SS-11s are not useful in attacking Minuteman silos, their use
would cost the U.S.S.R. nothing extra.)

It may perhaps be objected that, after all, the U.S.S.R.
would not attack the missile site radar first, because this
tactic would give the U.S. a few extra minutes in which to
fire its Minutemen before they are destroyed. However, if the
U.S.S.R. were going to worry about this contingency, they
would not attack in the first place, because the ballistic missile
early-warning system (BMEWS) and other systems would in
any case give the U.S. twenty to thirty minutes' warning of an
impending attack.

c. Low-altitude penetration aids.

It is probably possible for a technically sophisticated power
to exhaust the Sprints with a large number of decoys and/or
light warheads. Let us now see how effective and cost-effective the Safeguard system is against an attacker who uses these
tactics. The Spartans are assumed to be negated at negligible
cost by high-altitude penetration aids, so the burden of defense falls on the Sprints and on the missile site radars that
control them.

In the "Phase 1" Safeguard deployment, two Minuteman
wings are defended with two batteries of about 75 Sprints
each, each battery controlled by and guarding its own MSR. I
will assume that all the Sprints at both wings are within 25
miles of the radar, so that they are all able to protect it, even

though this leaves most of the Minuteman silos at the 200-mile-wide bases unguarded. According to Table 1, the 75 Sprints in each battery can be exhausted by attacking the radar with 33 RVs. The total of 66 RVs used for this purpose can be of light weight, and may cost as much to deliver as 22 RVs, which could destroy Minuteman silos. Thus the Phase 1 Safeguard system forces the attacker to increase his first strike from 2,100 silo-killing RVs to the equivalent of 2,122 silo-killing RVs. The attacker would also be spending a good deal on antisubmarine warfare (ASW) and air defense, so the Safeguard Phase 1 deployment pushes the cost of his first strike up by less than 1 percent.

For this "protection," the U.S. would pay $2.1 billion.[5] It would be just as effective to add 11 Minutemen, at one-thirtieth the cost. In this sense, Safeguard may be the *least* cost-effective system ever deployed. (We are not allowed to write off any of the cost of the Phase 1 deployment to defense of our population, because the offense could simply attack the unprotected parts of the U.S., which in Phase 1 would contain all our large cities.)

In the full 12-site Safeguard system 4 Minuteman bases are defended with 4 batteries of about 75 Sprints each and 4 MSRs. This deployment requires the attacker to increase his force by the equivalent of 44 silo-killing RVs, or less than 2 percent. For this defense we pay only about $330 million,[6] providing all costs of the system can be written off to city defense except for the 300 Sprints. However, it would be equally effective to add 22 Minutemen, at less than half the cost.

Thus the Safeguard system is an ineffective defense of our Minutemen, and is, as well, economically wasteful even as an add-on to a population-defense system.

If the Safeguard system as presently planned is so ineffec-

[5] Statement by Deputy Secretary Packard, Subcommittee on International Organization and Disarmament Affairs of the Senate Foreign Relations Committee, March 21, 1969.

[6] The Department of Defense has estimated ABM component costs as $130 million for each one-faced PAR, $160 million for each two-faced PAR, $165 million for each four-faced MSR, $1.5 million for each Spartan, and $1.1 million for each Sprint. The full cost of a first-generation Minuteman has been stated as "almost $8.75 million" by William C. Foster, "Prospects for Arms Control," *Foreign Affairs*, April, 1969, p. 418. Presumably the incremental cost is somewhat less, so I have taken the cost of adding Minutemen as $7 million each.

tive, what if we expand it? Let us consider an extended "Phase 2A" deployment, in which four Minuteman bases are defended, each with one MSR and a large Sprint battery. Obviously, the defense does become effective if enough Sprints are added. For instance, the cost of the ICBMs in a first strike is doubled if our defense requires the attacker to add a weight equal to 2,000 silo-killing RVs, or 6,000 radar-killing RVs, 1,500 for each MSR. According to Table 1, the number of Sprints which would necessitate this increase is 8,100 per radar site, or 32,400 Sprints in all, costing about $35 billion.

This is to show that such a defense can never compete in cost with just adding Minutemen. Each Minuteman we add requires the attacker to add at least two silo-killing RVs. For this cost, they could add at least 6 silo-killing RVs, which in a heavy attack would use up more than four times as many Sprints (see Table 1), or 24 Sprints. A Minuteman costs a good deal less than 24 Sprints, not to mention the radar cost! (Adding a Minuteman actually forces the attacker to add *more* than 2 RVs to keep the number of surviving Minutemen fixed.)

We are, incidentally, comparing the costs of deploying Sprints with adding Minutemen only as a convenient way of checking whether Safeguard is economical. We might well prefer to superharden Minutemen or to make them mobile, rather than to increase our offensive forces. It should be possible to go a long way in this direction for $35 billion.

A slightly more sensible advanced deployment would have extra MSRs as well as Sprints at each Minuteman wing. Only one of the MSRs need survive in order to continue the defense, so all must be attacked. This advantage can be exploited by the defense in either of two different ways:

a. All the MSRs and Sprints can be concentrated in a region small enough so that any Sprint can defend any MSR. At the beginning of the attack, the defense can determine which MSR has been targeted by the smallest number of offensive RVs, and can devote all Sprints to its defense, leaving the other radars to be destroyed.

b. The MSRs can be spread throughout each Minuteman base, with a Sprint battery of equal size defending each radar.

Table 2 shows the number of Sprints (with $P_k = 0.7$) and the cost (with Sprints at $1.1 million, MSRs at $165 million)

Table 2.   COST OF SPRINTS AND MSRs NEEDED TO GIVE 10
PERCENT CHANCE OF ONE MSR SURVIVAL

| | a. MSRs CLOSE TOGETHER | | b. MSRs SPREAD OUT | |
|---|---|---|---|---|
| MSRs | Sprints | Cost per base (billions) | Sprints | Cost per base (billions) |
| 2 | 3,600 | $4.29 | 6,900 | $7.92 |
| 4 | 1,590 | 2.41 | 5,770 | 7.01 |
| 6 | 970 | 2.06 | 5,140 | 6.64 |
| 8 | 680 | 2.07 | 4,710 | 6.50 |
| 10 | 520 | 2.22 | 4,370 | 6.46 |
| 12 | 410 | 2.43 | 4,100 | 6.49 |
| 14 | 340 | 2.68 | 3,870 | 6.57 |

of a defense which would give a 10 percent chance that at least one radar would survive an attack of 1,500 RVs.

We see that an optimum deployment would have about 6 MSRs and 970 Sprints close together at each Minuteman base, at a cost for four bases of about $8 billion. This defense requires the attacker to increase his force by 6,000 radar-killing RVs, or the equivalent of 2,000 silo-killing RVs, which could also be accomplished by adding 610 Minutemen, at a cost of about $4.5 billion. (In order to keep the number of surviving Minutemen fixed at 42, the offense would have to triple-target 770 of the 1,660 ICBMs and double-target the rest.) Thus even this optimal deployment is economically wasteful. It is, moreover, a high-risk defense, because it depends on the successful performance of a single MSR, and because the concentration of radars and Sprints makes them more vulnerable to blackout, jamming, electromagnetic pulses and so on. (Also, most Minutemen at each base are left unprotected.) These risks can be minimized by spreading out the MSRs and Sprints, as in deployment (b). Table 2 shows that each base would then have 10 MSRs and 4,370 Sprints, at a cost for four bases of about $25 billion. Such a defense would be grossly wasteful.

A cost-effective hard-point defense using Sprints and MSRs might be possible if Sprints could be fired sequentially at RVs, so that Sprints would not be wasted on warheads that had already been destroyed. This is, however, a very difficult tactic, because a typical RV will be within Sprint range for only about six seconds before impact, and because the defense would have no way of knowing whether or not the neutrons from a Sprint explosion had melted the fissionable material within an attacking RV.

## Bomber Defense: The Real Purpose

It had generally been supposed that bomber bases do not need an ABM defense, because 40 to 60 percent of the bombers can leave the ground with fifteen minutes' warning.[7] We would get a warning against attacking ICBMs on minimum-energy trajectories of perhaps twenty minutes from BMEWS and thirty minutes from our over-the-horizon radar and satellite systems.

The Administration has recently announced that our bombers are becoming vulnerable to attack from fractional orbital bombardment systems (FOBS) or submarine-launched ballistic missiles (SLBMs), which would not provide the bombers with the needed fifteen minutes' warning. This is the stated justification for locating up to seven of the twelve sites in the fully deployed Safeguard system at bomber bases.

But this justification makes no sense. Whether or not we deploy Safeguard, a great many bombers will escape any first strike. These include

a. The SAC bombers on air alert.

b. The SAC bombers warned by our antisubmarine or over-the-horizon radar systems of an impending SLBM or FOBS attack.

c. The nuclear-armed tactical aircraft in Europe and Asia.

In addition, a simultaneous attack on our Minutemen would have to make use of ICBMs on minimum-energy trajectories, because the yield and accuracy requirements for an effective attack on hardened silos preclude the use of SLBMs or FOBS. The preceding chapter by Jerome Wiesner points out that in this case there will also survive:

d. The SAC bombers warned by BMEWS twenty minutes before the attack on our Minutemen.

[7] Secretary of Defense Clark M. Clifford, "The 1970 Defense Budget and Defense Program for Fiscal Years 1970–74," Section II (C) 2.

The enemy can of course delay his attack on our Minutemen to avoid giving this warning, but then the attack on our bombers would alert the Minutemen to launch immediately or on BMEWS warning.

In order to mount a successful first strike, the Soviet Union would in any case have to have an air-defense system efficient enough to keep out all the aircraft listed above. If we deploy a perfect ABM defense of our bombers, the Soviets would at most have to improve their air defense to deal with a few more aircraft.

Furthermore, the Safeguard defense of bomber bases would be even less effective than its defense of Minutemen. Bombers are more vulnerable than radar, so the attacker would not have to direct a first wave of RVs at the radar; any RV aimed anywhere near the bombers would have to be met with enough Sprints to guarantee its destruction.

Even without going through the above analysis, it is obvious that any ABM defense of our deterrent should be concentrated on elements which are immobile and hard, like ICBMs, not mobile and soft, like bombers. I am forced to the conclusion that the only rational purpose for the seven proposed Safeguard sites at bomber bases would be to provide a thin area defense of our population with the Spartans, rather than to protect our deterrent.

### ABM Cost: Allocation by Function

When a salesman offers us a combination vacuum cleaner and bicycle pump, we like to know what part of its price is allocated to each of its functions, especially if we do not happen to need a bicycle pump. In the same sense, it is instructive to allocate the cost of the full Safeguard system among its main elements:

1. Components which chiefly serve to protect Minuteman bases against a heavy first strike from the U.S.S.R.
2. Components which chiefly serve to protect our population.
3. Components which substantially serve both purposes.

For the sake of clarity, it should be noted that there are several purposes which are *not* being considered here as valid objectives of an ABM system:

4. We exclude protection of our deterrent from a light attack. This is because even if China acquired 50 ICBMs, and even if by some miracle the 50 Chinese ICBMs destroyed 50 Minutemen, our deterrent would for all practical purposes be intact.

5. We exclude protection of our bomber bases. This is for reasons of vulnerability set forth in the previous section.

6. We do not distinguish between the ABM defense of Washington and of other cities, partly to simplify our calculations, and partly because some of the special functions of our National Command Authority can be handled by underground or airborne command-and-control centers. In the Sentinel deployment Washington would have been defended only by the general area coverage of the Eastern U.S., while in the Phase 1 Safeguard deployment Washington would not be protected at all. In any case, Washington is only one site out of twelve, so it would make little difference to our conclusions if we put the cost of this site in a special category.

Let us look in turn at each of the major components of the Safeguard system and ask what it is there for and what it costs.

*Spartans:* We have already seen that the long-range, high-altitude Spartan defense would be useless against a heavy and sophisticated attack on the deterrent. Thus the cost of the Spartans must logically be charged to the population-defense role of the Safeguard system. They cost $1.5 million each; so if the system employs about 400 Spartans, then this cost is $600 million.

It might be argued that the X-ray mechanism of the Spartan missile is still useful even in defending Minutemen, because its large kill radius forces the attacker to space his RVs many miles apart. This is supposed to make things somewhat easier for the computers and radars which control the Sprint defense. However, as we have already seen, the number of Sprints per radar site in the Safeguard system is so small that the system is ultimately limited by exhaustion of its Sprints, rather than by its data-handling capabilities. In any case, the attacker can first either black out the defense radars or exhaust the Spartan battery with a cloud of chaff or well-separated light decoys, and then send in a dense pack of RVs carrying warheads.

*PARs:* The function of the PAR—that is, the outlying perimeter radar—is to acquire and track incoming objects several thousand miles away, and then to hand over the trajectory information to an MSR at the actual missile site. The PAR is indispensable as an adjunct of the long-range Spartan missile, but for a Sprint defense these acquisition and track functions can be adequately handled by the MSR. This is demonstrated by the fact that the original Sentinel System was to have protected Hawaii with an MSR and Sprints but no PAR or Spartans.[8] Also, the PAR is very soft, and its long wavelength makes it unsuited for a defense of Minuteman silos against a sophisticated attack. The recent testimony of H. A. Bethe before the Senate Foreign Relations Committee indicated that neither Spartans nor PARs would be needed in an ABM defense of Minutemen.

To be conservative, we will nevertheless allocate the cost of the two proposed one-faced PARs at Minuteman bases to both Minuteman and population defense, while all other proposed PARs (one with one face, four with two) are charged to population defense. The one-faced PARs cost $130 million each and the two-faced PARs cost $160 million each; so this is $770 million for population defense and $260 million for dual purposes.

*Sprints:* We have been assuming that the Safeguard system would have about 300 Sprints at Minutemen bases and 100 Sprints throughout the rest of the U.S. All these Sprints partly serve to protect MSRs and PARs which are necessary for the Spartan defense of our population, but for simplicity we will charge 300 Sprints to the defense of our Minutemen and 100 Sprints to the defense of our population. (It would make little difference to our conclusions if these latter 100 Sprints were charged to bomber defense.) If Sprints cost $1.1 million, this is $330 million for Minuteman defense and $110 million for population defense.

*Sites (MSRs, computers, land, etc.):* The Safeguard sites at the four Minuteman wings clearly serve to protect both population and Minutemen, while the other eight sites are chiefly useful for population defense. If each site costs $225 million (of which $165 million is for the MSR), then this is $1,800 million for population defense and $900 million for dual purposes.

[8] News release, Office of Assistant Secretary of Defense for Public Affairs, No. 188–69, p. 3; March 14, 1969.

*Miscellaneous system-wide expenses:* The incremental component costs listed above add up to $4.77 billion. The Safeguard system is supposed to cost a total of $6.6 billion, so this leaves $1.83 billion for system-wide costs including some research, development, testing, evaluation, communications, command and control. The Spartans and PARs are useful primarily for population defense, the Sprints are useful primarily for Minuteman defense, and the MSRs and computers serve a dual purpose, so we will budget $800 million for population defense, $400 million for Minuteman defense, and $630 million for dual purposes.

The above cost analysis is summarized in Table 3:

Table 3. ALLOCATION OF THE COST OF THE SAFEGUARD SYSTEM ACCORDING TO THE PURPOSES OF ITS VARIOUS ELEMENTS

| TARGET DEFENDED | MINUTE-MEN | POPULA-TION | BOTH |
|---|---|---|---|
| | | Costs (millions) | |
| Spartans | $ 0 | $ 600 | $ 0 |
| PARs | 0 | 770 | 260 |
| Sprints | 330 | 110 | 0 |
| Sites (MSRs, computers, land, etc.) | 0 | 1,800 | 900 |
| System-wide expenses | 400 | 800 | 630 |
| | $730 | $4,080 | $1,790 |

Of course, these figures are based on a good deal of guesswork, and in any case should all be increased to allow for the usual escalation of defense costs. However, we may note that our estimates are reasonably consistent with the stated costs of two alternative deployments:

1. According to our estimates, the Phase 1 Safeguard deployment would cost $165 million for 150 Sprints, $260 million for two one-faced PARs, $90 million for 60 Spartans, $450 million for two sites, and $1,220 million for two-thirds the full system-wide costs for a total of $2.185 billion, in good agreement with the official estimate of $2.1 billion.

2. According to our estimates, the incremental cost of

adding two sites for Alaska and Hawaii would be $450 million for two sites, $130 million for a one-faced PAR in Alaska, $45 million for 30 Spartans in Alaska, and $33 million for 30 Sprints in Hawaii, for a total of $658 million, in good agreement with the official estimate of $600 million.[9]

But whether or not our figures are correct in detail, one conclusion seems inescapable: *Most of the cost of the Safeguard system is for components which substantially serve only to protect our population, not our ICBMs.* If the possible Safeguard deployments in Alaska and Hawaii are included, the proportion of the total cost that goes to protect our deterrent shrinks even further.

## *The Arms Race: The Logical Deductions*

What effect would the Safeguard system have on strategic stability? The best way to approach this problem is to look at Safeguard through the eyes of a Soviet defense planner, whom for brevity we will call Marshal S.

Perhaps Marshal S., like many Americans, received an initial impression from President Nixon's speech on March 14, 1969, that we were deploying a pure hard-point defense system to protect our deterrent. By carefully reading the President's statements, as well as subsequent Senate testimony of Defense Secretary Laird, he would soon have found that Safeguard was in fact going to retain the "thin" population-defense features of Sentinel. For instance, the written version of the President's Safeguard announcement listed the second purpose of the Safeguard system as "Defense of the American people against the kind of nuclear attack which Communist China is likely to mount within the decade."

In order to check the extent of this population defense, Marshal S. might then draw Spartan "footprints" on a map of the U.S. He would find that *the Spartan batteries are located so as to provide an area defense of every one of the twenty-five largest U.S. metropolitan centers.* The area defense provided by Safeguard is essentially identical with that provided by Sentinel; there are small gaps in Louisiana, Arizona and New Mexico, but the Spartan footprints still cover about 97 percent of the U.S. population.

[9] Statement of Deputy Secretary Packard, Senate Armed Services Committee, March 22, 1969.

At this point Marshal S. would begin to worry that an ABM defense that can protect U.S. cities against a Chinese first strike might be able to protect them from a Soviet *second* strike. Of course, he might believe those American scientists who think that this defense system is highly penetrable and probably unreliable, but as a prudent defense planner he would more likely give it the benefit of the doubt. In order to be certain of retaining the Soviet strategic deterrent, Marshal S. would have to consider the wisdom of increasing the Soviet offensive force.

Marshal S. would also wonder about American intentions. Is the population-defense capability of Safeguard merely a by-product of its deterrent defense role, or vice versa? He might do his own cost analysis and also find that most of the cost of the Safeguard system goes purely for population defense. He would further note that the defense provided by Safeguard for the U.S. ICBMs is ineffective and uneconomical, because its missiles and radars were not designed for that purpose. He would logically conclude that the primary motive of the U.S. in deploying Safeguard is to protect its population.

One crucial question would remain. Is the Safeguard system only a thin defense of our population against China, or is it a first step toward a thick city-defense system which might protect us from the U.S.S.R.? Defense Secretary Laird has said that while Sentinel could have been such a first step, Safeguard could not. This is supposedly because Sentinel would have had radars near some fourteen cities, and these MSRs could be used to control Sprints which would defend these cities in a thick ABM system, whereas in Safeguard the MSRs have been moved out of town to bomber bases (except that one site has been moved to Washington, D.C.). But in deciding his own next move, Marshal S. would take only cold comfort from Laird's distinction, for the following reasons:

1. The cost of a thick city-defense system was estimated by Defense Secretary McNamara as $22 billion to $40 billion.[10] Thus the importance of Sentinel or Safeguard as a foundation for a thick system is not that the incorporation of their missiles and radars would save a few billion dollars.

[10] Secretary of Defense Robert S. McNamara, "The Fiscal Year 1969–73 Defense Program and the 1969 Defense Budget," Sec. II (B) 1b.

Rather, the important thing is that it would save *time*, the time required for research, development, testing, evaluation and tooling.

2. The costs of expanding Safeguard or Sentinel into a thick system are not in fact very different. The *incremental* cost of deploying a Safeguard site, including the MSR, computers, communications, land, etc., has been estimated above as $225 million. Thus it would cost about $3 billion to put ABM sites back at thirteen cities. But Safeguard costs about $1 billion more than Sentinel, and most of this extra cost is for components which would be useful in a thick system, so the cost of expanding Safeguard into a thick system is only about $2.5 billion greater than for Sentinel. This is of course a lot of money, but it is only a third of the cost of the Safeguard system, and very much less than the full cost of a thick system.

3. It is not really clear that Safeguard will not have ABM sites which could control a Sprint city defense. Many U.S. bomber bases are fairly close to good-sized cities.[11]

At best Marshal S. would conclude that the U.S., in trying to defend itself from China, had inadvertently threatened the present and future Soviet deterrent. He would then have to advise an increase in Soviet offensive forces. At worst, Marshal S. would decide that the U.S. is covertly planning a first strike on the U.S.S.R., with our cities protected from Soviet retaliation by our ABM system. He would then probably advise that Soviet forces be put on a hair-trigger alert status. The world would be closer to war.

[11] In a news conference on March 14, 1969, Deputy Secretary Packard said that Safeguard ABM sites would not be near cities unless this was made necessary by the proximity of a city to a bomber base.

*Will there be time enough for the President*
*explicitly to authorize the firing of an ABM?*

# COMMAND AND CONTROL

## by BILL D. MOYERS

*Publisher,* Newsday
*Special Assistant to the President, 1963–1967*

THERE HAS NEVER been a serious challenge to the long-estab-
lished principle that only the President can decide to use
nuclear weapons. Senator Barry Goldwater appeared to suggest, in 1964, that military commanders in the field should be
permitted the discretion to decide when to employ tactical
nuclear weapons, but the country rejected the idea and its
author. In so doing, it reaffirmed the tradition of which President Johnson spoke that year when, in cataloguing the consequences of the atomic age, he said:

> For Americans, it means that controls over nuclear
> weapons must be centralized in the hands of the highest
> and the most responsible officer of government—the Presi-
> dent of the United States. He, alone, has been chosen by
> all of the people to lead all the Nation. He, alone, is the
> constitutional Commander in Chief of the Nation. On his
> prudence and wisdom alone can rest the decision which
> can alter or destroy the Nation.

There has been no real problem with that principle, which
has been at the heart of nuclear control since 1945. The
problem that now arises lies in the fact that to exercise such
prudence and wisdom in deciding whether to fire an ABM, the
President will have, if he is lucky, all of twelve hundred seconds. Certainly no more than that. According to recent testi-

mony from the Pentagon's Director of Defense Research and Engineering, "For attacks from the Soviet Union it could be as long as twenty minutes. For attacks off our coast, it would be only a few minutes."

Men have been known to exercise prudence and wisdom in less time, but given the shortness of time and the complexity of the technical issues, these are qualities which seem far less commanding than the inexorable momentum of the process itself, momentum which with the ABM either takes the decision out of the President's hands or all but determines it for him in advance.

Hear Herbert York, who served on President Dwight Eisenhower's Science Advisory Committee and was Director of Defense Research and Engineering under President Eisenhower: "We are getting to the point in complexity and in the time scale when there is not time for humans—and decisions are made by machines." Deployment of an ABM, Dr. York added, would accelerate the process by which "the power to make certain life and death decisions is passing from statesmen and politicians to more narrowly focussed technicians, and from human beings to machines."

Or, George Kistiakowsky, who once served as Chairman of the President's Science Advisory Committee and Special Assistant to President Eisenhower for Science and Technology: "The decision [to launch the ABM] has to be made automatically by a computer or by a comparatively junior military officer."

The key to the doubts of the experts is to be found in an analysis of the actual time interval between warning and launch. The time is shortened on one end by the necessity for accurate verification, and on the other by the carefully controlled process of the launch itself. We know more about that process as it affects offensive weapons than antiballistic missiles. In the speech referred to earlier, President Johnson outlined this procedure:

> The release of nuclear weapons would come by Presidential decision alone. Complex codes and electronic devices prevent any unauthorized actions. Every further step along the way from decision to destruction is governed by the two-man rule. Two or more men must act independently and must decide the order has been given. They

must independently take action. An elaborate system of checks and counter checks, procedural and mechanical, guard against any unauthorized nuclear bursts. In addition, since 1961 we have placed Permissive Action Links on several of our weapons. These are electro-mechanical locks which must be opened by secret combination before action at all is possible, and we are extending this system.

All of these checks and counterchecks are possible because our offensive weapons need not be fired in a spasm response to an enemy attack. They can ride out any attack, leaving the President time to decide how to respond. But the ABM must be fired in less than twelve hundred seconds.

What happens in an ABM firing is still classified information. If the controls are as strict, the time between verification and the decision to fire is further reduced. If they are less strict, another danger arises. Dr. York, in his recent testimony before the Disarmament Subcommittee of the Senate Committee on Foreign Relations, in fact pointed out a basic inconsistency between the requirement for a "hair trigger" ABM that is "continuously sensitive and ready" and a "stiff trigger" that "will never go off accidentally" or without proper authorization.

The key to the doubts of the experts is to be found in an analysis of the actual time intervals between warning and launch. With the ICBM targeted on a radar installation 6,000 nautical miles away, detection by over-the-horizon radar may occur immediately and detection by BMEWS may occur 10 minutes after launch, but accurate information on the missile's actual trajectory will be available only when the long-range radar acquires the track, 24 minutes after launch, and at a distance (along the ground) of 1,900 nautical miles. If the missile is not intercepted, it will arrive 10 minutes later. In order to intercept it with a Spartan missile, the trajectory data must be passed on to short-range, missile site radar, and the Spartan must be launched a few minutes later, in order to reach its target 8 to 9 minutes after acquisition.

For a missile launched from a submarine 1,200 nautical miles away, the whole sequence from launch to impact takes just 10 minutes, but radar acquisition is now just a half-minute after launch. In the case of an orbiting FOBS missile, it takes 23 minutes to go 6,000 nautical miles. The time from radar acquisition to arrival of a 100 n.m.–altitude FOBS missile is about 3.5 minutes, irrespective of the distance of the launch point.

The decision to fire an ABM obviously must be made sooner than the decision to retaliate with offensive weapons. To send off an ABM interceptor, the President will have almost no opportunity to weigh the evidence or to consult with his senior advisers. Although he can be in quick radio communications, the decision becomes all the more mechanical if at the critical moment he happens to be away from the command center in Washington.

The point is not that under these or any other circumstances the President relinquishes the actual command decision—he does not—but that the option when it reaches him is almost no option at all. If the system is to have any chance of intercepting actual enemy missiles, it is difficult to see how the President can avoid surrendering his decision-making authority to the computers and the junior military officers who stand over them. The command decision becomes little more than a hurried human reflex, devoid of political and moral consideration, to confirm what the machines say is inevitable.

There is, of course, an enormous difference between firing an offensive nuclear missile and a defensive nuclear ABM. But it seems important to bear in mind that deployment of an ABM system would in fact seriously erode the political and moral barriers that we have erected in the United States against the delegation of the essential Presidential control over the launch of nuclear weapons. In the light of all the other uncertainties surrounding ABM deployment, this concern over the loss of command adds significantly to the profound doubts about the wisdom of a deployment decision at this time.

# III

## SAFEGUARD SYSTEM:

## WILL IT WORK?

*Will the component parts of
the ABM work as described?*

# ABM RELIABILITY

## by LEONARD S. RODBERG

*Associate Professor of Physics,
University of Maryland
Chief of Policy Research, Science and
Technology Bureau, U.S. Arms Control
and Disarmament Agency, 1963–1966*

IN RECENT YEARS man has been responsible for some extraordinary technical achievements. But never before has he attempted to create anything approaching the complexity of the
ABM system. In this case, he must build and operate the
most sophisticated combination of rocketry, radars, computers, electronic equipment and other technology ever attempted. Not only must it all work, but it must function
perfectly the first time it is tried.

Few competent people in the field believe that it would.
There have been no full-scale tests thus far, least of all in an
operational environment. What's more, the history of initial
failures of far simpler systems suggests that the probability of
catastrophic failure of a defensive ABM system is quite high.
It is much higher, in fact, than for offensive systems which are
less intricate and more susceptible to adequate testing.

Once an ABM system was actually installed, it could never
be realistically tested—for an obvious reason. We could not
fire missiles at it since it would be located within the continental United States. Nor could we explode weapons above
it, so long as we adhere to the Nuclear Test Ban Treaty.
Many kinds of simulated tests could be devised for it, but the
first genuine test would have to be when it was used in
earnest. Although a model of part of the ABM system is being
tested on Kwajalein Island, these tests are conducted by

experts under laboratory conditions and cannot simulate a nationwide installation manned by GIs and technicians. In addition, the attack pattern is not realistic under such conditions, for we are testing against our own missiles, not enemy warheads, whose behavior we cannot be sure of.

From hard experience during recent wars, we know that far simpler devices fail to work the first time they are used. Early in World War II submarine torpedoes failed to work for six months until a systematic defect in their design was discovered. Of late, there have been significant improvements in the reliability of the individual components which make up modern military systems, but the complexity of these systems and the requirements placed upon them have been increasing even faster. For example, the greater speed of aircraft and the variety of countermeasures against air defense have more than kept pace with developments in antiaircraft systems. As a result, no one has succeeded in producing a system which could destroy more than 3 percent of the aircraft it faced. The poor performance of the advanced antiaircraft missiles installed by the Russians in North Vietnam testifies to this.

In spite of this kind of experience, a recent Defense Department press release makes the remarkable assertion that "theoretically it [an ABM system] can be 95 percent perfect." However, it goes on to note that even if such a high (and, in practice, certainly unattainable) reliability were achieved, it would not be sufficient. "In defending cities against an enemy with a large offensive force, such as the one the Soviet Union has today," the release continues, "95 percent is not good enough. One warhead getting through out of 20 can still kill a million persons."

The United States today has 30 metropolitan areas with populations of more than one million persons. If these were defended by such a high-reliability system and were each to be attacked by as few as three incoming warheads, one would expect (on a statistical basis) that 26 of these cities would survive; if they were each attacked by 30 warheads (something which is well within the capacity of the Soviet Union today), one would expect only 8 to survive.

## Reliability: Its Meaning

A system such as the ABM will function properly only if each of its major elements functions properly. Thus, the acquisition radar, missile site radar, interceptor missile and computer must each carry out its assigned tasks if a successful interception is to be accomplished. In such a system it is always less certain that the system as a whole will function properly than that any one of its components will be in working order. For instance, if each of these four components were to have a 95 percent chance of working properly at the time of an engagement, the total system would have slightly more than an 80 percent chance of meeting its objective.

The probability that a system or its components will function properly at any particular time depends on the mean time between failures of the system (usually denoted by MTBF) and the time required to detect a failure and repair it, when it occurs (this is usually called the "downtime"). Quantitatively, the probability that the element will be functioning—or the "availability"—is the ratio of the mean time between failures to the sum of that time and the downtime. For instance, if the MTBF is 98 hours and the downtime is 2 hours, the availability will be 98 percent.

The concept of mean time between failures is applicable to a system such as a radar or a computer, which is supposed to be operating continuously, but which will fail after a period of continuous operation. For such a system the degree of availability is a measure of the "reliability" of the system.

For an interceptor missile, a different concept must be used. Here the system remains quiescent on its launch pad, ready to be launched when a proper signal is received. For such a system the reliability is determined empirically by conducting a series of test firings and measuring the ratio of the number of launches in which the missile achieves its objective—destroying a single target—to the total number of launches. This ratio is the reliability of the missile, and indicates what probability there is that the weapon will successfully intercept its target once the button is pushed.

Continuously operating systems such as the radars and computers in an ABM system are subjected to repeated internal checks by monitoring the operation of particular components. Such test procedures allow the constant detection and replacement of inadequate components even while the whole system continues to function. Depending on the seriousness of the failure, the system may be inoperative for some time while the repair is made, but new modular techniques are being introduced to reduce the downtime by permitting simpler repair in the field.

Another method of testing is periodically to introduce signals which simulate an actual attack and to observe the response of the system. Naturally, such tests are substantially limited, since no one can foretell the course that an actual attack would follow. One can check individual components, but one can never be sure that the system as a whole will function properly in an unexpected circumstance. Through an unforeseen set of attack conditions, the computer system could be presented with a set of signals for which it had not been properly programed. The computer program would then misdirect the system or, at the limit, fail completely. The possibility of such a total failure is not included in the usual estimates of system reliability, since its likelihood cannot be quantified. It does appear to be, though, the single most likely occurrence that can cause the system to fail.

We nevertheless would want to make the "measurable" reliability as high as possible—just in case the programing should not fail! The requirements on individual components of an ABM system are roughly 100 times the reliability of components used on the Minuteman guidance and control system as recently as 1966, and 10,000 times higher than levels achieved in 1964. The use of integrated microelectronic circuits is increasing the mean time between failures by a factor of five, as compared with conventional transistors. As a result, electromechanical devices such as relays, switches and input-output devices are becoming the main source of failure in electronic systems.

In developing any technical system there are trade-offs between cost and reliability. The latter can be improved either by using more reliable, and thus more expensive, components, or by redesigning so that, even if individual components fail, the system will continue to operate. (This is usually done by introducing redundancy, that is, a duplication of components, into the system, to back up any that fail.) Either approach introduces significantly higher costs. And even after the system is deployed, as the system operators find unexpected sources of potential failure in the system and seek to improve further its reliability, increased expenditures will be called for.

In creating new weapons systems, designers consistently attempt to make advances in the state-of-the-art in general, and to use the most sophisticated forms of the technology involved—even when that technology is only in the earliest stages of development. This is as true of the Safeguard system—particularly its computer elements—as of any military system developed over the last twenty years. The use of advanced technology makes the system more attractive to the armed services, leads to higher projected effectiveness (if the new technology functions as predicted) and increases sales volume (since new technology is always more expensive than readily available equipment).

As a recent study[1] by an official of the Budget Bureau has shown, the result of this attempt to stay on the frontier of technology is that weapons systems consistently fail to live up to prior expectations, and their reliability is especially inadequate. The reason for this is clear: other measures of performance—such as the speed and range of an aircraft or the range and payload of a missile—can be determined easily at the time the weapon is produced. Reliability, on the contrary, can be determined only through extensive experience with the system, determining in practice how long the system functions between failures.

In the case of missiles developed during the 1950s, the mean time between electronic failures on three of four missile systems was 25 to 50 percent of the specified value (the fourth met specifications). The missiles also took an average of 50 percent longer to produce than had been forecast and had average cost increases of 100 to 240 percent. For systems designed in the last decade, a study of eleven high-risk electronic programs shows that they achieved an average mean time between failures of less than 50 percent of design specifications. This was worse than the experience during the 1950s. Follow-on programs demonstrated sharply reduced performance from that achieved in the parent program, averaging mean times between failure of only 30 percent of specifications.

Recent experience with the F-111 aircraft has shown how difficult and expensive it is to obtain reliable performance from a complex modern weapons system. This state-of-the-art system was put through a large number of flight tests and then authorized for use in Southeast Asia. When the plane was flown in combat, however, structural flaws showed up,

1 This study appears in the *Congressional Record*, February 7, 1969, page S. 1450.

and the Air Force was forced to ground the F-111 after several were lost. Even though the cost of the aircraft has increased by nearly 50 percent since production began, technical difficulties have continued to plague the program.

## Radars: The Rate of Availability

The most reliable elements in the ABM systems currently projected are likely to be the radars. The mean time between failures of most radars in use today runs typically from one to three days. However, these are mechanically steered systems with a single transmitting element, having the familiar rotating antenna fan. The radars used in an ABM system would have no moving parts, but would be steered by electronically changing the phase relations between the beams emitted by separate radiating units.

Such phased-array radars would have hundreds of thousands of individually controllable transmitting and receiving elements installed in a concrete base. The individual beams emitted by each radiating element interfere with each other, forming a narrowly focused beam which can be rotated through the sky by varying the phase relations between the elements.

Because the radar beam is generated by a large number of elements, it will persist even if some of these elements are inoperable. The radar uses about 5,000 independent transmitter tubes, each having a mean time between failures of about 3,500 hours. Thus there is typically about one failure per hour necessitating continuous maintenance and replacement of these tubes. The system is normally overdesigned, so that it can continue to function with reasonable precision if a nominal number of transmitter tubes or other components fail. The primary cause of severe difficulties would be the simultaneous failure of more tubes than expected. In that case the beam quality will be degraded, affecting the system's ability to locate incoming targets precisely and to contribute useful data for discriminating true warheads from decoys.

Today, phased-array radars are expected to have 95 percent availability. Because of the redundancy built into the phased-array concept, the radar turns out to be quite reliable, and most failures occur in the computer which controls the radar and processes the signals.

## Interceptor Missiles: Limits of Dependability

Guided multistage ballistic missiles are extremely complex pieces of military hardware; the Atlas missile, for instance, has 300,000 individual parts. Even with substantial flight testing, such weapons can have severe reliability problems. When deployed in operational sites, the Minuteman II missile was found to have severe problems which did not show up in any of the tests carried on during its production or in test firings. It is reported that Minuteman III has also had severe reliability problems, even though its designers were able to build on extensive experience with the earlier Minutemen.

The high reliability obtained in recent space launches should not mislead us into thinking that a similar reliability can be obtained in a military weapons system. In space shots a large number of people work on a single booster. Elaborate, hours-long countdowns accompany each flight, in which systematic checks are made of components to determine that they are functioning properly. On numerous occasions flights have been delayed or postponed because of defects in minute parts, as in the familiar "holds" associated with many launchings in the manned space flights.

Military missile systems must be maintained for long periods of time in the field by technicians having only a limited amount of experience and education. While the military services attempt to keep up the highest possible maintenance standards, there are inevitably losses in performance, as well as problems in maintaining instant readiness of all the systems involved.

The reliability of military missiles, as determined through flight test programs, generally ranges from 50 to 70 percent. Because many components are involved, it is generally very difficult and expensive to increase the reliability substantially above this, even under test conditions, and there is always some hard-to-measure loss in reliability when the system is deployed in the field.

## Computer: Largest and Most Intricate

The computer for an ABM system must perform a large number of tasks simultaneously: steering the radars, detecting potential targets, tracking them and predicting their trajectories, sorting out warheads from decoys, identifying and eliminating false targets, rejecting signals from prior nuclear explosions and residual blackout effects, allocating and then guiding interceptor missiles and checking the functioning of its own components—all in a matter of split seconds. It has been estimated that the data-processing facility necessary to perform these functions will have a capacity of a group of 100 of the largest commercial computers. Moreover, the internal programing, or software, would be the most intricate ever developed. Many computer engineers currently involved in the project profess uncertainty as to whether they will ever be able to design the software, much less assure that all sources of potential failure have been removed.

The complexity of the computer system is comparable, in its time, to that involved in the design of the SAGE air-defense system during the mid-1950s. There, too, the computer required by the over-all defense system involved a substantial advance over the computers then available, and optimistic projections of its eventual performance have not been borne out. Instead, the SAGE system has been plagued by continuing problems in the programing and operation of the computer system, and is currently being phased out.

The computer for the SAGE system contained more than 750,000 individual components (tubes, rectifiers, resistors and capacitors). It used duplex (redundant) operation, long-life components, continuous testing and modular packaging to aid maintenance. The designers attempted to have a ten-day mean time between failures, but in actual practice they were not able to achieve this. The system has suffered from poor reliability ever since it was installed, and the operators have had to fall back upon manual control because of their inability to obtain satisfactory automatic control.

Unlike the air-defense system, where the allocation of interceptors to individual targets can be made by human operators, the need in missile defense for split-second reaction times requires automatic allocation to targets by the computer. The role of human operators would be to monitor the operation of the computer system, not to make decisions.

Because of the large number of parts in the electronic systems of the ABM (running into the hundreds of thousands of individual components), even highly reliable components will lead to rather short mean times between failure. Thus, with the expected state-of-the-art of designing integrated electronic circuits, the mean times between failure of the system are likely to run around 200 hours, or 8 days. The chief component reliability problem in the computer system is not the computer itself, but other elements of the system, such as the device which converts radar signals into digital units which the computer can use. These converters generally have mechanical elements and are much less reliable than the computer. Because individual modules are used in the design of the computer, the repair time, once a defect is discovered, may be as short as 15 minutes. During that time, of course, the affected portion of the computer would not be functioning properly.

The brief duration of a mass missile attack would permit no time for human troubleshooting and repair. For this reason, approximately 10 to 15 percent of the data-processing system would be used solely for continuous self-monitoring and fault isolation in the system. It would attempt to pinpoint the location of failures, using periodic measurements of hundreds of individual subsystems and examination of these data to detect gradual deterioration in performance due to component aging. In some cases—provided this checking system could be designed and was operating properly—faulty subsystems could be bypassed and others used to carry out their functions. The system would be composed of a number of identical data processors (probably up to twenty). In the event of the failure of one of them, the work would automatically be distributed among the remaining ones. The primary consequence would be a small slowdown in the rate of data processing, if the remaining machines were operating at full capacity.

For some types of failures, of course, this replacement might not be possible, and the system would not function properly without manual replacement of the component—which would take some time. It is impossible to foresee all the ways in which the computer could fail. One can design around the foreseeable contingencies, hoping that no significant ones have been overlooked. But in such a complex system, it is impossible to know the effect of every possible component failure or combination of component failures.

In order to perform all of its functions the computer would use a "time-shared" programing approach. The central unit would work on a problem for a brief period, and then switch to other problems as they were presented by different aspects of the attack situation, doing this until it returned to the original problem. The central processing unit would determine what priority should be given to these problems, assigning them to individual processors in accordance with these priorities. It would then determine the allocation of computer time and storage space among the individual units of the computer.

So far there is only limited experience in the design of such computer systems. The first practical time-sharing system became operational only four years ago, and much development work remains to be done. Our largest computer firms have encountered severe difficulties, leading to delays of several years, in developing and marketing time-sharing systems which could function reliably on the small scale required for most commercial uses. So great is the variety of possibilities presented to the computer through the need to deal with a number of different calculations simultaneously, that it has proved difficult to analyze these different situations with complete thoroughness. The systems break down frequently, as new bugs in the computer program are discovered. Considerable time is then lost while these flaws are found and removed.

The combination of these many factors raises serious questions about our ability to achieve reasonable confidence in the computer programing. Judging from our experience with the SAGE air-defense system and other military command-and-control systems, the problem of programing the ABM computer system will take far more time and money to solve than many persons now expect. As one authority has said, "It is characteristic of dynamic-problem computer systems that the programing always seems closer to completion than it really is. In this respect, it is like driving toward mountain peaks which always prove more distant than they first appear." Many engineers feel that it will simply not be possible to program such a computer successfully in the near future.

## Conclusions

An ABM system would be the most complex and sophisticated electronic system ever constructed, and its design and maintenance would present an unprecedented problem in systems reliability. If all components of the system were to function at "rated" reliability (an unlikely eventuality under actual field conditions), the system would be available about 90 percent of the time (that is, the radars and computers would be functioning for that fraction of the time), and there would be a 50 to 70 percent chance of intercepting an incoming warhead if the single interceptor missile was functioning. This latter fraction could be raised to 75 to 90 percent by allocating two interceptor missiles to each incoming warhead. Although this is expensive and might nearly exhaust the available interceptors, it represents a potential option when defending the important target.

Assuming a single interceptor is used against each incoming warhead, between 4 and 10 cities would be expected to survive the kind of "light" attack envisioned earlier in this chapter (3 warheads on each of 30 metropolitan areas), and none would survive a heavy attack (30 warheads on each city). If two interceptors are used against each warhead, between 12 and 22 cities would survive a light attack and no more than 2 escape destruction in a heavy one. (Such calculations as these are of course idealizations. In an actual attack the offense would use penetration aids such as decoys and chaff which can saturate or confuse the defense and further decrease its effectiveness.)

There is a small chance (perhaps 5 to 10 percent) that, due to component failures in the radars or computers, the system's performance would be so degraded that it would fail to locate targets properly or to discriminate the targets from the decoys. In this case, there would be little chance of successfully intercepting many warheads. Last—but most important—there is a substantial likelihood that, in the course of a complicated engagement involving incoming warheads, decoys, chaff, electronic countermeasures, blackout explosions and other unpredictable effects, the system would fail completely, for totally unexpected reasons. No amount of prior study can foreclose this possibility which, on the basis of past experience with far simpler weapons systems, must be judged to be quite likely.

*Can we design computers and their
attendant programs with a reasonable
expectation that they will function?*

# UNDERESTIMATES AND
OVEREXPECTATIONS

## Assembled by J. C. R. LICKLIDER

*Professor of Electrical Engineering,
Massachusetts Institute of Technology*

DURING THE LAST three decades, the military-industrial complex of this country has had dozens of major experiences in
the design, development and deployment of large complex
systems. These have involved radar, communication, computer and other related electronic subsystems, all of which are
essential to the ABM. From these accumulated experiences,
lessons have been learned by individuals and to a lesser
extent by organizations. And as a result, it is now part of the
"common wisdom" of many scientists, engineers and administrators of technology that—particularly for a certain class of
systems—costs and times tend to be grossly underestimated
and performance tends to be mercifully unmeasured.

By all rights, it would be taken for granted that lessons
learned through past experience would have been applied in
evaluating the probable effectiveness of the proposed antiballistic missile system. But the "facts of life" about other
complex systems have never been incorporated adequately
into the basic procedure of procurement. Thus the elaborate
process of planning, proposing, awarding, funding, slipping
and overrunning continues almost as though it were a chain
of instinctive behavior, not modifiable by learning.

The class of systems for which costs and times are repeatedly underestimated and performance repeatedly over-
estimated have certain definable characteristics. These are:
(a) complexity and "sophistication"; (b) several interacting

technologies; (c) several or many concurrent but geographically separated instances; (d) operating conditions not mainly as envisoned by the designers or under the control of the operators; (e) the changing of the task with time; and (f) difficulties in the way of testing and practice. Some of the systems in this class are:

1. All-weather interceptors
2. Semiautomatic Ground Environment (SAGE) for air defense
3. Distant Early Warning (DEW) Line
4. Ballistic Missile Early Warning System (BMEWS)
5. Strategic Air Command Control System (SACCS)
6. Many others of the so-called "L" systems (intelligence and command-and-control systems)
7. Airlines reservation systems (e.g., SABER)
8. Electronic Switching System (ESS)

The closest things to counterexamples, we think, are Polaris and the Mercury-Gemini-Apollo series. Both are complex and sophisticated and involve several interacting technologies, and both have pretty good records. Note, however, that in both cases the operating conditions are mainly as envisioned by the designers or under the control of the operators and the basic task remains constant over time.[1] Moreover, a large fraction of an over-all Polaris system can be tested periodically, and every manned space mission is in essence a period of test and practice. And—we think a very significant factor in the case of the NASA systems—the spacecraft have been operated one at a time on a "fire when ready" basis by the original design-development-operation team; they have not been subjected to the rigors of "continual readiness" under field conditions and at the hands of nonprofessional personnel. Even relatively simple missile systems seem to run into trouble under pressure. The newspapers have reported five firings of Minuteman missiles in demonstrations to Congressmen. All five demonstrations failed.

If a wise decision is to be made about the ABM, it is necessary for high-level decision-makers to understand how

---

[1] When Apollo's LEM lands on the moon, the operating conditions may cease to be mainly as envisioned by the designers or under the control of the operators, and the basic task will change considerably— and, significantly, it is precisely at that time the confidence built up through the long series of orbital missions will need the most support from success in the ongoing operations.

the several factors work together to influence cost, time and performance—and how strong their combined influence is. Inasmuch as most of those decision-makers did not have close exposure to the technological experience provided by systems such as those listed, and inasmuch as there is no source that is both comprehensive and convenient, it may be necessary for the decision-makers to hear scientists, engineers and administrators on the subject.[2] Even with power of subpoena and much staff assistance, however, it would be difficult or impossible to develop truly authoritative data on the underestimation of cost and time or on the overestimation of performance. What could be reasonably developed, we think, is a subjective appreciation of the difficulties and uncertainties and of the distortions of perception and estimation that characterize the planning, development and deployment of complex systems even when they are in good hands. (Let us stress that the distortions of which we speak are not attributed either to stupidity or to villainy; they seem just to be characteristic of technological or organizational thinking in the complex-system field.)

## Interceptors: The First Test

Will an ABM system work when it is used for the first time? For obvious reasons, it will not have been tested as a whole.

Although the Air Force's all-weather fighter planes have not had to intercept enemy bombers, they have been "used" in tests with airborne targets. Perhaps the earliest full-scale tests were the Engineering Suitability Tests of the F-86 (North American), F-89 (Northrop), and F-94 (Lockheed), back in the early 1950s. Those aircraft were quite complex weapons systems by then-current standards, though not by today's. This is what happened the first time each aircraft fired rockets at a towed target: the F-86 had a malfunction of the rocket launcher; no hits. The F-94's rockets disturbed the air intake of the jet engines and caused a flame-out; no hits. The F-89 fired all its 104 rockets: 103 went off at an angle of about 45 degrees from the line to the target; one rocket

---

[2] Perhaps the closest approach to a comprehensive report is one that was circulating early this year in governmental and academic circles. See article by Bernard D. Nossiter, "Weapon Systems: A Story of Failure," Washington *Post*, Sunday, January 26, 1969. See also *Congressional Record*, February 9, 1969, p. S 1450, for the full text of this report.

wobbled erratically, departed from the others, and by the sheerest of flukes scored a direct hit on the target.

A direct translation of those experiences—which were by no means the worst offered by the all-weather interceptors—into the ABM context would, of course, spell out a horrible debacle.

## SAGE System: Idiosyncratic Behavior

What about the extrapolation from developmental tests of a precursor to deployment of a full-scale system? The Semiautomatic Ground Environment for air defense offered pertinent lessons.

The Cape Cod system had a few troubles, but it worked—surprisingly well—less than a year after it was undertaken. The SAGE system was to be essentially a scaled-up and replicated Cape Cod system, hence easy to estimate and schedule. Yet the number of man-years of programing required was underestimated by six thousand at a time when there were only about a thousand programers in the world. Up to a few weeks of the scheduled date of the first full installation-wide software test, the programing was "on schedule"—but then it slipped a year, and then another. Initially, it was thought that when the software was perfected for one installation, it would have only to be copied for all the others—but then it was found that each location was idiosyncratic and required time-consuming custom programing. And, of course, the computer technology advanced more rapidly than the system development. And the threat advanced more rapidly than the computer technology. SAGE was obsolete before it was completed. Although it was never subjected to a realistic test, the initial exercises made it obvious that SAGE could be brought under control, if at all, only step by step over a period of many months.

Another kind of lesson could be learned by dropping in on SAGE installations a couple of years ago—and probably still today. According to credible reports, there were makeshift plastic overlays on the cathode-ray displays, and the 'scope watchers were bypassing the elaborate electronics—operating more or less in the same "manual mode" used in World War II.[3] But perhaps we should not call that a lesson; it is part of

[3] Frederich B. Thompson, "Fractionation of the Military Context," *AFIPS Conference Proceeding*, Vol. 25, Spring Joint Computer Conference, 1964, pp. 219–230.

the bottled-up knowledge in most systems engineers' heads
that operational readiness simply cannot be maintained in an
inactive man-machine system, in a man-machine system that
is not repeatedly performing its essential function so that one
can repeatedly see how well or how poorly it performs. If you
try to achieve sustainable operational readiness by turning to
fully automatic design, you give up human control over the
crucial decisions. If you retain human control, you have to
remember the sad experience of SAGE and other man-
machine systems that tried to remain "ready" and "set" without ever receiving the word "go."[4]

## DEW Line: Changes on the Spot

The Distant Early Warning Line was a highly amplified
example of "hurry up and wait." According to a summary by
Donaldson,[5] it was "conceived in 1952," "born in 1953," and
"formally turned over to ITT Federal Electric Corporation by
the USAF for operation and maintenance in the summer of
1957." (Five years for design, development, and deployment.) Donaldson's summary says:

> Most of the electronic equipment, because of the urgency
> of the situation, did not have a normal development period.
> Equipment was manufactured directly from the bread-
> board design. Because of this, many operations and main-
> tenance problems arose which were not normal to a
> technician's daily work. The problem of modifications to
> electronic equipment and building and outside plant
> equipment to meet its new environment is discussed.
> Reliability of the detection and communication equipment
> and experience on remote area operation of a complex
> weapons system, in the face of ever increasing military
> operation requirements, and their solutions are reported.

## BMEWS: Moonbeams

Early in its operational life, the Ballistic Missile Early Warning System made its now-famous detection of "incoming

[4] Of course, the interceptors "scrambled" against "unknowns," but
that is nothing like going in earnest against a nuclear attack.

[5] W. G. Donaldson, "A Decade of Field Operations and Maintenance
of the DEWLINE," Conf. Proc. Mil-E-Con 8 (*International Convention
on Military Electronics*), p. 134, 1964.

ballistic missiles" that turned out to be the moon. Fortunately, cool wisdom in Colorado Springs—and lack of confidence in the new system—prevailed over the reflex of counterstrike, and what could have been the greatest tragedy in history became a lesson. Was the lesson merely to remember that large, distant objects can reflect as much energy as smaller, nearer ones? Or was it that men may not trust the advice of untested electronic systems enough to launch nuclear missiles? Or was it that men *should not* trust the advice of untested electronic systems?

## SACCS: The "Bug" Problem

The development of SACCS (Strategic Air Command Control System) updated the programing experience gained in the SAGE system. It showed dramatically that, when software gets very complex, you can pour more and more men and money into it without causing it to be completed. The programs get more and more complicated but not more and more operable. You begin to understand the possibility that they may literally never be "debugged" and integrated. You lower your aspiration level and accept what there is, working or not. You hope that the military computer people can finish the task the contractor's computer people could not—but you know that is only a hope, and you are happy that they can find things to do with parts of the contractor's unfinished product.

To put SACCS-like software into an ABM system would be folly—potentially hideous folly. To put perfected software into an ABM system would be—and this is the consensus of experienced system programers—impossible. All the large software systems that exist contain "bugs." There is no prospect for wholly perfecting any large software system in the next decade.

## Other "L" Systems

At one time, at least two or three dozen complex electronic systems for command, control and/or intelligence operations were being planned or developed by the military. Most were never completed. None was completed on time or within the initial budget. There should be a "History of the 'L' Systems."

## SABER: The IOC Factor

One of my associates had the experience of flying from De-
troit's Metropolitan to New York's LaGuardia the first day
American Airlines' SABER (airline reservations) system was
put into operation. He was trying to go to Boston, but the
Detroit-Boston flight for which he was ticketed was over-
sold—and he took the New York plane as the next-best thing,
a step in approximately the right direction, not realizing what
he was getting into. When he reached LaGuardia, about two
hundred people were milling about in the American Airlines
area, and all the other airlines were flooded by American's
overflow. Most of them had "reservations," but a reservation
on the first day of the computer system's IOC[6] turned out to
be worth just about as much as a letter of complaint to a
computerized billing system.

## The ESS: Double-time

The telephone company developed its Electronic Switching
system carefully and deliberately. The curve of "percent
programing completed" against time rose at about half the
projected rate, then bent over and approached one hundred
percent asymptotically.[7] Indeed, the curve looked very much
like curves for other large computer-based systems and added
another bit of confirmation to the rule that such systems turn
out to require at least twice as long for their development and
deployment as their planners think they will.

ESS was developed over a period of about three years;
tested, modified and augmented over a period of six months in
a pilot installation; improved; tested, modified and augmented
over a period of a year in a second installation; and then put
into wider service gradually. Hundreds of flaws were discovered and corrected in the process.

Although a great advance over the older electromechanical
systems, ESS is actually not very far out. It switches in milli-

---

[6] Initial operating capability, or the day on which a system is put into
operation for the first time.
[7] Edward E. David, Jr., "Effects on the Professions and on the
Character of Individual Contributions to Society," talk presented at
the 1968 Alumni Seminar, M.I.T., November 9-11, 1968.

seconds, not microseconds or nanoseconds. It switches lines, not messages. It is a far cry from the switched digital network that the nation ought to have. Note that such a conservative system as ESS can be deployed successfully only with much trial and error and gradual progression. How can one expect to make the much more radical ABM electronics work the first time out?

## Computer Programing: Endless Revisions

From experiences of the kind described in the preceding section, we have learned that the brash confidence of the "systems salesman" usually fades into the background soon after the development contract is let—and that the schedules slip, the costs mount and the delivered product falls short of the promise. We have learned that the misestimation of time, cost and performance are usually worst for the most complex subsystems. And we have learned that in many systems the most complex subsystem is the computer software, that is, programing. It seems worthwhile to focus attention, during the process of deciding about the ABM, upon its software subsystem. The following paragraphs deal with problems in the development and deployment of software that will probably be pertinent to the ABM software subsystem.

First, experience shows that computer programs that carry out regulatory and control functions are usually much simpler and easier to prepare than computer programs that involve target acquisition, pattern recognition, decoy discrimination, decision-making and problem-solving. If the ABM software were required only to handle clear signals and uncomplicated threats, and if it could be tested in an operational context, one might not expect more than a moderate amount of programing misestimation and trouble. On the other hand, if—as the case will actually be—the system will have to contend with weak signals and a sky full of man-made objects, some of them designed to resemble missiles or warheads, then, no matter how simple and straightforward it is expected at the outset to be, the ABM software will turn out to be very complex, continually in the process of revision and augmentation, and never free of bugs and "glitches."[8]

[8] Glitches are errors that, once they are located and understood, seem more glaring and blatant than bugs.

## *Fallibility: On the Research Frontier*

Because the matter of errors in the programing of complex computer software is so fundamental, let us take time to make it clear that the presence of such errors in a program is not evidence of poor workmanship on the part of the programers. True, the fewer errors the better the work and the more, the worse—other things being equal. But the essential facts are that all complex programs contain programing errors, that no complex program is ever wholly debugged and that no complex program can ever be run through all its possible states or conditions in order to permit its designers to check that what they think ought to happen actually does happen.

On the frontier of computer science, research people are working to overcome the obviously unsatisfactory situation just described, but they are not yet within reach of practical solutions. In the meantime, an important part of the software art is the part that concerns the practical mastery or "containment" of complex software subsystems. The techniques that have been successful involve continual operational testing of the over-all systems within which the software runs, careful recording of all detected anomalies of system behavior, taking the system out of operation periodically to make diagnostic tests and to track down the bugs and glitches and very careful revision and retesting of the programs. The revising has to be done very carefully because a programer is likely to do more harm than good when he makes a "corrective" change. Correcting one error may expose another, which, when it gets a chance, may disrupt the whole subsystem—which may then disrupt (or conceivably even destroy) the over-all system.

To a person who has been bombarded by phrases about "the fantastic speed and accuracy of the computer," the foregoing may appear to be either a heresy or grounds for barring computers from all functions that are vital to society. Actually, it contains a trace of both, but it is substantially neither. As we said, recognition of the facts of computer life is part of the common wisdom of knowledgeable computer scientists and engineers. Just as the foregoing assertions are facts of computer life, so also is the assertion that even quite complex software subsystems can be "mastered" (which is not the same as "perfected") and made to provide useful and effective service if they can be developed progressively, with the aid of extensive testing of systems (as well as subsystems and components), and if they can be operated more or less continually in a somewhat lenient and forgiving environment. A crucial question for consideration at this time, it seems to us, is the extent to which the ABM system and its environment will offer the conditions under which the essential software subsystem can be mastered in the sense and in the way just described.

## *Slowness and Cost: The "Retrofit" Factor*

The study referred to earlier (summarized by Nossiter in the Washington *Post*) notes that "complex electronic systems typically cost 200 to 300 percent more than the Pentagon expects and generally are turned out two years later than promised."[9] From the data presented by David[10] and from our own unsystematized observations, we have the impression that the two years is an underestimate of the typical schedule slippage, but it does not lead to a seriously distorted conclusion if one keeps in mind that a complex system may be delivered or deployed long before it is actually in fully operable condition. Indeed, complex systems ordinarily go through a long series of "retrofits" and field modifications. The F-111 swing-wing fighter-bomber leaps to mind as the example, of course, but perhaps the significant thing is that, although it seems to have been singled out for criticism, it is actually not much worse than quite a few other weapon systems.

In 1964, the rule of thumb for estimating the manpower requirement of the programing of large systems was 200 or 300 machine instructions per man-month. However, in a graph developed that year by Nanus and Farr,[11] summarizing experience gained in developing eleven complex systems, the function relating man-months to number of instructions curved upward rather sharply. It showed—on the average, though with quite a bit of variation—about 200 instructions per man-month on systems of 100,000 or 200,000 instruc-

[9] Nossiter, B. D., *op. cit.*
[10] David, E. E., *op. cit.*
[11] Burt Nanus and Leonard Farr, "Some Cost Contributors to Large-Scale Programs," talk presented at the Spring Joint Computer Conference, M.I.T., 1964.

tions, but fewer than 100 instructions per man-month on the largest of the eleven systems, which had 640,000 instructions. Such figures make it clear that the programing of large systems is governed by other factors than the capability of a typical programer to write a procedure: it would be difficult for a programer to write fewer than 100 instructions in a single morning. The governing factors have to do with the definition and organization of large programing tasks that involve several or many programers.

Many things have changed for the better in the world of software since 1964, but not the essential facts about the programing of large, complex systems. To obtain a rough check on the figures of Nanus and Farr, we made a quick calculation of the programing rate of the Multics system, a multi-access computer system developed jointly by General Electric, the Bell Telephone Laboratories, and M.I.T. For five years, it has been the focus of effort of a software group averaging about 50 people—which translates into 3,000 man-months. After having reached a size of well over a million instructions, it is now down to about half a million, and much better for having been made more compact. Thus Multics has yielded roughly 160–170 instructions per month for each of about 50 men. Perhaps one should take one instruction per hour for each of 100 men as a close-enough, easy-to-remember rule.

The instructions to which we have referred are machine instructions. To a first approximation, it may not matter how they were written—whether in a simple "assembler language" or in a high-level "compiler language." The significant thing is that the main causes of inefficiency lie outside the individual programer. If the 100 men were increased to 1,000, the hourly productivity of each would decline to one-third or one-fifth—or possibly one-twentieth. It may well be that, for any given state-of-the-art, there is an upper limit to the rate of production of complex, integrated software, and it may well be that it is now in the neighborhood of 10,000 or 20,000 instructions per month.

## Significance for the ABM: The Slow Software Pace

The significance of the foregoing discussion of slowness and cost lies in the slowness much more than in the cost. If a 10-billion-dollar ABM system required a 10-million-instruction software subsystem, the cost of the software, in and of itself, would be almost negligible. The trouble would come from the interaction of the software development and the development and deployment of the other subsystems. After each partial[12] system test, there would be weeks and months of reprograming—concurrent with the argument as to whether the failure of the test was due to the software or to other subsystems. Meanwhile, the threat would be changing—and the system would be continually improved and adapted—and the software would always be adjusting to changes in other parts of the system as well as to changes within itself. Thus the whole system effort would be reduced to the software's pace and to its state of confusion. On the other hand, the sad plight of the software system might be hidden from some of the other subsystems—and from the outside world—until the arrival of the hoped-against moment of truth. Then would the bugs come out.

We have, in sum, tried to set forth some of the considerations which we think should be held in mind by the decision-makers who determine whether or not to deploy an ABM system—and, if so, where, when and how. Most of the considerations pertain to the unhappiness that lies ahead for anyone who deploys a large, complex system that involves computers and software, that faces a changing and complicating threat and that cannot be tested continually as a whole. But we doubt that a mere description will serve to convince those not already convinced. We doubt that adversary proceedings are what are called for in the decision process of an issue so crucial to the future of life on this planet.

---

[12] There could not be a complete system test without exploding nuclear warheads.

*What is the likelihood of an enemy's overcoming an ABM by using various penetration aids and strategies?*

# COUNTERMEASURES
# TO ABM SYSTEMS *

## by HANS A. BETHE

*Professor of Physics, Cornell University*
*Nuclear Studies Laboratory, Cornell University*
*Member, President's Scientific Advisory*
*Committee, 1956–1959*
*Winner, Enrico Fermi Prize, 1961*
*Nobel Prize for Physics, 1967*

THE OBJECTIVE OF AN antiballistic missile defense can be quite succinctly stated: it is simply to send a nuclear-armed weapon close enough to an incoming attacker to destroy it. The execution of that plan, is, however, anything but a simple exercise. There are a number of ways that a defending missile can actually make a "kill." There are also a rather greater number of offensive devices and stratagems designed to confuse, deceive and elude defending rockets. These basic elements in any workable missile defense system deserve close examination.

## The Defensive Warhead: Three Effects

Much study has been given to the possibility of using conventional explosives rather than a thermonuclear explosive in the warhead of a defensive missile. The answer is that the "kill"

* The article by Richard L. Garwin and Hans A. Bethe, "Anti-Ballistic Missile Systems," *Scientific American*, March, 1968, continues to represent, in our view, the most authoritative analysis of penetration aids in the unclassified literature. This portion of the article, written by Dr. Bethe, is reprinted with the permission of *Scientific American*, and with the specific approval of Dr. Bethe. *Eds.*

radius of a conventional explosive is much too small to be practical in a likely tactical engagement. We shall consider here only the more important effects of the defensive thermonuclear weapon: the emission of neutrons, the emission of X-rays and, when the weapon is exploded in the atmosphere, blast.

Neutrons have the ability to penetrate matter of any kind. Those released by defensive weapons could penetrate the heat shield and outer jacket of an offensive warhead and enter the fissile material itself, causing the atoms to fission and generating large amounts of heat. If sufficient heat is generated, the fissile material will melt and lose its carefully designed shape. Thereafter it can no longer be detonated.

The kill radius for neutrons depends on the design of the offensive weapon and the yield, or energy release, of the defensive weapon. The miss distance, or distance of closest approach between the defensive and the offensive missiles, can be made small enough to achieve a kill by the neutron mechanism. This is particularly true if the defensive missile and radar have high performance and the interception is made no more than a few tens of kilometers from the ABM launch site. The neutron-kill mechanism is therefore practical for the short-range defense of a city or other important target. It is highly desirable that the yield of the defensive warhead be kept low to minimize the effects of blast and heat on the city being defended.

The attacker can, of course, attempt to shield the fissile material in the offensive warhead from neutron damage, but the mass of shielding needed is substantial. Witness the massive shield required to keep neutrons from escaping from nuclear reactors. The size of the re-entry vehicle will enable the defense to make a rough estimate of the amount of shielding that can be carried and thus to estimate the intensity of neutrons required to melt the warhead's fissile material.

Let us consider next the effect of X-rays. These rays carry off most of the energy emitted by nuclear weapons, especially those in the megaton range. If sufficient X-ray energy falls on a re-entry vehicle, it will cause the surface layer of the vehicle's heat shield to evaporate. This in itself may not be too damaging, but the vapor leaves the surface at high velocity in a very brief time and the recoil sets up a powerful shock wave in the heat shield. The shock may destroy the heat shield material or the underlying structure.

X-rays are particularly effective above the upper atmosphere, where they can travel to their target without being absorbed by air molecules. The defense can therefore use megaton weapons without endangering the population below; it is protected by the intervening atmosphere. The kill radius can then be many kilometers. This reduces the accuracy required of the defensive missile and allows successful interception at ranges of hundreds of kilometers from the ABM launch site. Thus X-rays make possible an area defense and provide the key to the Sentinel system.

On the other hand, the re-entry vehicle can be hardened against X-ray damage to a considerable extent. And in general the defender will not know if the vehicle has been damaged until it re-enters the atmosphere. If it has been severely damaged, it may break up or burn up. If this does not happen, however, the defender is helpless unless he has also constructed an effective terminal, or short-range, defense system.

The third kill mechanism—blast—can operate only in the atmosphere and requires little comment. Ordinarily when an offensive warhead re-enters the atmosphere it is decelerated by a force that, at maximum, is on the order of 100 g. (One g is the acceleration due to the earth's gravity.) The increased atmospheric density reached within a shock wave from a nuclear explosion in air can produce a deceleration several times greater. But just as one can shield against neutrons and X-rays one can shield against blast by designing the re-entry vehicle to have great structural strength. Moreover, the defense, not knowing the detailed design of the re-entry vehicle, has little way of knowing if it has destroyed a given vehicle by blast until the warhead either goes off or fails to do so.

### Penetration Aids: The Demands on Radar

The main difficulty for the defense is the fact that in all probability the offensive re-entry vehicle will not arrive as a single object that can be tracked and fired on but will be accompanied by many other objects deliberately placed there by the offense. These objects come under the heading of penetration aids. We shall discuss only a few of the many types of such aids. They include fragments of the booster rocket, decoys, fine metal wires called chaff, electronic countermeasures and blackout mechanisms of several kinds.

The last stage of the booster that has propelled the offensive missile may disintegrate into fragments or it can be fragmented deliberately. Some of the pieces will have a radar cross section comparable to or larger than the cross section of the re-entry vehicle itself. The defensive radar therefore has the task of discriminating between a mass of debris and the warhead. Although various means of discrimination are effective to some extent, radar and data processing must be specifically set up for this purpose. In any case the radar must deal with tens of objects for each genuine target, and this imposes considerable complexity on the system.

There is, of course, an easy way to discriminate among such objects: let the whole swarm re-enter the atmosphere. The lighter booster fragments will soon be slowed down, whereas the heavier re-entry vehicle will continue to fall with essentially undiminished speed. If a swarm of objects is allowed to re-enter, however, one must abandon the concept of area defense and construct a terminal-defense system. If a nation insists on retaining a pure area defense, it must be prepared to shoot at every threatening object. Not only is this extremely costly but also it can quickly exhaust the supply of antimissile missiles.

Instead of relying on the accidental targets provided by booster fragments, the offense will almost certainly want to employ decoys that closely imitate the radar reflectivity of the re-entry vehicle. One cheap and simple decoy is a balloon with the same shape as the re-entry vehicle. It can be made of thin plastic covered with metal in the form of foil, strips or wire mesh. A considerable number of such balloons can be carried uninflated by a single offensive missile and released when the missile has risen above the atmosphere.

The chief difficulty with balloons is putting them on a "credible" trajectory, that is, a trajectory aimed at a city or some other plausible target. Nonetheless, if the defending force employs an area defense and really seeks to protect the entire country, it must try to intercept every suspicious object, including balloon decoys. The defense may, however, decide not to shoot at incoming objects that seem to be directed against nonvital targets; thus it may choose to limit possible damage to the country rather than to avoid all damage. The offense could then take the option of directing live warheads against points on the outskirts of cities, where a nuclear explosion would still produce radioactivity and possibly severe fallout over densely populated regions. Worse, the possibility that re-entry vehicles can be built to maneuver makes it dangerous to ignore objects even one hundred kilometers off target.

Balloon decoys, even more than booster fragments, will be rapidly slowed by the atmosphere and will tend to burn up when they re-enter it. Here again a terminal ABM system has a far better chance than an area-defense system to discriminate between decoys and warheads. One possibility for an area system is "active" discrimination. If a defensive nuclear missile is exploded somewhere in the cloud of balloon decoys traveling with a re-entry vehicle, the balloons will either be destroyed by radiation from the explosion or will be blown far off course. The re-entry vehicle presumably will survive. If the remaining set of objects is examined by radar, the re-entry vehicle may stand out clearly. It can then be killed by a second interceptor shot. Such a shoot-look-shoot tactic may be effective, but it obviously places severe demands on the ABM missiles and the radar tracking system. Moreover, it can be countered by the use of small, dense decoys within the balloon swarms.

Moreover, it may be possible to develop decoys that are as resistant to X-rays as the re-entry vehicle and also are simple and compact. Their radar reflectivity could be made to simulate that of a re-entry vehicle over a wide range of frequencies. The decoys could also be made to re-enter the atmosphere—at least down to a fairly low altitude—in a way that closely mimicked an actual re-entry vehicle. The design of such decoys, however, would require considerable experimentation and development.

Another way to confuse the defensive radar is to scatter the fine metal wires or chaff. If such wires are cut to about half the wavelength of the defensive radar, each wire will act as a reflecting dipole with a radar cross section approximately equal to the wavelength squared divided by $2\pi$. The actual length of the wires is not critical; a wire of a given length is also effective against radar of shorter wavelength. Assuming that the radar wavelength is one meter and that one-mil copper wire is cut to half-meter lengths, one can easily calculate that 100 million chaff wires will weigh only 200 kilograms (440 pounds).

The chaff wires could be dispersed over a large volume of space; the chaff could be so dense and provide such large radar reflection that the re-entry vehicle could not be seen against the background noise. The defense would then not know where in the large reflecting cloud the re-entry vehicle was concealed. The defense would be induced to spend several interceptors to cover the entire cloud, with no certainty, even so, that the hidden re-entry vehicle would be killed. How much of the chaff would survive the defensive nuclear explosion is another difficult question. The main problem for the attacker is to develop a way to disperse chaff more or less uniformly.

An active alternative to the use of chaff is to equip some decoys with electronic devices that generate radio noise at frequencies selected to jam the defensive radar. There are many variations on such electronic countermeasures, among them the use of jammers on the re-entry vehicles themselves.

The last of the penetration aids that will be mentioned here is the radar blackout caused by the large number of free electrons released by a nuclear explosion. These electrons, except for a few, are removed from atoms or molecules of air, which thereby become ions. There are two main causes for the formation of ions: the fireball of the explosion, which produces ions because of its high temperature, and the radioactive debris of the explosion, which releases beta rays (high-energy electrons) that ionize the air they traverse. The second mechanism is important only at high altitude.

The electrons in an ionized cloud of gas have the property of bending and absorbing electromagnetic waves, particularly those of low frequency. Attenuation can reach such high values that the defensive radar is prevented from seeing any object behind the ionized cloud (unlike chaff, which confuses the radar only at the chaff range and not beyond).

Blackout is a severe problem for an area defense designed to intercept missiles above the upper atmosphere. The problem is aggravated because area-defense radar is likely to employ low-frequency (long) waves, which are the most suitable for detecting enemy missiles at long range. In some recent popular articles long-wave radar has been hailed as the cure for the problems of the ABM missile. It is not. Even though it increases the capability of the radar in some ways, it makes the system more vulnerable to blackout.

Blackout can be caused in two ways: by the defensive nuclear explosions themselves and by deliberate explosions set off at high altitude by the attacker. Although the former are unavoidable, the defense has the choice of setting them off at altitudes and in locations that will cause the minimum black-

out of its radar. The offense can sacrifice a few early missiles
to cause blackout at strategic locations. In what follows we
shall assume for purposes of discussion that the radar wavelength is one meter. Translation to other wavelengths is not
difficult.

In order to totally reflect the one-meter waves from our
hypothetical radar it is necessary for the attacker to create an
ionized cloud containing $10^9$ electrons per cubic centimeter.
Much smaller electron densities, however, will suffice for
considerable attenuation. For the benefit of technically
minded readers, the equation for attenuation in decibels per
kilometer is

$$a = \frac{4.34}{3 \times 10^5} \frac{\omega_p{}^2}{\omega^2 + \gamma_e{}^2} \gamma_e$$

Here $\omega_p$ is the plasma frequency for the given electron density,
$\omega$ is the radar frequency in radians per second and $\gamma_e$ is the
frequency of collisions of an electron with atoms of air. At
normal temperatures this frequency $\gamma_e$ is the number $2 \times 10^{11}$
multiplied by the density of the air $(\rho)$ compared with sea-
level density $(\rho_0)$, or $\gamma_e = 2 \times 10^{11} \rho/\rho_0$. At altitudes above
30 kilometers, where an area-defense system will have to
make most of its interceptions, the density of air is less than
.01 of the density at sea level. Under these conditions the
electron collision frequency $\gamma_e$ is less than the value of
$\omega = (2\pi \times 3 \times 10^8)$ and therefore can be neglected in the
denominator of the equation. Using that equation, we can
then specify the number of electrons, $N_e$, needed to attenuate
one-meter radar waves by a factor of more than one decibel
per kilometer: $N_e > 350\rho_0/\rho$. At an altitude of 30 kilometers,
where $\rho_0/\rho$ is about 100, $N_e$ is about $3 \times 10^4$, and at 60 kilometers $N_e$ is still only about $3 \times 10^6$. Thus the electron densities needed for the substantial attenuation of a radar signal
are well under the $10^9$ electrons per cubic centimeter required
for total reflection. The ionized cloud created by the fireball
of a nuclear explosion is typically 10 kilometers thick; if the
attenuation is one decibel per kilometer, such a cloud would
produce a total attenuation of 10 decibels. This implies a
tenfold reduction of the outgoing radar signal and another
tenfold reduction of the reflected signal, which amounts to
effective blackout.

The temperature of the fireball created by a nuclear explosion in the atmosphere is initially hundreds of thousands

of degrees Centigrade. It quickly cools by radiation to about 5,000 degrees C. Thereafter cooling is produced primarily by the cold air entrained by the fireball as it rises slowly through the atmosphere, a process that takes several minutes.

When air is heated to 5,000 degrees C., it is strongly ionized. To produce a radar attenuation of one decibel per kilometer at an altitude of 90 kilometers the fireball temperature need be only 3,000 degrees, and at 50 kilometers a temperature of 2,000 degrees will suffice. Ionization may be enhanced by the presence in the fireball of iron, uranium and other metals, which are normally present in the debris of nuclear explosion.

The size of the fireball can easily be estimated. Its diameter is about one kilometer for a one-megaton explosion at sea level. For other altitudes and yields there is a simple scaling law: the fireball diameter is equal to $(Y\rho_0/\rho)^{1/3}$, where $Y$ is the yield in megatons. Thus a fireball one kilometer in diameter can be produced at an altitude of 30 kilometers (where $\rho_0/\rho = 100$) by an explosion of only 10 kilotons. At an altitude of 50 kilometers (where $\rho_0/\rho = 1,000$), a one-megaton explosion will produce a fireball 10 kilometers in diameter. At still higher altitudes matters become complicated because the density of the atmosphere falls off so sharply and the mechanism of heating the atmosphere changes. Nevertheless, fireballs of very large diameter can be expected when megaton weapons are exploded above 100 kilometers. These could well black out areas of the sky measured in thousands of square kilometers.

For explosions at very high altitudes (between 100 and 200 kilometers) other phenomena become significant. Collisions between electrons and air molecules are now unimportant. The condition for blackout is simply that there be more than $10^9$ electrons per cubic centimeter.

At the same time very little mass of air is available to cool the fireball. If the air is at first fully ionized by the explosion, the air molecules will be dissociated into atoms. The atomic ions combine very slowly with electrons. When the density is low enough, as it is at high altitude, the recombination can take place only by radiation. The radiative recombination constant (call it $C_R$) is about $10^{-12}$ cubic centimeter per second. When the initial electron density is well above $10^9$ per cubic centimeter, the number of electrons remaining after time $t$ is roughly equal to $1/C_R t$. Thus if the initial electron density is $10^{12}$ per cubic centimeter, the density will remain above

$10^9$ for 1,000 seconds, or some 17 minutes. The conclusion is that nuclear explosions at very high altitudes can produce long-lasting blackouts over large areas.

The second of the two mechanisms for producing an ionized cloud, the beta rays issuing from the radioactive debris of a nuclear explosion, can be even more effective than the fireball mechanism. If the debris is at high altitude, the beta rays will follow the lines of force in the earth's magnetic field, with about half of the beta rays going immediately down into the atmosphere and the other half traveling out into space before returning earthward. These beta rays have an average energy of about 500,000 electron volts, and when they strike the atmosphere, they ionize air molecules. Beta rays of average energy penetrate to an altitude of about 60 kilometers; some of the more energetic rays go down to about 50 kilometers. At these levels, then, a high-altitude explosion will give rise to sustained ionization as long as the debris of the explosion stays in the vicinity.

One can show that blackout will occur if $y \times t^{-1.2} > 10^{-2}$, where $t$ is the time after the explosion in seconds and $y$ is the fission yield deposited per unit horizontal area of the debris cloud, measured in tons of TNT equivalent per square kilometer. The factor $t^{-1.2}$ expresses the rate of decay of the radioactive debris. If the attacker wishes to cause a blackout lasting five minutes ($t = 300$), he can achieve it with a debris level $y$ equal to 10 tons of fission yield per square kilometer. This could be attained by spreading one megaton of fission products over a circular area about 400 kilometers in diameter at an altitude of, say, 60 kilometers. Very little could be seen by an area-defense radar attempting to look out from under such a blackout disk. Whether or not such a disk could actually be produced is another question. Terminal defense would not, of course, be greatly disturbed by a beta-ray blackout.

### Blackout: Further Thoughts[1]

Summarizing the argument above, blackout can arise either from our own defense missiles or from enemy action. An enemy attacking us may explode a high-yield warhead above

---

[1] This subsection, an expansion of his analysis of blackout effects in the March, 1968, *Scientific American* article, was prepared by Dr. Bethe especially for this report. Dr. Bethe states that there has been no change in the technical situation since March, 1968.

the atmosphere, at an altitude of a hundred miles or so, and at a location close to our PAR radar. He will choose a warhead which gives a large amount of fission energy so as to create a maximum of radioactive fission products which then create blackout effects by their beta rays. He will use a high-yield weapon, of several megatons. By contrast our Spartan warhead will involve a minimum of fission insofar as compatible with proper design, so as to minimize the blackout. The exact figures are of course classified.

A given explosion will make blackout in two altitude regions. One is above the burst point, and is due to the fireball which has been created by the energy of the explosion, and which rises slowly with time. The other is due to the beta rays emitted by the radioactive fission fragments, the debris left over from the explosion. These beta rays go down into the atmosphere in much the same way as aurora streaks. But beta rays make most of their ionization (hence blackout) at an altitude between 30 and 40 statute miles.

Our knowledge of blackout is mainly theoretical. However, it is based on careful observations of test explosions at high altitude during the test series of 1958 and 1962. During these series, about seven nuclear devices of various yields were exploded at altitudes ranging from about 10 to 250 statute miles. Each of these was observed carefully, by taking ordinary, high-speed photographs and by measuring the spectrum of the fireball, and also by measuring radio propagation. Not every yield was investigated at every altitude, and it is this gap which has to be filled in by theoretical calculations.

It has sometimes been claimed that the Soviets may have more extensive knowledge in this field than we do. It is true that they carried out some test explosions at some altitudes and yields which we have not covered, and that their observation technique was different. However, on balance, I believe that our knowledge should be at least as good as theirs.

Because of the theoretical extrapolation required, there is some uncertainty about the exact extent of blackout in certain cases. However, the important conclusions are essentially independent of these uncertainties.

The area covered by blackout increases with the altitude of the burst and with the yield of the device. The exact numbers are classified. However, it is reasonable to expect a diameter of the blackout cloud of 120 miles (200 kilometers) for an explosion of a few megatons at a suitably high altitude. Since the beta blackout goes down to about a 30-mile altitude, the blackout disk will cover most of the sky if its center is over the radar. The duration of the blackout under these conditions is several minutes (perhaps ten) for UHF (ultrahigh frequency) radar such as will be used in the PAR. This is ample time for one or several further enemy missiles to "sneak in" unobserved behind the blackout cloud, because it takes about ten minutes from the time a missile first appears over the radar horizon until it hits its target. For higher frequency, the blackout duration is less; it goes about as the square of the radar frequency. Thus for S-band radar such as will be used in the MSR (missile site radar), the blackout due to beta rays will last only a few seconds.

The blackout due to the fireball has about the same duration, and is generally less damaging to radar observation because it is located at a higher altitude. This will be discussed in more detail below. However, it has an important lingering effect: even after the fireball becomes transparent to the radar waves, these are still refracted, like light is in going from air into water or glass. This gives rise to substantial errors in the estimate of the position of a missile when this is viewed through such a dead fireball. The error may amount to tens of miles, and there is no easy way to estimate it. The only possible way is to use radar of two widely different frequencies, such as UHF and S-band, to look at the same object. This can be done easily only if there are few objects in the sky, i.e., in the absence of chaff and of many decoys. A comparison of the observation by the two radars makes it possible to eliminate the position errors fairly well.

An enemy trying to black out our radars would have many tactics available. If he desired thorough blackout, he would need a considerable number of "precursor" explosions suitably distributed over our northern and western borders, perhaps something between ten and fifty. However, even a few high-altitude explosions designed to produce blackout can be quite effective.

If the enemy desires to attack one of the PAR radars itself, it is probably most advantageous for him to place the center of his blackout about sixty miles north of the PAR, so that the southern edge of the blackout is just over the radar. Then this radar will be able to look north only up to an angle of about 13°. On the other side, unevenness of terrain prevents the radar from looking at angles less than about 4° above horizontal. This means that the radar can look only into a narrow angular range of less than 10°, in which it can see incoming objects.

With such blackout, caused by a single incoming enemy missile, the radar could see a second missile directed against itself only at a considerable distance, namely, at more than one thousand miles. It would be somewhat difficult to calculate with any accuracy the future trajectory of such a missile from information obtained at such great distance. This would greatly impair the radar's ability to direct Spartans against the incoming missiles. This is, of course, the reason why Sprint missiles have been added to defend the PAR.

If the enemy wishes to attack a city down range, i.e., south of the PAR if the missiles come from the north, one possible tactic is to put the precursor blackout explosion directly over the PAR. If the city is 600 miles south of the PAR, the PAR could see a missile directed against the city until it was about 800 miles north of the PAR, or 1,400 miles north of its target. It could be seen again when it was about 350 miles north of its target. If the defense relies on computations in the early part of the trajectory of the enemy missile, i.e., at distance over 1,400 miles from the target, a very long extrapolation is needed, and the prediction of the further trajectory may be quite uncertain. If the defense tries to use observations *after* the enemy missile emerges from the blackout, this is rather late and requires that the Spartan intercept be made at an altitude of about 30 miles or lower. At this altitude, the effectiveness of the Spartan is already impaired, and it is also low enough so that the Spartan explosion may cause significant damage to the eyes of observers who happen to be looking at the explosion. This, however, may only be a minor consideration in case of nuclear war.

The defense is, of course, helped by the existence of several PARs which are connected by a communications network. It is hoped, when PAR I is blacked out, that PAR II, perhaps 1,000 miles distant, will be able to see the incoming missile. In this case, however, the high-altitude fireball blackout may be very troublesome. In the example of attack on a city 600 miles south of PAR I, while the enemy missile flies over PAR I (and is concealed from view by PAR I because of the low-altitude, beta blackout) it will also be in the midst of the fireball blackout at higher altitude. This will affect the observations which can be made by PAR II and may lead to very serious errors in the estimate of the trajectory of the enemy missile.

It is clear that blackout by *two* enemy precursor explosions, one north and one south of PAR I, would essentially put PAR I out of action (for the duration of the blackout), even for defense of cities substantially south of PAR I, and would seriously degrade observations by PAR II.

## Terminal Defense: Its Vulnerability and Cost

The foregoing discussion has concentrated mainly on the penetration aids that can be devised against an area-defense system. By this we do not mean to suggest that a terminal-defense system can be effective, and we certainly do not wish to imply that we favor the development and deployment of such a system.

Terminal defense has a vulnerability all its own. Since it defends only a small area, it can easily be bypassed. Suppose that the twenty largest American cities were provided with terminal defense. It would be easy for an enemy to attack the twenty-first largest city and as many other undefended cities as he chose. Although the population per target would be less than if the largest cities were attacked, casualties would still be heavy. Alternatively, the offense could concentrate on just a few of the twenty largest cities and exhaust their supply of antimissile missiles, which could readily be done by the use of multiple warheads even without decoys.

It was pointed out by Charles M. Herzfeld in *The Bulletin of the Atomic Scientists* a few years ago that a judicious employment of ABM defenses could equalize the risks of living in cities of various sizes. Suppose New York, with a population of about ten million, were defended well enough to require fifty enemy warheads to penetrate the defenses, plus a few more to destroy the city. If cities of 200,000 inhabitants were left undefended, it would be equally "attractive" for an enemy to attack New York and penetrate its defenses as to attack an undefended city.

Even if such a "logical" pattern of ABM defense were to be seriously proposed, it is hard to believe that people in the undefended cities would accept their statistical security. To satisfy everyone would require a terminal system of enormous extent. The highest cost estimate made in public discussions, $50 billion, cannot be far wrong.

Although such a massive system would afford some protection against the U.S.S.R.'s present armament, it is virtually certain that the Russians would react to the deployment of the system. It would be easy for them to increase the number of their offensive warheads and thereby raise the level of expected damage back to the one now estimated. In his recent forecast of defense needs for the next five years, Secretary McNamara estimated the relative cost of ABM defenses and the cost of countermeasures that the offense can take. He finds invariably that the offense, by spending considerably less money than the defense, can restore casualties and destruction to the original level before defenses were installed. Since the offense is likely to be "conservative," it is our belief that the actual casualty figures in a nuclear exchange, after both sides had deployed ABM systems and simultaneously increased offensive forces, would be worse than these estimates suggest.

Any such massive escalation of offensive and defensive armaments could hardly be accomplished in a democracy without strong social and psychological effects. The nation would think more of war, prepare more for war, hate the potential enemy and thereby make war more likely. The policy of both the U.S. and the U.S.S.R. in the past decade has been to reduce tensions, to provide more understanding, and to devise weapons systems that make war less likely. It seems to us that this should remain our policy.

*Does the influence of the military-industrial
complex have a serious impact on the
decision-making process regarding an ABM system?*

# THE PROBLEM
# OF MOMENTUM

## by ADAM YARMOLINSKY

*Professor of Law, Harvard University*
*Special Assistant to the Secretary of Defense,*
*1961–1964*

THE UNITED STATES military establishment is the largest
organization in the world. It spends almost 10 percent of the
U.S. Gross National Product, and it employs, directly or
indirectly, some 8.5 million people—3.4 million in the armed
forces, 1.3 million Defense Department civilians and 3.8 million industrial workers. This is one of every nine jobs in the
United States. Pentagon spending accounts for 43 cents of
every federal tax dollar, and one-third of all research activity.
For the sake of comparison, the automobile and truck industry sold products worth $23.5 billion in 1968, and the private
housing industry sold units valued at $22.4 billion, whereas
the Pentagon budget for the same year was almost $80
billion.

The economic activity produced by defense spending is
very widely distributed throughout the country, but it is
unevenly distributed. A number of areas are very heavily
dependent on particular kinds of defense work—and correspondingly vulnerable to shifts in defense procurement.
Nearly 30 percent of the personal income in Alaska, for
example, is directly attributable to defense spending. In particular metropolitan areas—Boston, Los Angeles, St. Louis,
Seattle—the concentration of defense work is even higher.
Nearly 60 percent of defense spending goes to ten states—
California, Texas, New York, Connecticut, Pennsylvania,

144

Ohio, Virginia, Massachusetts, Georgia and Missouri, in that order.

Companies engaged heavily in defense business seem to find it particularly difficult to diversify into the civilian market. One indication of this difficulty is the fact that 18 of the top 25 defense contractors in 1958 were also among the top 25 contractors in 1967, revealing their dependence year after year on military work. Another indication is the number of unsuccessful attempts by major contractors to establish themselves in the commercial market. Their lack of success may be attributed to the heavy emphasis on performance over cost-saving, and the difference between dealing with a single customer—the Pentagon—who plays a very large role in determining the internal management practices of its suppliers and dealing in the commercial market. Yet another indication is that the 25 top defense contractors in 1968 received 45 percent of prime defense contracts.

There is, therefore, a substantial and pervasive sector of the U.S. economy dependent on the maintenance of a relatively high level of military procurement and the development of new weapons systems to take the place of old systems, in order to keep the assembly lines running.

## Procurement: Coincidence of Interests

As Edward J. Lefevre, Washington Vice President for General Dynamics, explained his company's procurement philosophy to a Washington *Post* reporter late last year, "Our future planning is based on visible contracts. One must believe in the long-term threat."

The interest of the defense industry in maintaining a constant (or expanding) level of procurement coincides with the interest of military officers in developing new weapons systems for which they have been assigned program responsibility. It coincides also with the interest of labor union leaders in keeping their members on the job; with the interest of individual Congressmen in maintaining full employment and prosperity in their Congressional districts; and with the interests of lawyers, bankers, public relations men, trade association executives and journalists and a host of others whose professional and personal fortunes depend on this major sector of the U.S. economy.

The coincidence of these interests does not suggest any

nefarious combination or conspiracy among the various elements of the military establishment. The overwhelming majority is motivated by a genuine concern for national security. But when one view of the requirements for national security happens to coincide with personal and financial interests, and another view does not, it is difficult for an individual or a group to maintain an unbiased judgment of where the national security interest lies.

Some indication of the aberrations that this massive coincidence of interests can produce is to be found in the recent history of weapons development. Massive development projects, such as the nuclear-powered airplane (on which $1.025 billion was spent); the B-70 bomber ($1.5 billion); the Dyna-Soar ($405 million); and the Seamaster jet-powered seaplane ($361 million), were continued for some time after outside observers had concurred that further development was unfeasible and wasteful. Development of the Skybolt missile was only abandoned under circumstances that precipitated an international diplomatic crisis. And there is some reason to believe that the Department of Defense is still engaged in wasteful duplication of space systems developments paralleling those of the National Aeronautics and Space Administration. The system has a considerable momentum, and it is not easy to overcome, even when there is general agreement to change direction.

The *Congressional Quarterly*, in its May 24, 1968, issue, estimated that more than 15,000 companies could expect to be involved in the development and production of the proposed Sentinel ABM system. Listed among these were General Electric, Sperry-Rand, Raytheon, General Dynamics, McDonnell-Douglas and Thiokol Chemical. *CQ* quoted a brokerage firm report to its clients in the summer of 1967 on an expected decision to proceed with the ABM. It would be, the report said, the "day they will shake the money tree for electronic companies." Another authoritative observer estimated in March, 1967, that ABM development would employ some one million persons in 172 Congressional districts in 42 states.

Given these figures, and given the previous history of military weapons systems development, it seems reasonable to be concerned that initiation of even a "super thin" ABM system development would be difficult to keep within the limits of its initial procurement program, and that, once initiated, it would unleash powerful forces pressing towards elaboration and expansion of the system to the point where it might easily set off another major round in the arms race. The momentum of the ABM production line would tend to keep it going well beyond the point at which present plans call for it to be halted.

## Some Specifics: Width of the Web

A vast interwoven web of interrelationships lies at the root of this problem of momentum. Citing a few specific examples and considerations may help to illustrate how wide the web is. Some relate directly to the ABM; some do not. But they are all relevant to this discussion.

*First.* A recent Department of Defense survey showed that many members of the House, and many of the Senate, at one point in their lives held high-ranking positions in the armed services. It can be argued that this serves only to illustrate the laudable belief of these individuals in the necessity of each American responding to a call for military service; further, the fact that they reached high rank illustrates the courage and command abilities of those individuals. But in the context of this discussion, it uncovers one reason for the atmosphere of easy tolerance towards the recommendations of the Pentagon. The relationship between former high-ranking military officers who vote upon budget and program recommendations and present high-ranking officers who initiate the recommendations is of course a subtle one, and no one would suggest any impropriety in it. But the relationship, nevertheless, does exist, and it almost certainly has an impact.

*Second.* The Bureau of the Budget (BOB) in the Executive Office of the President has the primary government responsibility for weighing the merits of the requests of the various government agencies. In any typical year, the government agencies make proposals for programs and program funds to the BOB; the BOB must weigh these proposals for inherent soundness and conformity with both the President's over-all program and the Treasury receipts available before they are sent to Congress. It is not unusual for a Cabinet department to have the dollar amount of its proposals reduced by one-third by the BOB.

The BOB has some 500 professional staff personnel who serve as "budget analysts" in carrying out the review of the agency proposals. Only 45 of these 500 professionals are assigned to audit, control and program management of Defense Department programs. Thus, less than 10 percent of the personnel are assigned to defense programs which account for 50 percent of the federal government's budgeted funds. By way of comparison, according to material made available by Senator Jennings Randolph, there are 33 budget analysts assigned to natural resources programs, which account for less than 5 percent of budgeted funds.

The lesson of these figures seems clear: the BOB simply does not have the opportunity to perform the same rigorous examination of defense programs that it does on nondefense programs. There does exist a procedure for a joint BOB–Defense Department review of defense programs—but this joint review is not the type of arms-length, independent review accorded other federal programs; nor is it the type of review which might save us billions of dollars a year.

*Third.* Senator William Proxmire in March of this year released a tabulation which showed that the top 100 defense contractors employed some 2,072 retired military officers of the rank of colonel or Navy captain or above. This compares with a figure of 721 in 1959—an increase of 200 percent.

*Fourth.* The budget process of the federal government is at best abstruse, and only a handful of people in the country ever feel with any confidence that they understand its intricacies. The requests for funds for ABM activities in Fiscal Year 1970, which begins July 1, 1969, offers a good case in point. For Fiscal Year 1969, the Congress appropriated $1,195,600,000 for ABM activities (this excludes funds for classified work as well as funds for nuclear warheads). Yet only $861,200,000 of this will actually be spent in fiscal 1969; the remainder ($334,400,000) will be carried over to fiscal 1970, returned to the Treasury or used elsewhere in the Pentagon. The Administration has requested appropriations totaling $1,035,500,000 for fiscal 1970, for ABM activities which, when added to the amount carried forward from fiscal 1969, gives a total of $1,369,900,000 for potential ABM expenses in fiscal 1970. Yet the press repeatedly carries stories to the effect that the Administration has requested $900 million for Safeguard in fiscal 1970. While this may be technically true—the *authorization* request for military procurement for ABM activities is $905,400,000—it is an entirely inaccurate measure of the true costs of ABM activities in the coming fiscal year. One of the most difficult tasks facing our legislators—not to speak of the lay public—is to determine an accurate picture of government spending on defense programs. Yet there is no real purpose served by the obfuscation, and it should be ended.

*Fifth.* Another murky area is defense contracting procedures. The 1969 Report of the Congressional Joint Economic Committee commented on these procedures in the following terms:

> While over $44 billion was spent on the purchase of weapons and other military goods last year, only 11 percent of the contracts were awarded through formal advertising. Sole-source procurement accounts for 57.9 percent. It is the sole-source procurement of major weapons systems where much of the problem of excessive costs and cost overruns has occurred. Cost increases of 200 percent and more over original estimates have been common.

This raises no small problem: another Joint Economic Committee study showed that between 1950 and 1959, there were 38 million separate defense procurement transactions, with a dollar volume of $228 billion. One can only wonder if we can ever devise a procedure for an adequate and disinterested audit of all these transactions.

## Summary: To Make a Start

We all believe, in varying degrees, that we are the masters of our own fates. Sanity requires this to be so. Yet the more one delves into the problem of momentum surrounding the military establishment, the more one is impressed with the difficulty of controlling so powerful an engine. It is time to make a fresh start. But the pressure behind the ABM only serves, as the latest case in point, to underscore the profound difficulty of gaining more effective control over the military establishment.

# IV

## STRATEGIC BALANCE:

## WILL IT BE UPSET?

*How will the Soviets react to the U.S.*
*decision to deploy the ABM?*

# THE EFFECT OF ABM ON
# U.S.-SOVIET RELATIONS

## by MARSHALL D. SHULMAN

*Professor of Government and Director of the*
*Russian Institute, Columbia University*

THERE COMES A TIME in the affairs of men when it becomes necessary to exchange one cliché for another. The accepted Cold War image of two scorpions in a bottle has lost its power to impress. This is probably because we have come two decades into the nuclear age without deadly consequences—and two decades seem forever to the "now" generation. Perhaps we might now try for a while the image of two frogs in a pond, each puffing himself up to look more powerful than the other. In the jargon of the trade, the scenario has "alternative outcomes": (a) they puff up and out, or (b) they stop and ask: "Now what are we doing this for?"

The United States and the Soviet Union have fallen into a senseless contest over strategic weapons—senseless because it reduces the security of both. The game is exquisitely rational and speciously precise within its boundaries, but if anyone is watching from another planet, it must seem insane.

This is the context in which we must consider the effects of a decision by the United States to begin the deployment of an antiballistic missile system, whether it be called "Safeguard" or by any other deodorant code name. It is not ABM by itself which is the issue, but rather, ABM as another round in the upward spiral of strategic weapons.

This is not to minimize the need for an effective strategic

defense, nor to argue for more trust in our adversary, nor to anticipate a general détente. The question is: given the tough rivalry between the Soviet Union and the United States, which seems likely to continue for a while, can we keep the strategic weapons competition at a stable and moderate level? I think we can. I believe that conditions are favorable for breaking the senseless spiral at this time—and the opportunity may be ignored.

## Some Factors: The Soviet Perspective

Out of the history of the postwar period, it is possible to develop these brief considerations on the dynamics of the arms competition between the two superpowers:

(1) Until a few years ago, the strategic military relationship of the Soviet Union and the United States had reached a plateau of relative stability. This was based upon a gross balance of mutual deterrence, despite considerable disparities between the two arsenals. Experience had taught both countries a considerable measure of sobriety, and in practice there developed significant tacit restraints which introduced some measure of stability in their strategic military competition. However, the quest for superiority by each country and the appearance of a new generation of technological innovations now threaten to undermine that tenuous stability. By and large, the United States has been the pace setter, and the Soviet Union has been making a strenuous effort in recent years to catch up.

For all practical purposes, the deterrent balance cannot be improved in favor of one side or the other by any of the measures now under discussion. It can, however, be made less stable and more costly, and this will be the effect if the United States and the U.S.S.R. follow the upward spiral into new technological possibilities which are becoming available —improved accuracy, more target information from reconnaissance satellite photography, greater range and yield, multiple guided warheads, advanced computer technology and potential military uses of outer space and the sea bed. This is an important part of the context in which the ABM decision must be made.

(2) There has been a spiral of interaction between the two countries. Partly this results from the natural zeal of professional military men on each side, eagerly exercising their

responsibilities and protecting their particular services. Partly also it results from a tendency to overinsure against uncertainties of what the other side is doing, or may be planning to do in the future.

To a much greater extent than either side would care to admit, psychological apprehensions and bureaucratic politics tend to determine defense policies. Rational doctrine comes along as an afterthought. The interplay of forces and interests operating on the decision-making process within each country is affected by that on the other side. And the end result has been a reciprocal process of stimulation. However, there is often a lag in time involved, during which ideas are diffused, sink in and get translated into action. This means that we have often not recognized a reaction for what it is, but have taken it as a new initiative, reflecting a change in intentions. For example, it appears probable to me that the increased rate of intercontinental missile deployment by the Soviet Union, of which we became aware a few years ago, may reflect a decision taken in response to the steep rate of increase in our missile program foreshadowed in the 1961 U.S. budget, which was in turn a response to our estimate of what the Soviet missile program of 1958 might have projected—but did not. And the so-called Tallinn line in the Soviet Union, it seems likely, may have been an anticipatory response to our proposed B-70 bomber program—which we did not build. Thus, anticipation, overinsurance and unrestrained professional zeal provide the dynamism for the puffing up on both sides of the international pond.

(3) While on the United States side the impetus can be traced largely to military and certain industrial interest groups, on the Soviet side the upward thrust appears to come from the military and the orthodox wing of the Communist Party bureaucracy. The mark of this political union is a preoccupation with ideological conformity at home and the use of coercion against departures from orthodoxy in Eastern Europe. A further tightening of police and Party vigilance against "contamination by bourgeois ideology" may accompany any reduction in tension with the United States. This has been the case in the past, because this domestic coalition fears the corrosive effects of ideological coexistence.

(4) Economic interests, however, tend to tug the Soviet leadership toward less militancy and somewhat greater collaboration. The modernization of the economy within the

Soviet Union and in Eastern Europe raises inherent difficulties for tight Party control and limited contacts with the
West. More specifically, the Party leadership is now drafting
a Five-Year Plan for the allocation of resources for the period
1971–1975. It is clearly concerned about the drain on resources generally and upon advanced technology in particular
as it contemplates the costs of an upward-spiraling arms race.
One year ago, the Soviet leadership was engaged in a hard-
fought debate on the question of entering into talks with the
United States to  damp down the strategic arms race. By the
late spring of 1968, this issue was settled in favor of entering
into such talks. It is not clear how far the Soviet leadership
would be prepared to go in actual negotiations. It may be
that the only agreement reached at that time was to let the
talks begin. But it does appear that a serious concern about
economic costs has impelled the Soviet leadership to want to
find out how far the United States is prepared to go in
checking the upward spiral of the strategic arms race.

(5) The rise in publicized hostility between the Soviet
Union and Communist China is a factor that may operate in
several contradictory directions. The Soviet Union definitely
appears more interested in a period of quiescence in its relations with the United States since its intensified conflicts on
the Chinese border began. More than that, it has shown deep
anxieties about the possibility of an alliance between China
and the United States. On the other hand, the Chinese border
conflicts also serve to increase Soviet defense requirements,
which complicates its efforts to reach even *de facto* agreements with the United States.

(6) As of this moment, Moscow's attitude toward the new
Administration in Washington is tentatively hopeful. Soviet
fingers are crossed. The Soviet press and leadership, despite
past feelings about the new President and anxiety about
pressures toward the militarization of American society, appear to believe that "objective circumstances"—meaning domestic social tensions in the United States, budgetary pressures and the pacific inclination of the American people—
together with the practicality of the President, may create a
fresh opportunity for moderating the strategic arms race.

(7) In recent years, serious analytical writing on the ABM
has virtually dropped out of Soviet publications. With regard
to the U.S. decision to deploy Sentinel or Safeguard, the
Soviet press has not until recently expressed deep concern,

except for the worry that a thin ABM might soon put on more weight. Although evidence is lacking, I believe the ABM by itself may be of less concern than the ABM in its full context. This includes the deployment of MIRVs and other technological refinements, especially the improvement of missile accuracy. Taken together, these may give some plausibility to the arguments of those in the U.S.S.R. who claim the United States is bent on achieving a first-strike capability—just as Defense Secretary Laird, with less basis, has claimed about the Russians.

If we proceed with the deployment of Safeguard, I do not believe it will automatically deter the Soviet Union from entering into talks with us. But I do believe it will make it much more difficult for those talks to be productive. In the end, what the Soviet Union says about U.S. ABM deployment is of less significance than the decisions it makes in research and development, procurement and deployment, accelerating its own rate of technological innovation. We may well feel there is no logic in such a response, but the Soviet Union is not likely to be any more coolheaded than the United States: against a Soviet ABM deployment involving around half as many missiles, much less impressive than ours, we responded by moving into MIRVs *and* an ABM system. When the Soviet Union has responded to Safeguard, we will then point to whatever they do as evidence of their aggressive intent, requiring a further response from us, and so the puffing goes on.

## Some Conclusions: Risks and Opportunities

I believe that the deployment of Safeguard should be put on "hold." At the same time, U.S. research and development of various antiballistic missile systems should continue. There are risks to such deferment. But I believe they are less than the risks and costs of stimulating the upward spiral of the strategic arms race. And they are certainly less than the risks involved in delaying and complicating a leveling-off of that race.

Even more important would be a serious effort on our part to begin negotiations with the Soviet Union aimed at curtailing the strategic arms race as soon as possible. What is needed is a clear indication of the seriousness of our intention to achieve stability, leveling-off and, when possible, arms reduction. One essential mark of our seriousness would be our willingness to exercise restraint in the further deployment of Poseidon, Minuteman III and other advanced offensive weapons. There are also risks to this course, but if our security is best advanced by a stable deterrent balance at a moderate level, such risks are neither disproportionate nor irretrievable.

We should avoid creating undue expectations for early and dramatic results in any negotiations with the Soviet Union. It seems likely that these arms talks may take a long time, that they may involve procedural wrangles and setbacks and that they may at best produce tacit and reciprocal restraint rather than treaty agreements. We should not expect these talks automatically to produce a general détente, or a settlement of other political differences. The prospects for an era of good will with the Soviet Union do not appear to be bright at the present time. Still, we should be absolutely clear in our minds about one thing. There is a real distinction between a full détente and a damping down of the strategic arms race. Whether the level of tension is high or low, the U.S. and the U.S.S.R. share a mutual interest in strategic arms control.

It follows from this that while the Administration should be commended for its effort to move ahead on a number of political issues with the Soviet Union, the missile talks should not depend upon the successful outcome of these efforts. If we make arms negotiations conditional on the settlement of other issues, we will invest the missile talks with a political significance that will seriously complicate our relations with our allies. What is more, we will blur what must be kept distinct: the separation between the strategic confrontation and the political rivalry.

It follows also that it would not be wise to begin to deploy an ABM system in the belief that it would improve our bargaining position in relation to the missile talks. To do so would be more likely to strengthen the position of those on the Soviet side who are only too ready to argue that the United States is committed by its system and its pressure groups to an arms race.

I would not argue that every level of antiballistic missile deployment under every circumstance is necessarily destabilizing. I can conceive of circumstances arising, once the negotiations have begun, in which the Soviet Union might indicate it would not wish to contemplate the dismantling of its ABM installations, whether because of the Chinese or for whatever reason. Similarly, if we then chose to deploy some moderate level of ABM protection, specifically designed to reduce the future vulnerability of our fixed-site missiles, our command-and-control installations and our Strategic Air Force as a stabilizing factor in the deterrent balance, I believe the Soviet Union might be able to accept such a deployment. But it would be absolutely essential to make clear, by Presidential declaration and by physical disposition of ABM facilities, that they will not be used as the building blocks of a thick ABM system and a first-strike capability on our part. None of these circumstances applies to a present deployment of the Safeguard system. It is not well suited for the task of protecting missile sites. It is designed for area defense. And, finally, it is to be deployed in the context of continuing advances in U.S. offensive systems.

These several observations all point toward one final significant conclusion. The present moment offers an unusual opportunity for stabilizing the strategic balance between the Soviet Union and the United States. In spite of the pressures within each country for puffing up, I believe the Soviet leadership has a present interest in exploratory arms negotiations. This is because of the economic costs of missile systems, because of China's bellicosity along the Russian border and because Moscow believes it has achieved something like parity. At best, arms negotiations will be devilishly complicated, but the alternative is even more unsatisfactory. If serious talks do not start at this time, it seems likely that in another year or two the weapons systems then deployed will be several times harder to stabilize and reduce. Both we and the Soviet Union will continue to pour out our vital forces in a senseless endeavor, all the while increasing costs and risks. This, in sum, is an opportune time for both sides in the arms race to stop and ask: "Now what are we doing this for?" And if the Administration will not break the spiral, perhaps the people and their Congress will.

*How serious is the threat of a nuclear attack by the Chinese Communists?*

# THE CHINESE NUCLEAR THREAT

## by ALLEN S. WHITING

*Professor of Political Science and Associate of Center for Chinese Studies, University of Michigan Formerly Chief of Intelligence and Research, Far East, Department of State*

WHEN SECRETARY OF DEFENSE Robert McNamara announced the 1967 decision to go forward with deployment of the Sentinel ABM, he introduced an entirely new element into the dialogue of nuclear defense and deterrence. For the first time, he identified Peking's emerging nuclear capability as a principal threat to the continental United States. The Sentinel, he said, would be "Chinese oriented." Over a year later, the new Administration recast the case for deploying the Safeguard ABM so that the Chinese specter was somewhat subordinated to the traditional Soviet threats. Still, the prospect of nuclear-tipped attack missiles from the Chinese mainland has now been officially raised and that, in turn, has raised two key questions: what kind of ICBM capability is Peking likely to have, and when; and what are the likely nuclear motivations and intentions of the Red Chinese leaders?

On the question of Peking's ability to build a missile capable of striking at U.S. cities, Secretary McNamara in 1967 estimated that there could be an operational Chinese ICBM as early as 1973. The more probable date, he said, was 1975. On March 20, 1969, however, Deputy Secretary of Defense David Packard downgraded that prospect. He testified that "the Chinese threat is not much further along today than it was three years ago." A month later, on April 18, 1969, President Nixon reported that the Chinese "have not moved as fast recently" as in earlier years. But he nevertheless estimated that by 1973 or 1974 "they would have a significant nuclear capability." These varying official estimates on the state of Peking's missile technology only underscored the need for a more precise definition of Red China's ICBM capabilities and intentions.

## Chinese Capabilities: How Much, How Soon?

The confusion and uncertainty are understandable. The fluctuation in intelligence projections is partly the result of the wide-ranging turmoil unleashed on the Chinese mainland by Mao Tse-tung's Cultural Revolution. At its inception, the Cultural Revolution officially excluded forays in the field of science. But those protective barriers failed to stand. As mob violence and armed clashes spread throughout China's urban areas, the original restraints on the Revolution disappeared. And as they did, China's missile chief, Marshal Nieh Jung-chen, came under repeated Red Guard poster and pamphlet attacks.

Some measure of the resulting disruption can be judged from the fact that China's thermonuclear experiment in December, 1967—the first after its successful test in June, 1967—went unannounced by Peking. It was analyzed by the U.S. Atomic Energy Commission as a probable failure. No test at all occurred in the spring of 1968, breaking a pattern that had held since the program began in October, 1964. A clue to the source of turmoil came in April, 1968, when Chou En-lai met in an all-night session trying to unite two key feuding scientific factions, both responsible for the nuclear weapons program. Chou failed, as reflected by subsequent Western newsmen's reports from Peking, which told of Red Guards ransacking the offices of one of the scientific factions.

On December 27, 1968, China held its first successful test in eighteen months with an estimated 3-megaton explosion. However, no ICBM test had occurred by the time of Deputy Secretary Packard's testimony, nor did one appear to be in the offing. Under these circumstances, it is still likely that an official Nixon revision of the original McNamara estimate will move the possible Chinese acquisition of an operational ICBM forward from the time frame of 1973–75.

This assumes, of course, that Peking will proceed immediately from testing to production and deployment. Such an assumption may seem reasonable enough, but it need not be taken for granted. The famous proclaimed "missile gap" of the late 1950s arose because of American assumptions that the first Russian Sputnik would be followed by immediate ICBM production. However, Soviet strategists decided against this, preferring to delay an operational capability until a more reliable, quick-responding and secure system was available. This, as well as other constraints of policy, might delay China's ICBM capability well beyond the initial test stage.

Moreover, there is the unresolved question of whether Peking will allocate its scarce resources for a single missile system or spread its investment over a wider range of weapons systems, principally for the political effect of a diversified token capability. Alice Hsieh of the RAND Corporation has already called attention to the political and military gains accruing from shorter-range MRBMs and IRBMs, which would bring virtually all important capitals and U.S. bases in Asia under targeting within 750- to 1,000-nautical-mile ranges of China. Testing an ICBM would give Peking the prestige of showing it could match Soviet and American capability if it wished. But producing and deploying less costly and more reliable systems might well prove a more attractive route to Chinese leaders. In addition, various reports of plans for a nuclear-armed Chinese submarine force suggest still another alternative to the ICBM should Peking be forced to choose amongst various nuclear weapons systems.

In sum, there is no basis for justifying an ABM in the United States now because of a possible Chinese ICBM capability by 1973. At the outside, there is a hypothetical possibility of a Chinese ICBM capability in 1975. But even this prospect depends upon a series of uncertainties, including the rate and success of actual testing and some decision on actual allocation of limited Chinese resources to an ICBM weapons system.

### Chinese Intentions: How Calculable?

Even assuming the eventual Chinese acquisition of an ICBM capability, we must assess Peking's motivations and intentions in order to justify translating capability into threat. Moreover this threat must be both credible and critical if we are to supplement our massive nuclear retaliatory deterrent with an antiballistic missile system that has definite economic and political costs. These costs necessitate designing a defense system against some reasonable range of potential enemy behavior. While "worst-case" projections are useful in war games and in alerting responsible officials to the inevitable inadequacies in any defense system, they cannot be the single basis for determining the design of such systems.

It is difficult enough to project the nature and outlook of any political regime five years or more hence. This is further complicated, however, by the probable passing of Mao Tse-tung from power during this forthcoming period and the uncertainties of the successor struggle which is certain to follow. Even so, the People's Republic of China is almost twenty years old. Its major military and political figures have been on the scene for forty years. Thus we have fairly good evidence for evaluating the range of likely Chinese actions in the foreseeable future. In particular, we can reasonably assess the probability of irrational behavior or miscalculation by Mao's immediate successors.

These two possibilities, irrationality and miscalculation, underlie almost all the attempts at justifying an ABM in terms of an alleged Chinese threat. The first views the Chinese leadership in the mid-seventies as willing to launch a thermonuclear attack against the United States despite the absolute certainty of retaliatory nuclear devastation in China. An alternative argument views our confrontation and conflict with Peking as eventually triggering a Chinese miscalculation, escalation and sudden—if suicidal—ICBM attack on the United States.

Basic to both long-range arguments is the assumption that the Chinese will be fundamentally different from the Russians in their handling of nuclear weapons and in their response to the threat of nuclear devastation. Even the so-called worst-case projection of Chinese nuclear capabilities shows that throughout the next decade Peking's strength will be at much greater disparity vis-à-vis American nuclear power than was true for the Soviet Union throughout the past two decades. Yet we successfully faced down the Russians in Berlin and Cuba, knowing they had weapons capable of striking American cities. We found that American deterrence worked. No Soviet attack occurred. At present and throughout the foreseeable future, our nuclear power in land, sea and airborne systems will remain more than sufficient to destroy half of

China's population and virtually all of its agricultural and industrial base. But, strangely, proponents of the ABM argue that this destructive force will not deter the Chinese as it deterred the Russians.

There is no basis in fact or theory for attributing a significantly higher likelihood of irrationality to Chinese as compared with Russian decision-makers. To be sure, the Chinese are far more strident than the Russians in verbal support of "people's wars" and "national liberation movements." But this is rhetoric. Peking has no more than Moscow rendered open aggressive support—or risked nuclear retaliation—for foreign insurgencies. Moreover, despite continued U.S. intervention in the Chinese civil war, protecting Chinese Nationalist forces on Quemoy within gun range of Chinese Communist batteries on the mainland, there has been no compulsive or reckless risk-taking on the part of Peking.

It is true that Chinese Communist forces engaged us massively in the Korean War while Russia stood aside. But it should be emphatically remembered that the Chinese gave no help to the North Korean invasion of South Korea in June, 1950. They intervened only when that regime was about to be driven off its territory by advancing United Nations forces under the command of General Douglas MacArthur, acting in defiance of an explicit Chinese warning against crossing the thirty-eighth parallel. American military action in Hungary in 1956 or in Czechoslovakia in 1968 would almost certainly have led Moscow to take risks similar to, if not greater than, Peking took in Korea. In sum, any similar effort to roll back Communist rule in East Europe would have run an equally grave risk of provoking an identical, or worse, Russian reaction.

Since the Korean War, the only major action involving Chinese troops has been the several weeks of limited war with India in the disputed Himalayan border area. Indeed the preponderant weight of evidence shows that the Chinese leadership to date has used force beyond its borders with a consistently deliberate control so as to minimize risks. Nowhere has this deliberation been more apparent than in the Quemoy crisis of 1958. Chinese Communist shore batteries submitted the offshore island to intensive bombardment. After a few days of promising effort, units of the United States Seventh Fleet escorted Chinese Nationalist ships to within three miles of the mainland. At that point, Chinese Communist guns promptly lifted their bombardment, awaiting the full pattern of U.S. involvement. But once they discerned that the three-mile limit was operative, they resumed shelling, carefully targeting their fire so as to hit between the American escort screen and the Quemoy garrison.

Much of this analysis is directed at alleged Chinese irrationality. But it also pertains to the alternative assumption of Chinese miscalculation. Two strategic situations might be hypothesized. Peking either attempts nuclear blackmail, its bluff is called and it is "locked in" with no alternative but to proceed, regardless of the consequences. Or, Chinese confrontation with the United States or its allies reaches a boiling point which seems to threaten a nuclear attack on China. Peking thereupon decides it must pre-empt such an attack or lose its small, highly vulnerable ICBM force to enemy attack. This latter scenario was, in fact, the explicit justification advanced by Assistant Secretary of Defense Paul Nitze during the original McNamara justification of an ABM.

## Chinese Blackmail: How Likely?

Any such hypothetical propositions cannot be assessed *in vacuo*. They must be applied to specific situations—past, present or future—so as to assess their real likelihood. Blackmail must have a purpose; confrontations must offer credible gains as well as credible risks. For instance, the most familiar aspect of Chinese Communist propaganda is Peking's avowed support for "people's wars." But, to make this a plausible basis for projecting Chinese nuclear blackmail we must  go well beyond simple patronage. We must hypothesize serious, direct and overt Peking support for an insurgency that effectively risks nuclear devastation of the entire Chinese mainland.

Between 1949 and 1969 not one such insurgency has arisen, either on China's borders or at more distant points overseas. Despite a serious border dispute with New Delhi, one which eventually triggered actual war in 1962, Peking has not given massive support or taken significant risks on behalf of Indian Communist insurrectionary movements or anti-Indian minority uprisings. The Telangana uprising in 1949 failed, as did the Naxalbari revolt in 1968. Both applied Mao's maxims of armed struggle in the countryside. Both times Peking anathematized New Delhi as a fascist regime, acting as an anti-Chinese tool for foreign governments. Yet China never took any serious steps to keep these insurgencies alive, much less to see them through to victory.

Similarly anti-Indian movements or actual uprisings, in the sub-Himalayan states and principalities of Nepal, Bhutan and Sikkim, or amongst the Nagas of Assam, have failed to win significant Chinese aid. Incitement and subversion may be attempted through propaganda and, to a modest extent, through money, arms and training as well. Beyond this, however, Peking has refused to go. This pattern has remained fairly constant, despite the heightened militancy associated with China's Cultural Revolution.

Equally relevant is the low degree of Chinese involvement in Burma's various insurgencies. At no time since 1949 has the Rangoon regime been able to pacify the entire country. Much of the territory adjacent to China has been controlled by various armed groups hostile to Rangoon's rule. As in India, Peking's patronage, both overt and covert, has encouraged and equipped Communist insurrectionists and anti-Burmese separatists. Yet neither the amount nor the kind of such aid has seriously threatened the regime. The situation has ebbed and flowed and today seems no worse than in the past, at least in terms of Chinese involvement.

Thailand, of course, has won considerable attention as a public target of Peking's propaganda. Over the past few years actual armed insurrection has spread through provinces in the northern, northeastern and southern sectors of Thailand. Most recently Meo revolts have further challenged Bangkok's authority. Some support for these various insurgencies comes from Hanoi; most comes from Peking. Defectors provide graphic evidence of training and direction from Chinese sources on the mainland and in Thailand. Presumably China could easily infiltrate a well-trained guerrilla force that would be wholly Thai in composition, recruited from the 200,000 ethnic Thais in the nearby Chinese province of Yünnan. But, in actual fact, the present insurgents remain a scattered, poorly equipped, uncoordinated force of less than two thousand. This small effort is what lies behind Peking Radio's grandiose claims for "people's war" in Thailand.

In short, after twenty years of such unstable situations all along the unpoliced borders of a nation with 600 or 700 million people supposedly "supporting" armed struggles abroad, we must ask: What has kept China from doing more?

Has it been the fear of U.S. retaliation? This could hardly apply in remote Nagaland or amongst the hill peoples of neutralist Burma. Chinese troops or an indigenous fifth column could march into adjacent territory with overwhelming force and establish a "liberated area" without fear of U.S. power being unleashed against the Chinese mainland. Moreover, where China's interests have been viewed by Peking as truly vital, such risks of U.S. retaliation have indeed been taken—overtly in Korea and covertly in Vietnam.

Thus by focusing less on Peking's words and more on Peking's actions, we can separate out the lesser from the greater Chinese interests. The clear fact of the matter is that Peking does not believe its vital interests include giving significant material support to foreign revolutionary movements. In fact, Mao's doctrine explicitly describes national liberation struggles as essentially dependent on local resources, a do-it-yourself philosophy. This doctrine serves Chinese ethnocentric and practical interests as well. First, it points to the Chinese as the models for guerrilla warfare and prolonged struggle without outside help. The message is clear: "We did it basically on our own; you can too." Second, China's practical interests are served because this general doctrine excludes the necessity of choosing between safe and unsafe situations in allocating Chinese assistance. All people's wars will be treated equally; no major risks will be taken because no Chinese aid will be that important. This is the real constant in Chinese policy, whether with neutral Burma, hostile India, or American-allied Thailand.

## Chinese Policy: How Rational?

There is no plausible reason for these Chinese calculations to change five years hence. Neither in the first flush of victory in 1949 nor in Mao's last political convulsions during the Cultural Revolution did Chinese armies move across borders on behalf of "people's wars." Mao's successors are unlikely to react any differently to the role China should play in advancing Communism abroad. They might even conceivably scale down their lip service to "national liberation struggles." But certainly there is no reason to believe they will take greater risks in staking their prestige, and possibly their country, on a local insurgency through a show of force or nuclear blackmail.

Indeed, were one to concede any plausibility to this possibility of a Chinese resort to nuclear blackmail, it would have far more relevance to Chinese deployment of an intermediate-range ballistic missile system, targeted against U.S. bases on China's immediate periphery or against the cities of our Asian allies. A Chinese ICBM and a U.S.-based ABM would be largely irrelevant to a serious and systematic effort by Peking to back local insurgencies with nuclear force. But even the IRBM alternative assumes so fundamental a change in Chinese doctrine as to raise serious questions of probability.

Moreover, so long as U.S. nuclear power remains capable of devastating China, the credibility of any such blackmail by Peking—whether through ICBMs or IRBMs—is so low as to, in all likelihood, discourage its use. If we assume a burgeoning nuclear missile program in China, we also assume the concomitant infrastructure of technological modernization and all that is entailed in supporting so costly and complicated a military system. This developmental process has a double effect. First, it educates an elite in the long and painful process of pulling a backward country somewhere near the levels of advanced nations. Moreover it increases the nuclear vulnerability of their society, no longer dependent on scattered rice fields but now locked into an urban complex. In short, China's acquisition of an operational nuclear missile capability should reduce, not increase, the willingness of Peking to risk nuclear war.

If we shift attention from so-called people's wars to conventional types of conflict, the past twenty years do indeed give somewhat more cause for concern in projecting the future. The important uses of Chinese force, with varying degrees of anticipated risk, occurred in Korea, 1950–53; Quemoy, 1954–55 and 1958; India, 1962 and 1965; and Vietnam, 1965–68. Several characteristics link these events together. Every clash occurred in immediate proximity to, if not actually on, China's border. In every case Peking regulated the level and tempo of its military actions so as to minimize the risk of escalation spilling over into China, although accepting some such risk as basically unavoidable. After Korea, Peking never again openly courted U.S. attack against the mainland. On the contrary, it very carefully controlled its actions in the Taiwan Strait crises and its words in the Vietnam War, so as to avoid provoking the United States to use either conventional or nuclear force against targets in China.

Looking at the specific issues involved in each clash, these events obviously differ, one from another. The first Sino-Indian conflict of 1962 grew out of a festering border dispute, complicated by Chinese assumptions of foreign exploitation of internal vulnerabilities in the disastrous aftermath of Mao's Great Leap Forward. China's subsequent attack in 1965 was part of the Pak-Indian conflict, within which Peking had a limited interest on behalf of Pakistan as well as itself. In both Korea and Vietnam, Chinese assistance came on behalf of a besieged neighbor sharing a common Communist ideology against a commonly perceived enemy, "U.S. imperialism." Finally, the two Quemoy crises arose in the context of China's unfinished civil war, into which we interposed our force nineteen years ago and from which we have never disengaged.

One can examine this record much as one looks at the doughnut or the hole. On the one hand, it shows the careful deliberation behind China's use of force in conventional situations commonly encountered in international relations over the past two hundred years. This is the way nations behave, Communist or not, Chinese or not. On the other hand, it does show Peking's willingness to take risks and to use its force in situations other than clear and immediate self-defense.

## China's Strength: How Dangerous?

I would suggest that combining both points of emphasis permits us logically to project forward to the time when China will have acquired nuclear weapons. We can anticipate a Chinese situation that is neither wholly reassuring nor wholly frightening. I suspect this uneasy condition will be true for all countries so long as nuclear weapons remain in anyone's hands, and it will increase should they proliferate beyond the present nuclear powers.

There is one basic aspect of the Chinese situation, however, which is unique compared with our relationship to other nuclear powers: we did indeed intervene and continue to intervene in the Chinese civil war. Moreover, in the second Quemoy crisis of 1958, we provided the Chinese Nationalist forces with eight-inch howitzers publicly identified as capable of firing nuclear shells. Aside from whatever role our threats to use nuclear weapons in 1953 may have played in bringing about a truce in Korea, our nuclear deployment in the West Pacific has taken on a particular salience for Peking. This is because it has provided the ultimate deterrent against Mao's pursuit to the end of his more than thirty years' struggle with Chiang Kai-shek.

Here a bit of historical perspective is in order. For more than one hundred years, China—long confident of its civilization's superiority to the outside world—suffered invasion and exploitation by foreign powers, large and small, European and Asian. This was largely because of China's material inferiority, especially in weapons. We call it the period of "gunboat diplomacy." The Chinese—whether Nationalist or Communist—call it the period of "Unequal Treaties and Foreign Imperialism." Peking's determination to gain sufficient military strength to prevent foreign interference in China's internal affairs made the development of nuclear power in China virtually inevitable. Whether against American dominance or Soviet dependence, China's nuclear capability would provide at least psychological and political strength, if not an actual strategic equalizer.

I do not doubt that significant elements in the Chinese leadership—certainly Mao himself—believed their interpretation of Secretary of Defense McNamara's announcement of an ABM because of the Chinese threat. The decision, they said, was a step "taken by U.S. imperialists to continue with their nuclear blackmail and nuclear threats against China" and "another anti-Chinese measure adopted to intensify the Administration's collusion with the Soviet revisionist leading clique." If we continue with the ABM we will perpetuate the suspicion, if not the conviction, in Peking that we are determined to maintain maximum military superiority over China. In the Chinese view, our objective is to act at will in pursuit of our interests, regardless of the consequences for Peking. Given our confrontation over Taiwan and the offshore islands, anything which perpetuates or intensifies the sense of bitterness and frustration in the Chinese leadership must have the strongest justification in order to help offset this very real cost. Viewed from this perspective, the ABM is not at all a guarantee against Chinese irrationality or miscalculation. More likely, it is the reverse. Deployment of the ABM may simply act as a further goad to deeply rooted Chinese assumptions of U.S. malevolence and enmity.

*Does the American decision to deploy an*
*ABM upset the balances of power in Asia?*

# ASIA AND THE ABM

### by ALLEN S. WHITING

Professor of Political Science and
Associate of Center for Chinese Studies,
University of Michigan
Formerly Chief of Intelligence and Research,
Far East, Department of State

INSTALLATION OF AN antiballistic missile system poses clear
problems and raises disturbing implications for an already
taxed and troubled U.S. policy in Asia. As a general proposition, to the degree we stress the dangers of Chinese irrationality, miscalculation or deliberate use of nuclear weapons for
blackmail or actual battle purposes, we cannot but inflate the
Chinese threat in the eyes of other Asian leaders. This might
suit our national interest were we trying to corral all Asian
countries into an alliance headed by the United States.
Alternatively, it might be justified were our policy similar to
that of Soviet Russia: that is, a deliberate effort to isolate the
Peking regime from all other governments through any means
at hand.

However, we are not seeking to extend our commitments to
more countries in Asia than are already bound to us by
mutual security treaties and multilateral alliances. Nor do we
have any real hope of regional security arrangements coming
into force within the foreseeable future beyond those already
in effect. Finally, we are explicitly and properly committed in
our public policy, whether under Democratic or Republican
administrations, of seeking an end to China's isolation in
world affairs.

Therefore no positive purpose would seem to be pursued
by inflating still further the extant levels of Chinese threat as

perceived by Asian elites. They have lived with a China that dominated Asia in general, and many of their own societies in particular, for too many generations to be ignorant of the power realities, of China's sense of itself as the middle kingdom amidst lesser tributary states, and of the resurgent strength manifest in China's transformation from a divided and weak country to one which could both hurl back the United Nations forces in Korea and could develop its own nuclear weapons without any Soviet assistance over the past decade.

However, considerable harm can be accomplished by justifying extraordinary American security systems, such as the ABM, in terms of an alleged Chinese threat. The disparity of power between China and its Asian neighbors is tolerable in many cases because of calculations concerning Chinese self-restraint in the use of force, or Chinese calculations of self-interest in the levels of risk that could accompany overt aggression. For more distant neighbors, particularly those off shore, Chinese weakness in naval and air power coupled with an apparent inability to mount a successful invasion of even the islands of Quemoy and Matsu permits confidence in standing firm against any verbal threats from Peking.

Once Peking demonstrates its missile capacity through test flights of various-range missiles, whether regional or intercontinental in reach, some of the foregoing confidence will be undermined. But this should not reach panic proportions so long as the United States places the Chinese nuclear capability in its proper perspective, especially with regard to the improbability of use given China's continuing vulnerability to nuclear devastation in any retaliatory attack. Conversely, we will undermine the confidence of Asian nations in withstanding Chinese pressures to the extent that we portray Peking as prone to irrationality and miscalculation. The consequence for other Asian countries might be a tendency to avoid Chinese pressure by seeking separation from America. Alternatively, for those with the technological capacity, there might be a drive to acquire some form of nuclear defense system against missile attack. Finally there would be the prospect of increased Asian pressures for ironclad, hair-trigger commitments of American nuclear protection against a Chinese nuclear attack.

We cannot predict the course of politics in each of the eighteen nations which lie in the arc of Asia adjoining China, from Japan to Pakistan. We can, however, examine a few of the more salient cases with respect to the three alternative reactions which might follow installation of an American antiballistic missile system on the grounds of a Chinese nuclear threat. In so doing, we shall accept two assumptions of present and prospective American policy. First, it is not in our interest nor that of world peace to increase the number of nuclear powers. Second, it is not in our interest to take the decision to use our nuclear weapons out of the hands of the President of the United States at the actual moment of contemplated use. These two principles have underlain our policy, both at home and abroad, since we acquired nuclear weapons more than twenty years ago. They would seem equally valid throughout the next decade when China also will acquire a nuclear capability.

## *Japan: Nuclear Neutrality?*

Japanese political attitudes toward Chinese nuclear weapons are a composite of the many divergent forces which have emerged out of the Japanese experience since 1945. It is easier to identify them as isolated factors than to evaluate them as a political mix operative four to five years hence. However, even a simple enumeration can illustrate the Pandora's box of troublesome tendencies which we might open by exaggerating the threat of Chinese nuclear attack.

Obviously the most basic relevant attitude in Japan is abhorrence of nuclear weapons and the fear of radiation once again repeating the horrors of Hiroshima and Nagasaki. This is a mixed blessing, however, so far as American policy is concerned. On the one hand, it deters Japanese political and military leaders from pressing to acquire nuclear weapons. On the other hand, it could make Japan more susceptible to nuclear blackmail. Moreover, the Japanese abhorrence of nuclear weapons cannot be assumed as a constant in weight. It can easily erode with time, or it may become so total and absolute an attitude as to be an unquestionable fact of political life.

It is possible to make some projections from developments in the past few years which have seen a growing acceptance of discussions concerning various strategic alternatives, chiefly in connection with the non-proliferation treaty debate but also in connection with the problem of Okinawa and the continuation of the Japan-U.S. mutual security treaty. These seem to indicate that the abhorrence against acquisition of nuclear weapons, at least for deterrence or defense, will lessen during the next decade. Should this be true, a logical Japanese application of the American argument stressing Chinese irrationality and miscalculation would call for placing an ABM around Japanese cities. Such a decision would assume some promise of technical feasibility despite the markedly shorter range and therefore shorter response time for Japan as compared with the United States.

An American refusal or ambivalence on accommodating such a Japanese request would not necessarily lead to development of an independent Japanese nuclear capability. It could hardly help American relations in Japan, however, and might well increase the strength of neutralist or pro-Communist forces who argue that American protection is both unreliable and provocative. Much more certainty on these various possibilities will emerge in the course of the Japanese mutual security debate in 1970. But none of the prospects provoke much confidence that an anti-China ABM in the United States will leave the nuclear issue in Japan where it has remained for the past decade.

Another factor complicating Japanese political attitudes in this matter is the deep-seated ambivalence toward China itself. The conflicting attitudes cutting through public opinion polls and private political discussions include a sense of guilt over Japan's treatment of China during much of this century, awe over China's accomplishments in the past twenty years, ambition to compete successfully with foreign traders in the China market and hope of increasing Japan's international stature without increasing its international risks by being more independent of the United States, on the one hand, and, on the other hand, showing both China and Russia that it is a power worth dealing with as an equal.

Moving from generalities to specifics, the practical issues facing Japanese leaders considering the China question are particularly complicated by the problem of Taiwan. Paradoxically, Taiwan offers Japanese investors and traders greater promise, now and in the foreseeable future, than does mainland China. But will this continue indefinitely? And what will be the final disposition of Taiwan itself? What will the combination of a post-Mao, post-Chiang set of regimes in

Peking and Taipei mean for flexibility or intransigence, accommodation or aggression, on the part of either side? How will the increasingly powerful indigenous Taiwanese population play a part? Will Washington stand firm or stand aside in the event change threatens the status quo?

None of these questions can be answered today, but neither will they disappear tomorrow. Already complicated enough, they will be given still another dimension with the Chinese acquisition of nuclear weapons capable of reaching Japan, Okinawa and Taiwan. How Japan's leaders and public alike guess the answers to these questions is certain to be influenced by the way in which we predict and react to the Chinese nuclear capability. Our differentiating this situation from that of Soviet Russia, with which we and the Japanese have lived for twenty years, is quite likely to increase the polarization in Japanese politics among those who insist on a strong American alliance with firm nuclear guarantees, those who argue for Japan's acquiring its own independent nuclear shield and those who advocate a nonnuclear neutrality as the only course consistent with Japan's self-interest. Given the emotional volatility of the nuclear issue and the ambivalent attitudes toward China, the outcome of such a debate is uncertain. But the odds are against continuing the status quo of Japan's relations with China and the United States.

## India: Nuclear Commitment?

India, like Japan, has the capability of going the nuclear route should it so choose. Unlike Japan, there is far less abhorrence of nuclear weapons in the Indian body politic, but also unlike Japan, India has neither the technological resources nor economic wealth to pursue a nuclear weapons program easily. On balance, then, the prospects for India are as uncertain as for Japan, and any position taken by the United States concerning the Chinese nuclear threat must be regarded as of potential influence in determining future Indian choices.

A critical variable which differentiates India from Japan, however, is its present enmity with both of its neighbors, Pakistan and China. Internally this places definite constraints and pressures on political leaders responsible for military preparedness. Internationally, India's fear of a two-pronged attack, manifest in the short-lived Indian-Pak and Indian-Chinese hostilities of 1965, compels New Delhi to seek continuing and escalating guarantees from Moscow and Washington. Fundamentally, however, the uncertainty of those guarantees forces greater reliance on Indian internal military preparedness.

It is clear in retrospect that Indian assumptions concerning the nature and extent of Chinese intentions in 1962 were wholly overdrawn. Indian fears of a massive Chinese lunge down the Chumbi Valley through Nepal, or of Chinese air raids over Indian cities, seriously misjudged the limited nature of Chinese military action. These limitations were imposed both by the logistics of the situation, principally Tibet's distance from China proper and the terrain over which supplies must move to the sub-Himalayan front, and by Peking's own sense of the political costs which accompanied the use of force. The error in Indian assumptions, however, diverted scarce resources from the civilian to the military sector and continued to prepare needlessly for a war that was never to be.

The prospect would be far more serious for all powers concerned—India, Pakistan and the Soviet Union, as well as the United States—should we reinforce or raise Indian anxieties concerning the prospective Chinese nuclear threat. Should we so act, then we, alone or with the Russians, must provide New Delhi with a completely credible and irrevocable commitment to retaliate against Chinese nuclear attack. Otherwise, the logic of our justifying an ABM in terms of an eventual Chinese ICBM, as with Japan, would compel India to seek its own nuclear defense. Aside from what this would mean for the Indian economy, its implications for the Indo-Pak dispute are so ominous and obvious as not to require argumentation.

Somewhat less evident at first glance, however, are the implications of an absolute U.S. nuclear guarantee in the context of the Sino-Indian dispute. Practically speaking, this commitment would bind the President of the United States to attack China with nuclear weapons in the event of either a sudden escalation in the Sino-Indian border conflict or of an accidental misfiring of Chinese missiles against India. Whatever may be the odds against the latter occurrence, they do not rule it out altogether. But the odds are far lower against serious fighting breaking out along borders that China holds in dispute, as evidenced by the Sino-Indian war of 1962 and the Sino-Russian incidents of 1969.

The moral imperatives and the material consequences both argue against a commitment to use nuclear weapons under any but the most extreme and vital situations. How and when this will arise must be determined by each President, but certainly it should not be anticipated in advance as likely, much less inevitable, under such circumstances as attend Sino-Indian relations.

## Thailand: Nuclear Alarm?

Unlike Japan and India, Thailand does not have the practical option of acquiring its own nuclear defense or nuclear weapons. It might seem that there could be few harmful effects in Bangkok from whatever Washington said about an alleged Chinese nuclear threat and the need for an ABM in the United States.

Such, however, is not the case. The Thais justifiably pride themselves on having preserved their independence through a century of colonialism that surrounded them, as well as through the Japanese offensive of World War II. They have blended accommodation and alliance so as always to keep their political options open. It would seem incumbent on any regime in Bangkok to hedge against the possible withdrawal of American military power from the mainland of Asia. This hedge would, in all likelihood, take the form of some rapprochement with Peking, at least along the lines of an informal, quiet understanding.

Should the United States portray the Chinese nuclear threat as so serious, however, as to require unique measures to defend the United States, alarm in Bangkok might well reach unmanageable proportions from the standpoint of relations with Washington. A sharp reversal in Thai policy could easily result, eschewing any ties with the United States that might seem provocative to Peking, counting on Chinese self-restraint to safeguard future Thai independence. Even the credibility of American assurances would come into question were the United States to portray the Chinese as not deterrable by the American retaliatory capability and therefore requiring an American ABM. Thai leaders would justifiably doubt whether in any real confrontation with Peking, Washington would risk American cities for the sake of Bangkok.

## Other Asian Reactions: Nuclear Nightmares?

The concerns of Thailand would be shared, to a greater or lesser extent, by the governments of Laos, Cambodia, Burma, Malaysia, Singapore, Indonesia and the Philippines. Whether because of proximity to China, local large Chinese populations or strong anti-Communist sentiments, the Chinese threat looms sufficiently large in the minds of political leaders throughout these countries as to make any additional emphasis on the threat a risky proposition at best. This is especially true when the emphasis comes from the United States because it is assumed that American estimates on Chinese capabilities and intentions must be exceptionally accurate, given the tremendous American resources for intelligence collection and analysis. Moreover, any American interpretation of a Chinese ICBM threat carries with it the question: At what point will the United States lower its readiness to defend Asians at the risk of American cities?

Generalizations for this varied a group of countries under the circumstances which might prevail five years hence obviously must remain extremely tentative. It is difficult, however, to envisage positive benefits, from the American point of view, accruing in these Asian countries from any exaggeration of Chinese military intentions. But the disparity of power in the region and the distance of the United States from the region caution against stating the case in anything other than its sober but reassuring reality.

In the absence of an overseas invasion capability, the People's Republic of China remains essentially a continental power. It may be able to extend a nuclear strike capability off the mainland, for hundreds and perhaps thousands of miles. It would have no means of following this up with any invasion. Moreover, it would risk such mammoth destruction in the wake of any nuclear aggression as to make such a threat wholly incredible. Should these propositions appear invalidated by unforeseen changes in Chinese leadership behavior and capabilities, the United States can address the issue, together with its Asian friends, in the terms that are seen as likely to prevail at that time. Until then, however, it is incumbent on us not to proliferate nuclear nightmares in Asia, any more than we would proliferate nuclear weapons.

*Will ABM deployment fracture or*
*reinforce the NATO Alliance and our*
*relations with the rest of Western Europe?*

# THE ABM AND
# WESTERN EUROPE

## by THEODORE C. SORENSEN

*Partner, Paul, Weiss, Rifkind, Goldberg,*
*Wharton & Garrison, New York City*
*Special Counsel to the President, 1961–1964*

No AMERICAN CITIZEN can pretend to know with certainty how those in Western European countries will react to an ABM weapons system not yet deployed or even fully defined. The Europeans will differ among themselves on such a matter. Much will depend upon how the Russians react, what political and military events lie ahead and how the Pentagon attempts to justify the Nixon Administration's latest ABM proposal. Nevertheless it seems to be inevitable that no matter how strenuously the Pentagon argues that the new ABM, by safeguarding our retaliatory power, will increase our capacity to deter any attack against the West, many if not most West Europeans will believe instead that the United States is increasing its capacity to ignore some future Soviet nuclear threat which European nations cannot escape.

Their opposition may be regarded in Washington as only a minor consideration on matters directly affecting the national security of this country. But those in other nations not caught up in the emotional, political and economic arguments that today swirl about the ABM issue in the United States may be better able than most American officials to measure the hard facts and logic of the situation. Moreover, President Nixon has already crossed the ocean to assure West Europeans that their opinions are important to this country, that their sense of security is high on our list of priorities, and that a spirit of

togetherness must now characterize an alliance that has been
slowly fading in recent years.

## An American ABM: Will It Help Western Europe?

If in fact the Soviets now or in the future possess long-range
missiles of sufficient accuracy to reach a targeted missile
launcher, there is still no convincing evidence to indicate that
an ABM would effectively intercept them, that the presently
proposed ABM system would not be technologically obsolete
in a few years, that it could not be rendered useless by decoys
and penetration devices, and that it could in any way defend
against a saturation attack by a multiple increase in enemy
missiles.

The deployment, limited or unlimited, of so uncertain a
system will not add to the West Europeans' sense of security
for the future, much less their sense of confidence in the
United States. More importantly, having assured the West
Europeans for some years that, even after suffering a first
strike, we possessed a second-strike capacity of weapons
systems in the ground, underwater or in the air sufficient to
destroy any attacker several times over, we will have a difficult task convincing them now that an ABM system is needed
to make this deterrent effective. Killing the enemy off once or
twice should be enough, in their unsophisticated view. To
argue that it may be needed in the distant future will not
persuade them that we are wise to begin immediate deployment now of an uncertain system, instead of waiting one or
more years to ascertain whether we really needed it and
whether we could not reach an agreement with the Soviets
first.

Our allies understandably find it difficult to believe that we
mean it when we say that we will risk our cities to save theirs.
Now that the proposed ABM system no longer protects
American cities, it offers no assurances to the Europeans
along these lines. Any American President who realizes that
his own cities would be wiped out in a nuclear exchange is
not likely to be much emboldened in any future showdowns
on the brink by the hope that at least part of his retaliatory
capacity would survive. Thus the ABM cannot make Europeans feel more secure, more certain of our coming to their
defense. On the contrary, the more Americans talk about a
defense against ballistic missiles, the more those in Europe

will be fearful that we are preparing to let them be the choice targets of any future nuclear war while we stand by, invulnerable and alone. That conclusion may be illogical; our NATO obligations may be solemn commitments which this country is bound to honor; but our role in the world is often influenced more by what others think we will do than by what we say we will do.

## An American ABM: Will It Facilitate Arms Control?

An arms control agreement, after all, is Western Europe's only hope for security in the long run. The citizens of that part of the globe want some relief from the thousands of Soviet intermediate-range missiles targeted on them now; and they see no relief in a system that at best protects only a portion of the American missile arsenal. On the contrary, history has made all too clear that the Soviet Union's ultimate response to an American ABM is likely to be an acceleration in its own missile development in order to overwhelm, offset and adjust for such a defense. That kind of renewal of the arms race can only increase anxieties among the Western Europeans. A firm rejection by the United States of this new weapons system, on the other hand—even if it were done because its reliability is uncertain, even if it were only a postponement for a year or more to await both diplomatic and technological developments—would do much to improve the atmosphere for talks on strategic arms limitations. It is the product of those talks to which Western Europe looks for real security.

## An American ABM: Will It Strengthen the Alliance?

Consider how the world will look to the West European in the ABM era. He will see his own country's military capability falling further and further behind the two superpowers, casting doubt on Western Europe's ability to influence events, to deter an attack or to protect itself in the event of an attack. He will see the United States going it alone on a new weapons system of its own, one that could not possibly permit consultation with the Allies before it is fired, one that could even deceive Americans into thinking they could sit out the next war and return to isolationism, and one that could embolden the United States to take provocative actions regarding China (whose response may be aimed at Western European interests in Asia as well as American).

None of this is likely to encourage in the West European renewed feelings of devotion to the Alliance, trust in the United States and determination to make whatever sacrifice is necessary to fulfill NATO and other Alliance obligations. On the contrary, the atmosphere engendered by the American ABM may well be one in which the French can claim justification for developing their own independent weapons system, the Germans assert the need for a greater military capability, the smaller nations seek separate arrangements with the Soviet Union, and in which Western Europe, generally, sees less reason for playing an active role. The preservation of the Alliance, and particularly progress toward Western Europe's political integration, depends upon a downgrading of nationalism. An ABM system in which no ally can play any role is necessarily a boost to nationalism.

One non-European member of NATO—Canada—is a special case, particularly since it is the nation with whom we share the defense of the North American continent. Since World War II, it has been clear that the defense of the territory of the United States against some of the likeliest threats—for example, bomber attacks over the polar regions—has depended on the assent and indeed the active cooperation of Canada. The existing BMEWS early-warning radar, which might be the first to pick up a developing missile attack a good ten minutes before any PAR could see it, is installed on Canadian soil.

The proposed ABM system, in either Sentinel or Safeguard configuration, would involve intercepts by Spartans and even some Sprints above Canadian territory. Some of the defensive missiles would pass through Canadian air space if ever they are launched. ABMs that do not intercept will fall, with their nuclear warheads, upon Canadian soil, in all probability to spread some radiation even if the fail-safe mechanisms operate to prevent a nuclear explosion. Spartan explosions may burn the retinas of people looking at the fireball, producing visual impairment of unknown magnitude and duration.

It is easy to see, therefore, why the prospect of ABM deployment along our northern border has stirred deep anxieties in Canada, anxieties that may ultimately not only contribute to disaffection with the Alliance but further complicate relations with the United States. Here again, the ABM question has become a source of division rather than of unity and strength.

I do not wish to exaggerate the effect on Western Europe and Canada of a limited ABM deployment. But experience teaches me that small military systems eventually become large military systems, and that the proposed ABM is at least a step in the wrong direction at the wrong time for the wrong reasons.

# V

ARMS CONTROL:

WILL IT BE SET BACK?

*Do the arms control experiences of the past
twenty-five years teach us any lessons
about the meaning of deploying an ABM?*

# ABM AND ARMS CONTROL

## by BERNARD T. FELD

*Professor of Physics, Massachusetts Institute
of Technology
Past Director, Laboratory for Nuclear Science
Consultant, Brookhaven National Laboratory*

THE HISTORY OF arms control negotiations since World War II
has been characterized by large ideas and small results. The
outstanding example is the Oppenheimer-Lilienthal plan,
which called for the truly radical step of placing under
international control *all* developments of nuclear technology,
in recognition of the intimate connections between peacetime
nuclear power applications and the production and utilization
of fissionable materials for atomic weapons. This proposal,
though for years uppermost on the international disarmament
agenda, came to nothing, in part because of the one-sided
nature of its formulation by Baruch and the paranoid response of the Stalin regime.

Only now, more than twenty years later, after a score or
more nations have advanced, by virtue of the inevitable
developments of peacetime nuclear technology, to the thresh-
old of nuclear weapons production, has it been possible to
resurrect some features of this plan in the Nuclear Non-
Proliferation Treaty. But the treaty is, in many ways, ambivalent: it excludes the major powers from the restraints placed
on nations which do not possess nuclear weapons; and the
nuclear guarantees provided by the "haves" to the "have-
nots" are to some degree equivocal. Thus, acceptance of and
continuing adherence to the treaty by many of the technologically highly developed countries remain open questions.

One of the most important aspects of the Non-Proliferation Treaty (Article VI) consists of an undertaking on the part of the nuclear powers "to pursue negotiations in good faith on effective measures relating to cessation of the nuclear arms race at an early date and to nuclear disarmament. . . ." With the signing of the treaty on July 1, 1968, and its ratification by the Senate on March 13, 1969, this frequently professed goal of previous administrations has become official policy.

## The Test Ban: Half a Loaf

But policy or goal, progress has been exceedingly slow. Until 1963 the only arms control agreement achieved was the treaty providing for the nuclear-free status of the Antarctic Continent. (Latin America has recently been made a nuclear-free zone in a treaty which, however, has not yet been signed by a number of important countries.) The outstanding arms control achievement to date is, of course, the Test Ban Treaty of 1963, prohibiting nuclear explosions in the atmosphere, in outer space and in the oceans. However, this treaty permits underground explosions. As a result, only half of the intended purposes of the treaty have been fulfilled: radioactive contamination of our atmosphere from nuclear explosions has been drastically reduced (tests in the atmosphere are still carried out by France and China, neither of which has signed the treaty); but the treaty's major arms control objective—that of inhibiting further developments in nuclear weaponry —has been effectively circumvented by the possibility of underground testing.

The limited test ban agreement strikingly illustrates the major difficulties in the way of achieving meaningful arms control arrangements in the face of vigorous and uninhibited research and development programs in military technology. At the time of negotiation of the treaty, it was not extended to underground testing because of a difference of opinion between the Soviet Union and the United States concerning the adequacy of three, as compared to six, mandatory on-site inspections per year for monitoring compliance. At that time, seismological techniques for detecting and identifying underground explosions, against the background of naturally occurring earthquakes, were in a relatively early stage of development, so that there was still some uncertainty as to their capabilities. Furthermore, the political pressures—exerted by the military establishment, by our weapons laboratories and by the more Cold War–oriented members of the Senate—opposing any apparent concession to the Russians and wanting to retain the possibility of further weapons development through underground testing, made it expedient to reject the Soviet compromise in order to avoid a political battle which might have jeopardized ratification of the treaty.

Thus, even though improvements in seismological detection techniques now assure the adequacy of three yearly on-site inspections (in fact, a large number of experts maintain that an underground test ban could now be satisfactorily verified by national detection systems alone), the opportunity for a comprehensive test ban treaty (*with* on-site inspection) was lost, perhaps irretrievably.

The pace of underground testing was rather slow in the years immediately following the adoption of the treaty—in large part owing to the backlog of weapons data resulting from intensive programs of atmospheric testing by both sides just prior to its adoption. But the technology of testing underground advanced at a prodigious rate. (Indeed, the efforts put into such technological developments have far exceeded those invested in seismological improvements.) As a result, the number, variety and magnitudes of the underground explosions conducted by the two superpowers are quite comparable to those of the years immediately preceding the test ban. In addition to "Plowshare" (peaceful uses for nuclear explosives) tests, new weapons and weapons types, as well as weapons of a size exceeding even a million tons (megaton) of TNT equivalent, are regularly tested, so that military weapons development programs can hardly be said to be inhibited by having to test under the ground.

## ABM Deployment: The Russian Response

It has been worth dwelling at such length on the history of the test ban because of the lessons which can be drawn for present and future arms control efforts. Generally speaking, this history of arms control provides an excellent illustration in the advantages enjoyed by offensive as compared with defensive developments. Specifically, and more important, it provides a striking example of the difficulty—if not the impossibility—of inhibiting new technological developments

by any measures short of their prohibition; and it demonstrates most vividly the futility of trying to stabilize or
dampen the nuclear arms race under conditions which permit
the free introduction of technological improvements and innovations.

These lessons should be applied to the decision to deploy
an ABM.

The ABM decision assumes crucial importance for the
whole future of arms control because it comes at a time when
both sides appear to be leveling off on the number of their
nuclear weapons, at levels which, for all practical purposes,
could be characterized as having a rough parity, albeit a
parity of gigantic overkill capacity for both. (The assertions
by some Administration officials of a potential "first-strike"
capability on the part of the Russians are not substantiated
nor do they appear tenable.)

The decision to deploy an ABM—be it the Sentinel system
of the Johnson Administration or the Safeguard system of the
Nixon Administration (which is to a very large extent Senti-
nel-in-disguise)—is unnecessarily provocative; as such, it is
bound to elicit a response from the Russians, most likely in
the form of an increase in the number of their deployed
ICBMs but probably also in further Russian ABM deployment beyond the present ineffective and obsolete system
surrounding Moscow. Hence our ABM is likely to set off a
new, upward spiral in the nuclear arms race. In the end, as a
result of the probable large increase in numbers and sophistication of nuclear weapons, our security and that of the
Russians will have been decreased.

The "thin" ABM provides an opening wedge for the
eventual deployment of a more extensive system, despite
protestations from the Administration to the contrary. In concept, it is an open-ended system which, perforce, calls for the
incorporation of improvements resulting from a vigorous research and development program to eliminate them. In fact,
the very deficiencies of the system—and they are serious and
well documented—demand their own serious research and development programs. Whether such programs fail, which will
mean the deterioration of our deterrent capacity in the face of
increased Soviet delivery capabilities, or whether they succeed, in which case the Soviet deterrent will have been
threatened, the result will upset the none-too-delicate balance
of nuclear terror.

## Conclusion: History's Judgment

All of which adds up to the conclusion that our ABM deployment must inevitably trigger reactions, on the part of our potential adversaries, which will adversely affect our security —increased numbers and sophistication of Russian and Chinese deployed missiles and defenses; increased tension on the international scene; decreased likelihood of any serious concerted action to curb the arms race.

More dangerous still is another type of reaction—that of spurring new technological developments, aimed specifically at circumventing the ABM. Such new developments will have the effect that, if successful, they may completely upset the strategic balance, destabilize the East-West military confrontation, and increase incomparably the difficulty of arriving at meaningful arms control agreements.

One such development is already on the horizon: the multiple independently targeted re-entry vehicle, or MIRV, now being vigorously tested by us, with deployment in both land- and sea-based missiles scheduled for the near future. This development was our response to the rudimentary beginnings of Russian deployment of an ABM some years ago; it was intended as a device which could overwhelm the Russian defenses by sheer numbers; and there is no question that it would succeed in so doing, as could the utilization of MIRV by the Russians succeed in overwhelming any ABM deployed by the United States. The danger of MIRV, besides that resulting from the increase in numbers of deliverable warheads, is that it is a profoundly destabilizing weapons system in that it can lead to the illusion of "first-strike" capability by its possessor and, conversely, places a very large premium on a first strike against the side possessing it in times of crisis. In addition, once MIRVs are deployed, it will no longer be possible, as it is today, to verify unilaterally a freeze of missile numbers by counting the number of missile sites from satellites.

A somewhat similar, though not so insidious, development is the fractional orbital bombing system of FOBS, which was devised by the Russians to counter the possibility that we *might* start to deploy ABMs. This is a missile launched into a satellite orbit, but removed from orbit before completing it, and brought to the target on a trajectory which cannot be precomputed by the detecting radar, and at an altitude at which it would be extremely difficult to track. Despite the 1967 treaty on space exploration, which prohibits the stationing of nuclear bombs in satellites, the possibility of such a weapon (or the American Air Force program for a manned military satellite, for that matter) demonstrates again the tendency of new technological advances, when uninhibited, to undermine arms control agreements.

If merely the prospect of deploying ABMs, or the actual deployment of a "thin" system alleged to be reassuring rather than threatening, has already led to such unfortunate developments, what can we expect in the way of new, destabilizing technology once ABMs of equivocal effectiveness start to be deployed? History is by no means reassuring on this score.

What we are dealing with here is the tendency until now for arms control negotiations and agreements to lag behind weapons technology. If we and the Russians continue to insist on the criterion that an agreement be both foolproof and riskproof before it is accepted, while at the same time being willing to deploy new weapons systems whose operations and implications retain considerable uncertainties, then arms control will continue to lag hopelessly behind military technology. And the arms race will continue on its merry but deadly upward spiral.

If, after years of patient diplomatic groundwork and mutual education, having finally arrived at a situation where the Soviet Union is anxiously requesting talks on the freezing and limitation of both *offensive and defensive* nuclear armaments, we then delay these talks while proceeding with the installation of new systems which will render such limitations more difficult, then we are foolishly risking long-term stability for short-term military or political advantage.

Technology will not stand still while we equivocate and manipulate. Each new spiral in the arms race has left all nations less secure than before. Every indication points to the prospect that this next round—on which we are now unnecessarily embarking with the decision to deploy the ABM—will leave both us and the Russians more vulnerable than ever before. It is high time that we took the courageous decision to break into this vicious cycle—to substitute the reality of arms limitation for the illusion of military superiority. Toward this end, the decision to forego ABM deployment while vigorously pursuing a missile limitation agreement will signal new hope that humanity may yet avert a nuclear disaster.

*How well does surveillance-by-satellite*
*enable the United States to keep*
*track of Soviet missile strength?*

# CAN THE COMMUNISTS
# DECEIVE US?

## by JEREMY J. STONE

*Member, Council of the Federation of*
*American Studies*
*International Affairs Fellow, Council on*
*Foreign Relations, New York City*

SEVERAL YEARS AGO the Defense Department began to speak
with remarkable new assurance about Soviet missiles. It was
obvious from the Secretary's annual statements on the subject
that he felt unusually confident not only of his estimates of
the number of missiles but also of the security of his source of
information. The explanation for this certitude was apparent:
The United States was using orbital satellites to watch Soviet
missile progress.

"I know how many missiles the enemy has," President
Johnson said on March 16, 1967.[1] He went on to say that the
value of satellite reconnaissance alone had justified the nation's
expenditure on space ten times over. Spy-in-the-sky technology may permit the Soviet Union and the United States to bypass the previously formidable obstacle of reaching agreement
on on-site inspections. It may make comprehensive agreement
possible without physical intrusion simply because it so
sharply reduces the risk of a surprise enemy build-up.

Most of the details about satellite reconnaissance have
always been classified. But enough information has appeared
so that it is possible to make an appraisal of reconnaissance
capability from public journals. As long ago as 1961, a
government official was quoted as saying of a U.S. satellite
that "the information it sends back . . . provides better

[1] Evert Clark, "Satellite Spying," *New York Times,* March 17, 1967.

surveillance of Russia than any ever received from the years of U-2 overflights that ended officially in May, 1960."[2]

After Gary Powers was shot down over the Soviet Union, President Eisenhower showed photos from thirteen miles up that revealed four-inch painted stripes in a parking lot of a San Diego air base.[3] The nation was astounded. This was an enormous improvement over the aerial photography of World War II; in those days, photographs taken at only thirty thousand feet had a "ground resolution of perhaps 15 or 20 feet."[4] Yet even that crude equipment would have been able to detect the IRBM bases that the Soviet Union put into Cuba.

In 1967 one source noted that "objects as small as three feet in diameter, such as garbage-can lids, probably are picked up on a routine basis."[5] Another reported that even in 1963 the supersensitive cameras of SAMOS (Satellite and Missile Observation System) could produce "clear images of objects the size of a basketball."[6]

The advances have continued. Cameras with 240-inch focal lengths have been used by NASA, and there has been discussion of 960-inch focal lengths. Using film with 40 lines per millimeter (easily available commercially), a 960-inch-focal-length camera 200 miles high could obtain about a 1-foot resolution. But secret films are probably as much better than commercial films as secret cameras are superior to the cameras we know of. One observer was quoted as saying that the new technique of retrieving film from orbit—by ejecting a film capsule and recovering it—provides intelligence officers with up to one thousand times the quality and resolution of the early satellite photos, which had to be transmitted from space.[7]

It can be calculated that "atmospheric turbulence can produce an error in observing the ground of four inches." (This statistical error is almost independent of altitude for aero-

[2] New York Times, February 1, 1961.

[3] Howard Simons, "Our Eye in the Sky," Washington Post, December 8, 1963.

[4] Amrom Katz, Observational Satellites: Problems and Prospects, p. 13.

[5] J. S. Butz, Jr., "Under the Spaceborne Eyes," Air Force and Space Digest, L, No. 5 (May, 1967), pp. 93–98.

[6] "Spies in Space," U.S. News & World Report, September 9, 1968.

[7] Ibid.

space craft flights above twenty miles.)[8] Obviously, the technology is getting close to being limited by atmospheric turbulence. In 1968 one report noted: "U.S. officials used to brag that they could take a picture of an object as small as a dinner plate. Now they claim they can pick out a button on a man's shirt."[9] Another report, several years ago, claimed that a skilled photo interpreter, looking at a photograph taken on a clear day from one hundred miles up, could pick out a telephone wire because, although the wire is only one-eighth of an inch wide, its length would make it observable.[10]

## Seeing Through Camouflage: Missiles Under the Grass

Can the new satellite reconnaissance cope with camouflage—for example, of missile silos? The answer apparently is yes, thanks to devices that use portions of the electromagnetic spectrum other than optical light. Thus one source notes:

> Another recent development . . . is the use of multi-spectral systems. In this technique, observations are made simultaneously in several portions of the electromagnetic spectrum. . . . One of the pleasant surprises of recent years is that a comparison of these images made in several portions of the spectrum yields far more information about the situation on the ground than any single sensor ever would. The visible-light camera shows small objects. The other sensors, which do not have as high a resolution, complement by revealing the thermal emission, reflectivity, and color characteristics of the objects. Altogether these data reveal a truly astounding variety of information . . . including missile silo emplacements with grass growing over the top. . . .[11]

Another article reports:

> Ultramodern versions of World War II radar, circling in outer space, now penetrate cloud covers and forest vegeta-

[8] John C. Ervard, "When to Give Design a Second Look: Philosophy of Reexamination," *Aeronautics and Astronautics*, August, 1968, p. 68.

[9] George C. Wilson, "Scorpions Match Stings," Washington *Post*, September 15, 1968.

[10] Peter T. White, "The Camera Keeps Watch on the World," *New York Times Magazine*, April 3, 1966, p. 27.

[11] J. S. Butz, Jr., *op. cit.*

tion to reveal objects such as hidden missile sites, tanks and even troops. Infrared sensors in satellites can uncover "hot" objects—such as a submerged submarine, a missile launching or, in some cases, even a running truck motor.[12]

A third says:

It is important to realize that skilled photo-interpreters can extract vastly more information from such photographs than is apparent to the untrained observer. . . . By analyzing the significance of each feature in the overall context of a scene, the expert can spot inconsistencies which help him identify decoys or camouflaged facilities. By combining skilled observation with extensive background knowledge about the types of facilities of interest, he can even estimate industrial production capabilities or detect significant changes in weapon system capabilities.[13]

In practice this has meant that, for example, reconnaissance experts were able to find 98 percent of a thousand military vehicles hidden around an Army post in Texas and to determine that the first surface-to-air missile photographed in North Vietnam was a dummy without supporting gear.[14]

Despite the "multispectral systems," both the Soviets and the Americans evidently prefer to photograph during cloudless periods, when optical light can be used effectively. In the journal *Spaceflight*, G. E. Perry noted that launchings in the Russian Kosmos series seem to be correlated with cloudless periods over the United States.[15] One source noted that the United States Air Force is using "high quality photographs obtained by its 417 weather reconnaissance satellites to determine when the view of the earth by surveillance satellite would not be obscured by cloud cover."[16] Indeed, the United States continuously monitors the weather around the globe, and the United States and the Soviet Union now routinely exchange weather photos taken by satellite.

On the average, 60 percent of the earth is covered by clouds, and there is also the problem of darkness. Thus on the

[12] *U.S. News & World Report, op. cit.*

[13] General Electric, General Engineering Laboratory, Schenectady, N.Y., Report No. 62G–L78 (July 27, 1962), p. 986.

[14] *New York Times Magazine, op. cit.*

[15] G. E. Perry, *Spaceflight*, October 31, 1967.

[16] *Aviation Week and Space Technology*, LXC, No. 4 (January 27, 1969), p. 13.

average a satellite can see the sunlit surface of any given point on earth only about 20 percent of the time. Some areas tend to be cloudier than others, of course. For example, there is statistically only about a 5 percent chance that less than three-quarters of the noon sky over Moscow will be covered by clouds.[17] Smoke and dust may also impede photography, and this factor makes periods after a rain more desirable for surveillance. But reconnaissance satellites are now being developed that "will be able to maneuver and change orbits to take advantage of breaks in the weather."[18] (Satellites may even be able to "swoop down as close as 50 miles above the earth for close-up pictures—presumably by a zoom lens.")[19]

Cameras are not the only surveillance devices that satellites carry. Radio receivers in U.S. satellites apparently listen in on Soviet conversations. One such satellite, nicknamed Ferret, is said to pass over Moscow twice a day monitoring such transmissions as messages "from Moscow headquarters to ships and submarines at sea or even signals between military units on maneuvers."[20]

## Satellites and Arms Control: Free Inspection

For arms control inspection purposes, it is necessary to inspect only often enough to discover changes in the other side's strategic posture. Most important changes take many months. And it is evident that any changes are now being carefully monitored. In our efforts to penetrate the secrecy of the Communist countries we have, in effect, already created a unilateral arms inspection system. To use it to enforce an arms control agreement would cost us scarcely one additional dollar.

It is hard to imagine that Soviet leaders, knowing their country is under such close observation from the sky, would think they could get away with cheating—by building, for example, large numbers of missiles or submarines, antimissile defenses, improved bomber defenses, and new antisubmarine warfare capabilities. Such an action would risk disclosure to the United States through some other means as well, including defectors, spies and so on.

[17] General Electric, *op. cit.*
[18] *New York Times Magazine, op. cit.*
[19] Wilson, *op. cit.*
[20] *U.S. News & World Report, op. cit.*

But what if the Soviet Union did try to cheat—would we know in time? Would our reconnaissance warn us soon enough of Soviet violations that might undermine our nuclear deterrent? The answer is that the United States would see no less, and be able to act no less promptly, in the presence of a suitable agreement than in its absence. Suppose, for example, that the Soviet Union decided to build a large-scale missile defense network. The United States would be able to see quite early in the deployment process the detailed signs of the construction—just as it now knows that the Russians have precisely seventy-two interceptor missiles around their Moscow defense line. With or without an agreement, the United States would have ample opportunity to observe and respond to Soviet efforts to shift the balance.

*What are the consequences for the
Nuclear Non-Proliferation Treaty
of the ABM deployment decision?*

# ABM AND
# NON-PROLIFERATION

## by MASON WILLRICH

*Professor of Law and Director, Center for the
Study of Science, Technology and Public Policy,
University of Virginia*

OF OVERRIDING IMPORTANCE to the world community in the nuclear age is the avoidance of nuclear war. In relation to this goal, a major objective of United States foreign policy is the prevention of the spread of nuclear weapons among the nations of the world. This position has been embraced by every President, Democrat and Republican, from Truman to Nixon. The basic justification for this policy is quite straightforward. It is the increasing risk of nuclear war as more and more nations acquire their own nuclear weapons.

Two important steps have already been taken toward an effective non-proliferation policy: the Nuclear Test Ban Treaty signed in 1963 during the Kennedy Administration; and the Non-Proliferation Treaty negotiated by the Johnson Administration, still to be ratified by the Nixon Administration.[1] But with more and more nations developing the scientific and technological know-how to build nuclear weapons, much remains to be done if nuclear weaponry is not to proliferate. In the final analysis, the success of efforts to prevent the spread of nuclear weapons depends on whether or not nations such as Japan, India, Israel and West Germany can

---

[1] For a full analysis and discussion of the treaty by the author, see Mason Willrich. *Non-Proliferation Treaty: Framework for Nuclear Arms Control* (Charlottesville: The Michie Co., 1969).

be convinced that their security does not require them to acquire their own nuclear weapons.

It is pertinent, therefore, to ask how deployment of an ABM system by the United States would affect the objective of non-proliferation in general, and the successful implementation of the Non-Proliferation Treaty in particular.

### Choice of Systems: Thick, Thin or Neither?

At the present time, no one is advocating the immediate deployment of a thick ABM system capable of defending the United States against a large-scale Soviet nuclear attack. Even the strongest proponents of ABM deployment admit that the technology needed to deploy such a system is not now available. What the United States *could* do in the near future, however, is deploy a so-called thin ABM system—the Safeguard system. Even this thin system is subject to modification, depending on the deployment of the short-range Sprint component.

If a thin ABM system is deployed with Sprint missiles located around land-based strategic nuclear forces, then the most reasonable interpretation would be that the system is intended to assure the survival of our strategic nuclear deterrent forces against a Soviet nuclear attack. If, on the other hand, a thin ABM system is deployed with Sprint missiles located around major urban centers, then the best explanation would be that the purpose of the system is to protect the cities from the sort of nuclear attack that China might be able to launch during the period five to fifteen years from now.

It does not make sense, therefore, to argue that Sprint deployment around land-based strategic nuclear forces will help defend against Chinese nuclear attack, because for the foreseeable future, China will be limited to a counter-city strategy. China will possess enough intercontinental missiles to penetrate the Spartan defenses, but clearly will not be able to mount an attack on our strategic nuclear deterrent forces.

Two further reasons have been offered in the past and may be offered again in favor of the thin ABM system. The first is that the system, especially the Spartan component, is intended to defend against the possibility of accidentally launched missiles. This rationale is inadequate for it would be extremely difficult to justify the expenditure required for a thin ABM system simply for assurance against accident. The risk of accident is probably less now than in the past in view of improvements made in the quality of the Soviet strategic nuclear forces.

The second reason is that the decision to deploy an ABM system will strengthen our position vis-à-vis the Soviet Union in arms control negotiations. I believe that it may be argued with considerably more force and logic that the United States position would be much stronger *before* the decision on ABM deployment is made. This negotiating tactic would keep in reserve the threat of a possible future deployment should negotiations fail. Even assuming that deployment now would initially strengthen our hand in arms control talks, it would certainly be a wasting asset. For if deployment were to proceed during protracted negotiations on complicated questions such as a freeze on strategic offensive and defensive weapons, there might well, in the end, be nothing left to freeze.

## ABM Deployment: Soviet Orientation

If we should decide to deploy a thin ABM system, how will other governments interpret our actions? Will nations presently without nuclear weapons be encouraged to develop their own? Will they feel secure enough to limit unilaterally their nuclear capabilities in the face of our decision?

The focus of our inquiry can be narrowed to the key nations involved: Japan, India, Israel and West Germany. Many other nations including Australia, Canada, Italy, Sweden and Switzerland have, or are rapidly acquiring, the scientific and technological capabilities for a nuclear weapons option. But whether these nations exercise that option in the future will probably depend on what Japan, India, Israel and West Germany decide to do. Deployment of a Soviet-oriented and/or a China-oriented ABM defense by the United States must be analyzed separately in relation to the nuclear ambitions of each of these four countries.

Taking the implications of a Soviet-oriented ABM system first, what would be the effect in Asia were the United States to set up a Soviet-oriented, hard-point ABM defense? At the moment, the incentives to develop nuclear weapons in both Japan and India are being fueled primarily by the threat of China's growing nuclear power. For that reason, China would probably welcome the deployment by the United States of a Soviet-oriented ABM system. It would mean that cooperation

between the United States and the Soviet Union in arms
control or any other political area would be more difficult in
the future. China might well perceive that in deploying an
ABM system, the United States was jeopardizing any possible
cooperation with the Soviet Union on the containment of
China, and at the same time was not effectively canceling
out China's nuclear strike capability against the United
States.

Furthermore, if the two superpowers pushed on with a
nuclear arms race, both Japan and India would probably lose
all hope that the United States and the Soviet Union were
ever contemplating serious arms control efforts in accord with
their prospective obligations under Article VI of the Non-
Proliferation Treaty. Accordingly, the incentives for such development of nuclear weapons in these nonnuclear-weapon
Asian nations undoubtedly would be intensified.

Deployment of a thin, Soviet-oriented ABM system in the
United States would probably be received with mixed emo-
tions in Israel. Such action by the United States might not
substantially or directly affect the development of nuclear
weapons in Israel since incentives for such development are
generated primarily by the long-term threat to a conven-
tionally armed Israel by the surrounding Arab countries. But
an ABM decision might be applauded in Israel, since it
would tend to drive the United States and the Soviet Union
further apart and reduce the likelihood of a settlement in the
Middle East imposed by the two superpowers acting in
concert. On the other hand, Israel will perhaps recognize that
in the long run it could be disastrous to its own security if the
United States and the Soviet Union were ever to confront
each other directly in a future war over the Middle East.

With respect to West Germany, U.S. deployment of a thin,
Soviet-oriented ABM system could have numerous implications. The West German Government, or some factions of it,
might welcome a move driving a wedge between the two
superpowers. The apparent inconsistency between deployment of the ABM and Article VI of the Non-Proliferation
Treaty might quite logically provide the West German Government with an added reason for withholding its signature
from the Non-Proliferation Treaty. In the long run, it is to be
hoped that West Germany will see that its own security is
strengthened, not weakened, by an accommodation between
the United States and the Soviet Union on nuclear arms con-

trol. For in the wake of such an accommodation the United States and West Germany together would be in a strong position to insist that the Soviet Union assume its share of the responsibility for creating a political climate in Europe in which West Germany will not feel it is giving up something for nothing in adhering to the Non-Proliferation Treaty—a climate in which both parts of Germany, whether remaining apart or gradually moving together, will be willing to accept nonnuclear-weapon status for the long-term future.

## ABM Deployment: Chinese Orientation

The implications of an ABM system directed primarily against China are no more encouraging for the policy of non-proliferation. The United States deployment of a thin, China-oriented ABM system might simply cause Peking to accelerate its own offensive missile production, much as we would expect the Soviet Union to respond to U.S. deployment of a Soviet-oriented ABM. In this regard, the dynamics of a technological race work against both the Soviet Union and the United States. Improvement in relative position will be less difficult for China to achieve than for the nuclear superpowers, which are both already pressing against existing technological boundaries. Therefore, China's growing nuclear capability could be the catalyst for a major new round in the Soviet-American nuclear arms race, especially if continuing technological pressure from China's strategic nuclear posture induces the United States to thicken its own ABM defense after initial deployment.

As for Japan and India, how would deployment of a thin, China-oriented ABM system influence their decisions on nuclear weaponry? They might well consider it a desperate, although ineffective, move by the United States to insulate itself against China, signaling our withdrawal from Asian affairs. If our action caused China to accelerate her own nuclear weapons program—or even announce that it was doing so—Japan and India might not only feel isolated but fear that their own security was deteriorating rapidly. Thus, the deployment of a system which is judged ineffective could substantially increase the pressure on the Japanese and Indian governments to build their own nuclear arsenals.

If Japan or India were convinced of the invulnerability of the U.S. system against China—a doubtful possibility—the result would be the introduction of a potentially dangerous ambiguity in their relations with the United States. We might be regarded as having insulated ourselves against China at the very moment Japan and India were being subjected to the threat of China's growing intermediate-range missile force. The issue then is clearly drawn. Would an American ABM system provide assurance to our Asian allies that we intended to deter the Chinese nuclear threat, and thereby contribute toward the non-proliferation of nuclear weapons? Or would the construction of a nuclear shield be interpreted as the beginning of an American shelter behind which we are with-drawing—a Fortress America for the nuclear age? It seems plausible to conclude that as Japan and India are subjected to an increasing nuclear threat from China, both countries, influenced by our example, could be expected to look to nuclear weapons of their own for security.

The deployment of a thin, China-oriented ABM system by the United States would probably have only a marginal effect on the nuclear weapons incentives in Israel and West Germany. Both these countries, however, might perceive the U.S. action as an effort to maintain—or reconstruct—a bipolar world. This in itself could be an unattractive prospect for these nations. It would lend support to those within each government who advocate the Gaullist doctrine that nuclear weapons are an essential ingredient of independence and national sovereignty in the nuclear age. In any case, it is difficult to see how U.S. deployment of a China-oriented ABM system would decrease incentives for the acquisition of nuclear weapons in either Israel or West Germany.

## Summary: Adverse Effects

From the preceding analysis of the probable effects on nuclear weapons incentives in Japan, India, Israel and West Germany, it is apparent that deployment by the United States of either a thin, Soviet-oriented or a thin, China-oriented ABM system would adversely affect our proclaimed policy of non-proliferation. Such adverse effects are especially apparent in Asia, where any United States ABM deployment seems to strengthen China's hand and not effectively nullify her growing nuclear power.

The Nixon Administration's compromise is to deploy an ABM defense—the Safeguard system—initially around two missile complexes in remote areas in Montana and North Dakota and, subsequently, around nine other strategic nuclear missile and bomber bases and one city, Washington, D.C. The ABM decision has been explained primarily as giving us a marginal improvement in our capabilities both to deter the Soviet Union and to defend ourselves against a Chinese nuclear attack. But for the reasons given, such a compromise decision may very well prove to be the worst possible course of action for the United States, especially in regard to the prospects for preventing the spread of nuclear weapons in the world. The resulting configuration of the Safeguard ABM system will be highly ambiguous and could well be interpreted by other nations simply as a move by the United States to lay the foundation for a future thick ABM defense of both strategic nuclear forces and cities.

Should this happen, our nuclear non-proliferation policy will suffer an early demise.

*Do the serious concerns of the other nations of
the world over nuclear proliferation and the
arms race have relevance for the ABM decision?*

# THE ATTITUDE OF
# THE WORLD COMMUNITY
# TOWARD THE ABM

## by ARTHUR J. GOLDBERG

*Partner, Paul, Weiss, Rifkind, Goldberg,
Wharton & Garrison, New York City
U.S. Ambassador, United Nations, 1965–1968*

As PART OF MY responsibilities as U.S. Ambassador to the
United Nations, I was charged with guiding the Nuclear Non-
Proliferation Treaty (NPT) through the General Assembly
and with seeking in that forum the maximum possible support
from the one hundred twenty-two nonnuclear members of the
U.N. This responsibility gave me a unique opportunity to
learn the views of the world community with respect not only
to the NPT but also to the entire question of limiting nuclear
weapons, both offensive and defensive. From this experience,
I do not hesitate in stating that the world community views
with apprehension what appears to them to be the escalation
of the nuclear arms race through deployment of competitive
ABM systems.

In reporting this deep concern, I have in mind not only the
intensive private negotiations which went on between nuclear
and nonnuclear states both at Geneva and in New York, I
have in mind as well the amply supported public record of the
Eighteen Nation Disarmament Committee (ENDC) and of
the U.N. General Assembly—and the fears and expectations
voiced before both bodies by the nonnuclear states.

Their views are not to be disregarded lightly. Our nation,
from its inception, has affirmed the principle of showing a
decent respect for the opinions of mankind. Today, the ABM

decisions of the United States and the Soviet Union will have a profound effect on the signatories of the NPT in light of the acknowledged link, in fact and in the provisions of the NPT itself, between future self-denial of nuclear weaponry by the nonnuclear states and the willingness of the superpowers to show reciprocal self-restraint.

Perhaps a good place to begin is when I first reported to the General Assembly on September 21, 1967, and announced the decision three days earlier by our government, a decision to embark on deployment of a "thin" ABM system. I said explicitly at that time, with the full authority of our government:

> However, we have no illusions that construction and deployment of missiles of any kind is the preferred road to security. It is not. The events which have led to our decision simply underscore the urgent importance of pursuing negotiations on a limitation of strategic offensive and defensive missiles. Despite our lack of success thus far, the United States remains ready to open talks on this subject at any time.

This expression of our willingness to open talks, I must candidly say, did not satisfy the world community. As is evidenced by the legislative history of the NPT, the non-nuclear states insisted upon and obtained more substantial assurances by both the United States and the Soviet Union that the new superpowers would undertake solemn treaty obligations in the total area of limiting nuclear armaments, an area which was understood to include the nuclear-based ABM system. This insistence had arisen early in the negotiations of the ENDC which began in Geneva in 1964.

The determination of the nonnuclear states to obtain matching commitments of self-restraint from the superpowers was reflected not only at Geneva. It reached a point of procedural crisis at the United Nations itself in late 1967. At issue was the strong desire of the nonnuclear states to hold a separate conference of their own, prior to submission by the ENDC of a draft treaty to the General Assembly. In contrast, the nuclear states supported a resolution which provided for submission of a draft treaty by the ENDC directly to the First Committee of the General Assembly, and then to the General

Assembly itself, before convening of a conference proposed by the nonnuclear states. Many among the nonnuclear states felt that a conference under the sponsorship of the nonnuclear states prior to General Assembly consideration of the NPT would redress what they conceived to be an imbalance in negotiating power, and would bring about changes in the treaty more responsive to their wishes and needs. The nuclear states, however, felt strongly that they were at long last on the verge of an agreement which would be imperiled by further delay. They felt also that the proposed treaty would reflect a proper balance of obligations between nuclear and nonnuclear states.

In the end, the nuclear and nonnuclear states reached a compromise agreement on the following package proposal: As an essential condition for support by the nonnuclear states of the resolution authorizing the ENDC "urgently to continue its work" and to report a draft treaty by March 15, 1968, the nuclear states (who previously were lukewarm about the nonnuclear states conference and had not committed themselves to participating) agreed to support the convening of the conference and to join in its discussions. In addition, the nuclear states agreed to amend operative paragraph 2 of the resolution by adding language calling upon the ENDC to give "all due consideration to all proposals submitted to the [ENDC] as well as the views expressed by Member States during the twenty-second session." The compromise was embodied in another resolution, which was subsequently adopted by the General Assembly on January 5, 1968.

At this stage, the draft treaty tabled at Geneva on August 24, 1967, by the United States and the U.S.S.R., as Co-Chairmen of the ENDC, did not contain any operative provisions on the nuclear disarmament question. But it declared in the preamble an "intention to achieve at the earliest possible date the cessation of the nuclear arms race," and a further statement as follows:

> Desiring to further the easing of international tension and the strengthening of trust between States in order to facilitate the cessation of the manufacture of nuclear weapons, the liquidation of all their existing stockpiles, and the elimination from national arsenals of nuclear weapons and the means of their delivery pursuant to a treaty on general and complete disarmament under strict and effective international control . . .

And even these preambular statements, it should be noted, arose from the request embodied in an August 19, 1966, joint memorandum on the question by the eight nonnuclear nations participating in the ENDC negotiations. They did not arise from the initiative of the nuclear states.

It was obvious from the discussions at Geneva and from the viewpoints of the nonnuclear nations at the U.N. that the August 24 draft treaty was unacceptable to the nonnuclear states on a number of grounds. Among them, in addition to differences over peaceful uses of nuclear energy and the conduct of nuclear explosions, was the failure of the treaty in its operative provisions to impose obligations of self-restraint on the superpowers. In deference to this criticism, and faithful to the compromise reached at the U.N., the draft treaty of August 24 was radically amended in renewed negotiations by the ENDC. Among the changes was the addition of Article VI in its initial form, which was included in the revised draft treaty presented by the Co-Chairmen on January 18, 1968. The article provided:

> Each of the Parties to this Treaty undertakes to pursue negotiations in good faith on effective measures regarding cessation of the nuclear arms race and disarmament, and on a treaty on general and complete disarmament under strict and effective international control.

Yet even the inclusion of Article VI in this form, and the revisions in other sections of the treaty, were not regarded as satisfactory by the nonnuclear states. Consequently, still further changes were made in the treaty between January 18, 1968, and the submission of the final draft on March 14, 1968. In particular, Article VI was revised and strengthened to read, as in the final treaty, as follows:

> Each of the Parties to this Treaty undertakes to pursue negotiations in good faith on effective measures relating to cessation of the nuclear arms race *at an early date* and to nuclear disarmament, and on a treaty on general and complete disarmament under strict and effective international control. (Italics indicate additions.)

Even these extensive changes in the treaty, however, were deemed insufficient by the nonnuclear states, who freely voiced their misgivings in the extensive debate which took

place in the First Committee of the General Assembly following the submission by the ENDC on March 14, 1968, of a
revised draft in accordance with the compromise agreement.
These misgivings were not made just for the public record. I
can testify that behind the scenes the very same fears, hopes,
misgivings and expectations were expressed by the nonnuclear
signatories of the NPT. These views are a sincere, profound
and justified concern with the risks inherent in the escalation
of both offensive and defensive weaponry—which of course
includes the ABM.

The nuclear states were not insensitive to these concerns,
and, as a result of this debate, still further changes were
made in the draft treaty in negotiations at the U.N. Although
Article VI was unaltered, the ninth paragraph of the preamble was strengthened by the addition of the words "and to
undertake effective measures in the direction of nuclear disarmament." Other changes dealt with the still-continuing
dispute over peaceful uses of nuclear energy and over
weapons testing.

In addition, the draft resolution endorsing the treaty was
likewise strengthened. As submitted on March 1, 1968, the
draft resolution requested "the ENDC urgently to pursue
negotiations on effective measures relating to cessation of the
nuclear arms race at an early date and to nuclear disarmament, and on a treaty on general and complete disarmament
under strict and effective international control." As finally
approved on May 31, 1968, the request for strategic talks was
directed not only to the ENDC, but also to "the nuclear-
weapon states."

A further paragraph of the resolution as first presented
read:

> Convinced further that an agreement to prevent the
> further proliferation of nuclear weapons must be followed
> by effective steps on cessation of the nuclear arms race and
> on nuclear disarmament and that the non-proliferation
> treaty will continue to this aim . . .

But as finally approved on May 31, 1968, this paragraph too
was strengthened:

> Convinced further that an agreement to prevent the
> further proliferation of nuclear weapons must be followed
> *as soon as possible* by effective measures on the cessation of

the nuclear arms race and on nuclear disarmament, and that
the non-proliferation treaty will contribute to this aim . . .
(Italics indicate additions.)

Still other changes were made in the treaty provisions
dealing with peaceful uses of nuclear energy and with access
to the scientific results of nuclear tests.

On June 10, 1968, the treaty, with changes made in its
endorsing resolution and its preamble paragraphs so as to substantially strengthen the obligations on the nuclear states in
the area of nuclear arms limitation, was approved by the First
Committee by a vote of 92 in favor, 4 against, with 22 abstentions. Two days later, on June 12, 1968, the treaty received
the approval of the General Assembly by a vote of 95 in favor,
4 against, with 21 abstentions.

Our government's view of the spirit of Article VI of the
NPT and related parts of the preamble and resolution merits
quotation. These official statements convey the way in which
we viewed the treaty and, in turn, suggest the light in which
the nonnuclear states viewed us.

On April 29, 1968, I presented to the First Committee our
government's view of the obligation imposed by Article VI. I
said then:

> The commitment of Article VI should go far to dispel
> any lingering fear that when the [NPT] is concluded the
> nuclear-weapon Parties to it will relax their efforts in the
> arms control field. On the contrary, the Treaty itself re-
> quires them to intensify these efforts. The conclusion of it
> will do more than any other step now in prospect to
> brighten the atmosphere surrounding all our arms control
> and disarmament negotiations. . . .
>
> Following the conclusion of this Treaty, my Government
> will, in the spirit of Article VI and also of the relevant
> declarations in the preamble, pursue further disarmament
> negotiations with redoubled zeal and help—and with
> promptness. And we anticipate that the same attitude will
> be shown by others.
>
> As President Johnson said, "No nation is more aware of
> the perils in the increasingly expert destructiveness of our
> time than the United States. I believe the Soviet Union
> shares this awareness. This is why we have jointly pledged
> our nations to negotiate toward the cessation of the nuclear
> arms race. This is why the United States urgently desires to

begin discussions with the Soviet Union about the build up of offensive and defensive missiles on both sides. . . . The obligations of the [NPT] will reinforce our will to bring an end to the nuclear arms race. The world will judge us by our performance."

President Johnson reaffirmed these views when he addressed the General Assembly on June 12, 1968, immediately following General Assembly approval of the NPT:

> In keeping with our obligations under the Treaty we shall, as a major nuclear Power, promptly and vigorously pursue negotiations on effective measures to halt the nuclear arms race and to reduce existing nuclear arsenals.
>
> It is right that we should be so obligated. The nonnuclear States—who undertake with this Treaty to forego nuclear weapons—are entitled to the assurance that powers possessing them, particularly the United States and the Soviet Union, will lose no time in finding the way to scale down the nuclear arms race.
>
> We desire—yes, we urgently desire—to begin early discussions on the limitation of strategic offensive and defensive nuclear weapons systems.

On July 1, 1968, the Soviet Union and the United States each signed the NPT, and the leaders of the two superpowers took the occasion to announce the willingness of their governments to open talks on the limitation of offensive and defensive strategic weapons.

Just as our government expressed its understanding of the spirit of Article VI, the nonnuclear states too have expressed their understanding of the obligations of the superpowers. Most revealing of their views, and of the direct connection between Article VI and the ABM question, is the resolution adopted by the Conference of Non-Nuclear Weapon States held in Geneva in August and September of 1968, pursuant to the compromise agreement described earlier. This resolution reads in part:

> *The Conference of Non-Nuclear Weapons States*
>
> . . .
>
> *Recalling* that Article VI of the Treaty on Non-Proliferation of Nuclear Weapons embodies an undertaking of the

Parties to the Treaty to pursue negotiations in good faith on effective measures relating to cessation of the nuclear arms race at an early date and to nuclear disarmament,

. . .

*Deeply concerned* at the imminent danger of a renewal of the strategic nuclear arms race and its escalation to new levels which would become uncontrollable and of the consequent grave threat to the security of all States,

. . .

*Conscious* of the vital need of mankind for a diversion to peaceful purposes of the resources at present consumed by the maintenance and augmentation of nuclear destructive power,

*Urges* the Governments of the Union of Soviet Socialist Republics and the United States of America to enter at an early date into bilateral discussions on the limitation of offensive strategic nuclear-weapons delivery systems of defense against ballistic missiles and systems.

In reporting this viewpoint of the world community concerning arms control in general and the ABM in particular, I do not say that the NPT contains express provisions which prohibit deployment of an ABM or require any moratorium. There was no need, as the Senate properly recognized, for the reservation urged by Dr. Edward Teller to preserve the right of the United States to deploy an ABM. That legal right exists under the treaty. But what also exists, as is apparent from what I have reported, is a strong viewpoint of the world community that good-faith talks should occur between the superpowers toward mutual limitations of their offensive and defensive nuclear might, before deployment momentum builds.

Implicit in this viewpoint is the expectation that neither the United States nor the Soviet Union will take actions which would prejudice the chances of such talks to put a halt to an escalating arms race, and to reduce existing nuclear arsenals. The negotiating record shows that this is the spirit of the treaty. Finally, it is pertinent to observe that there is nothing in the negotiating history which would justify linking talks on strategic weapons with talks on other matters of profound disagreement between the superpowers. Indeed, many of these other matters, such as the Middle East, were the subject of sharp disagreement at the U.N. and elsewhere, precisely in the period when the NPT was being negotiated, and it was never even implied that settlement of these issues was a precondition to strategic arms limitation talks.

In summary, it seems evident to me that the world community justifiably expects the United States and the Soviet Union to undertake, with a sense of urgency, talks on the limitation of offensive and defensive nuclear weapons, including the ABM, and to refrain from escalating the nuclear arms race pending the outcome of such talks. It is true that in matters affecting vital national security, world opinion, while important, cannot override the requirements of national defense. But it is equally true, on the ABM question, that good-faith respect for world opinion and for the spirit of the Nuclear Non-Proliferation Treaty makes it mandatory that decisions taken in the name of vital national security in fact serve that goal.

# VI

## APPENDIX

# GLOSSARY

ABM. Either (a) a missile designed to intercept and neutralize an incoming enemy warhead or (b) a system of radars, computers and missiles designed to defend some specified target or geographic area against an enemy BALLISTIC MISSILE attack.

ABMIS. The airborne equivalent of SABMIS. If developed, it would intercept enemy missiles in mid-course with missiles. It would also guard against submarine-launched missiles.

ACTIVE DEFENSE. Defense utilizing aircraft or missiles to intercept attacking enemy aircraft or missiles.

AMSA. The Advanced Manned Strategic Aircraft, a proposed replacement for the B-70.

ASROC. Antisubmarine rocket: a U.S. rocket-torpedo with either nuclear or conventional warheads, for use by surface vessels against subsurface targets.

ASSURED DESTRUCTION CAPABILITY. The ability to inflict some specific level of damage on an adversary with a very high degree of confidence. It generally does not include the ability to destroy enemy military forces. A high level of assured destruction capability has, by the United States and the U.S.S.R. in recent years, been widely recognized as the condition precedent for deterrence of nuclear war.

ASW. Antisubmarine warfare.

ATLAS. A type of U.S. intercontinental BALLISTIC MISSILE.

217

AWACS. Airborne Warning and Control System: a system using large aircraft (the C-5) carrying radars, computers and communication facilities, to control engagements between U.S. interceptor fighter planes and adversary enemy bombers. AWACS has been proposed as a replacement for the present ground-based warning and control system (DEW, SAGE, etc.) because of the vulnerability of ground-based systems to attack by enemy missiles.

B-47. An early strategic bomber, now phased out.

B-52. A large intercontinental subsonic bomber. The United States now has about six hundred operational B-52s. The latest models will continue to be part of the operational force of the 1970s.

B-58. A large intercontinental supersonic bomber.

B-70. A large intercontinental supersonic bomber, designed to fly at three times the speed of sound. The program was discontinued upon the realization that defense penetration at high altitudes would be much more difficult than low-altitude penetration. Only two B-70 aircraft were built; one crashed and the other is in the Air Force Museum.

BADGER. A Soviet intercontinental subsonic twin-turbojet aircraft (TU-16), generally regarded as comparable to the phased out U.S. B-47. It is being replaced by the BLINDER aircraft.

BALLISTIC MISSILE. A missile that along most of its trajectory moves freely, under the influence of gravity alone.

BEAR. A Soviet four-engine turboprop bomber (TU-95) with a range of 7,800 miles, which carries the KANGAROO standoff missile as part of its armament.

BETA PATCH. The ionized region of the atmosphere produced by beta rays from high-altitude nuclear explosions. See IONIZATION and D-REGION.

BIG BROTHER. A Soviet BOOSTER rocket with an estimated 100-megaton-bomb orbiting capability; in 1965 the Big Brother placed a 13.5-ton payload in orbit.

BISON. A four-engine Soviet turbojet strategic bomber comparable generally to the U.S. B-52.

BLACKOUT. The phenomenon caused by a nuclear explosion in space. Radar rays are reflected, refracted, or absorbed in blackout areas. See BETA PATCH and FIREBALL.

BLAST. The pressure pulse (shock wave) in air initiated by the expansion of the hot gases produced by an explosion.

BLINDER. A supersonic, medium-range Soviet manned bomber (TU-22), now replacing the Badger.

BMD. Ballistic Missile Defense. See ABM.

BMEWS. Ballistic Missile Early Warning System: a U.S. electronic defense network, based in Greenland, Scotland and Alaska, established in the early 1960s to give early warning of incoming transpolar missiles.

BOB. Bureau of the Budget.

BOOSTER. The large first stage of a rocket.

CEP. Circular error probable: a measure of accuracy of missile attacks on point targets. It is the radius of a circle about the target within which half of the attacking missiles will fall.

CHAFF. Bits of metal or other material dispersed about an incoming warhead to confuse radar by reflecting multiple signals.

COST-EXCHANGE RATIO. The ratio of the cost of a defense to the cost of the offensive force needed to overcome it.

COUNTERFORCE CAPABILITY. The ability to destroy an enemy's strategic offensive forces, implying a first-strike attack on the enemy's missiles and bombers before these can be launched. The term is also used to describe an attack against enemy forces at any time during a nuclear exchange.

C.P.R. Chinese People's Republic (Communist China).

CRUISE MISSILE. A missile like the V-1 which along most of its trajectory flies like an airplane.

DAMAGE DENIAL. The ability to prevent any damage whatsoever from an enemy nuclear attack. Damage denial could be accomplished by a FIRST-STRIKE ATTACK against the adversary's forces, by ACTIVE DEFENSE and PASSIVE DEFENSE or by a combination of such actions.

DAMAGE-LIMITING. A term describing the measures to reduce or limit damage to a country from a nuclear attack by an enemy. These measures include COUNTERFORCE attack against adversary forces, ACTIVE DEFENSE and PASSIVE DEFENSE.

DECIBEL. A unit used to describe fractional changes in radar-signal intensity. One decibel is a factor of 1.26; ten decibels is a factor of 10.

DECOY. A penetration aid designed to complicate the problem of defending against a missile attack. A decoy or decoys might be detached from a warhead, to increase the number of targets with which a defender must contend.

DEPRESSED TRAJECTORY. A ballistic missile trajectory lower than a MINIMUM-ENERGY TRAJECTORY; in other words, a trajectory flatter than that normally used to fly missiles from one place to another.

DISCRIMINATION. The art of distinguishing DECOYS and other PENETRATION AIDS from nuclear warheads.

D-REGION. The layer of the ionosphere at altitude 45 miles, within which most BETA-PATCH IONIZATION occurs. See BETA PATCH and IONIZATION.

DYNA-SOAR. A discontinued U.S. combined atmospheric-space manned craft, capable of assuming orbit and/or landing at specific touchdown targets.

ECM. Electromagnetic countermeasures.

EMP. Electromagnetic pulse.

EXOATMOSPHERIC INTERCEPTION. Interception of enemy warheads before they re-enter the earth's atmosphere.

F-12. Proposed advanced supersonic interceptor aircraft to be used with AWACS system.

FB-111. Bomber version of the F-111 (TFX).

FIREBALL. The luminous sphere of hot gases produced by a nuclear explosion.

FIRE STORM. A phenomenon occurring in very large fires. The updraft produced by the fire causes winds to blow in toward the fire from all directions. Such storms are produced in large forest fires and were evident in some of the large bombing raids in World War II and in the bombing of Hiroshima. In a fire storm, virtually all the combustible material within the area covered by the fire is burned.

FIRST-STRIKE CAPABILITY. Ability to destroy adversary offensive weapons by delivering a PRE-EMPTIVE ATTACK, using missiles or aircraft or any combination.

FLIGHT. As applied to MINUTEMAN forces, ten MINUTEMAN missiles, grouped in a loose cluster at an Air Force base.

FOBS. Fractional Orbital Bombardment System: a system involving the delivery of nuclear weapons from low-altitude orbital trajectories. FOBS requires the use of reverse thrust to bring the warhead down to target. Because the trajectory is lower than in the case of ICBMs, detection using conventional long-range radars is more difficult. The payload delivered by a given propulsion system is generally smaller than with an ICBM, and the accuracy is generally poorer.

FOOTPRINT. The area of the United States protected by one ABM missile site.

FY. Fiscal year.

GALOSH. The NATO code for the Soviet defensive missile, which is already partially emplaced around Moscow. It is considered comparable to the NIKE-ZEUS, which the U.S. ruled inadequate for operational use. The Galosh system includes about 70 missiles, with their supporting radars and computers.

GOLEM. A Soviet submarine-launched missile of IRBM class.

GRIFFON. A Soviet short-range ABM comparable to the U.S. SPRINT missile.

ICBM. Intercontinental ballistic missile: a long-range (6,000 to 8,000 miles) multistage rocket capable of delivering nuclear warheads. U.S. ICBMs include ATLAS (phased out), TITAN I and II (Titan I phased out) and MINUTEMAN I, II, and III. Soviet ICBMs include the SS-9, SS-11 and SS-13.

INTERCEPTOR MISSILE. Surface-based missile used as part of either an air or an antiballistic missile defense system. They are divided into two classes: those designed for EXOATMO-SPHERIC INTERCEPTION, such as the SPARTAN, and those designed for TERMINAL INTERCEPTION, such as the SPRINT.

IONIZATION. The break up of air or other substances into electrons and positively charged ions. Ionized substances conduct electricity, and therefore reflect, refract or absorb radar signals.

IRBM. Intermediate-range ballistic missile: a ballistic missile with a range of roughly 2,000 to 4,000 nautical miles.

KANGAROO. A Soviet standoff (tactical) missile used as armament by BEAR-type aircraft.

KILOTON. A unit of explosive force equal to 1,000 tons of TNT.

KIPPER. A Soviet standoff missile, with a range of approximately 450 miles, used on BADGER-type aircraft.

KITCHEN. A Soviet standoff missile used on BLINDER medium-range strategic bombers.

LOFTED TRAJECTORY. Any BALLISTIC MISSILE trajectory higher than a MINIMUM-ENERGY TRAJECTORY.

MAR. Multifunction array radar: a U.S. detection and command system designed originally for use with the nonde-ployed NIKE-X ABM system.

MINIMUM-ENERGY TRAJECTORY. The particular elliptical path followed by a BALLISTIC MISSILE for which the fuel needed to deliver a given payload at a given target is a minimum.

MINUTEMAN. The basic U.S. ICBM presently in deployment. The warhead for Minuteman I yields about 1 megaton; that of Minuteman II has a higher yield and/or can carry PENETRATION AIDS; that of Minuteman III can carry MIRVs.

MIRV. Multiple Independently Targetable Re-entry Vehicle: a system of multiple warheads carried by one re-entry vehicle (ICBM, etc.), which can be maneuvered on independent courses to separate targets. MIRVs are being developed by both the United States and the Soviet Union.

MRV. Multiple Re-entry Vehicle: a system of multiple warheads carried by one re-entry vehicle, which are not independently targeted but are dispersed for a general target area.

MSR. Missile site radar: part of the SAFEGUARD ABM. Performs surveillance and detection, target track, missile track and command functions for the SPRINT and SPARTAN missiles.

NAUTICAL MILE. Unit of length used by naval and air forces. The length of one minute of latitude. One nautical mile equals 1.15157 statute miles or 1.853248 kilometers.

NEUTRON KILL. The destruction of a nuclear warhead by neutrons from an ABM nuclear explosion.

NIKE-X. A U.S. ABM system, designed in 1963, employing the long-range ZEUS missile and the short-range SPRINT missile in combination with the MAR and MSR. The NIKE-X system has not been deployed.

NIKE-ZEUS. A U.S. ABM system, authorized about 1957 but never deployed.

NPT. Nuclear Non-Proliferation Treaty: treaty approved by the United Nations in 1968 and ratified by the Senate in 1969. Each nonnuclear signatory would undertake not to acquire nuclear weapons; each nuclear power would agree not to assist nonnuclear powers in acquiring nuclear weapons.

OVERPRESSURE. The pressure produced by a nuclear explosion in excess of ambient air pressure. Usually measured in pounds per square inch.

OVER-THE-HORIZON RADAR. A long-range BALLISTIC MISSILE warning system that uses radar waves which are reflected back and forth between the earth's surface and the ionosphere, and can therefore propagate over the horizon.

PAR. Perimeter Acquisition Radar: a long-range radar of the SENTINEL/SAFEGUARD ABM. Used for surveillance and tracking in conjunction with the SPARTAN missile.

PASSIVE DEFENSE. Defense of population or military facilities by protective shelters, hardening, dispersal, mobility, etc.

PENETRATION AIDS. Devices to aid the entry of aircraft or missiles through enemy ACTIVE DEFENSES. Penetration aids for missiles include DECOYS, CHAFF and electronic jammers. Other techniques are delivery of large numbers of warheads and decoys almost simultaneously in order to saturate radar and computer capabilities, targeting of radars rather than primary targets, and nuclear explosions at high altitudes to produce ionization interfering with radar detection and tracking.

PHASED-ARRAY RADARS. Radars in which the beam is steered electronically and which therefore do not involve moving parts. They have an advantage over the older mechanically steered radars because they can handle many targets simultaneously and can be steered quickly from one target to another.

POLARIS. U.S. nuclear-powered missile-launching submarine, carrying sixteen missiles. The term also refers to the missiles, of which there have been three versions. The first two, Polaris A-1 and A-2, each carried single warheads with a yield of around 1 megaton. Polaris A-3 carries three smaller warheads which are not individually targetable (MRVs). Forty-one Polaris submarines have been launched.

POSEIDON. The advanced U.S. nuclear-powered missile-launching submarine now being deployed. Poseidon missiles have better accuracy, longer range and higher payload than POLARIS and will probably carry MIRVs.

POSTURE STATEMENT. Official U.S. summaries of our defense posture, prepared each year by the Secretary of Defense.

PRE-EMPTIVE ATTACK. First strike designed to knock out the adversary's offensive forces, population or industry in anticipation of a possible strike by him.

RADAR CROSS SECTION. The effective reflecting area of an object observed with radar.

RV. Re-entry vehicle: that part of a missile which is designed to re-enter the earth's atmosphere, and at least part of which is to reach the earth's surface without burning up.

SABMIS. Sea-based antiballistic missile system: defensive missiles mounted on surface vessels to intercept enemy warheads in mid-flight, before the land-based defensive system can reach them, so as to destroy an enemy missile before it scatters a number of separate warheads and decoys.

SAC. Strategic Air Command: the U.S. force of intercontinental bombers.

SAFEGUARD. The modification announced by President Nixon on March 14, 1969, of the SENTINEL ABM system.

SAGE. Semiautomatic Ground Environment: a U.S. defense system designed to provide instantaneous information by computer for air defenses.

SAM-D. Advanced Soviet surface-to-air missile defense system for use against bomber aircraft.

SANDAL. A Soviet IRBM.

SARK-SERB. A Soviet submarine-launched IRBM system.

SASIN. A Soviet two-stage liquid-propellant rocket of ICBM range, roughly comparable to the early U.S. ATLAS.

SAVAGE. See SS-13.

SCAD. Subsonic Cruise Armed Decoy: a relatively long-range bomber-launched cruise missile now under development.

SCAMP. A mobile Soviet IRBM.

SCARP. See SS-9.

SCRAG. See SS-11.

SECOND-STRIKE CAPABILITY. The capability to destroy an enemy after absorbing a first strike.

SENTINEL. The American ABM system as announced by President Johnson.

SLM. Submarine-launched missile: a missile mounted on long-range nuclear-powered submarines, which can be fired from under water. Also referred to as SLBMs and FBMs.

SOFT FACILITIES. Missile sites, command and control centers or other facilities that have not been provided with protective shielding against nearby nuclear explosions.

SPARTAN. A missile which is a part of the U.S. ABM system. This missile carries a nuclear warhead and has a range of 300 to 500 miles.

SPRINT. A missile which is a part of the U.S. ABM system. This missile carries a nuclear warhead and has a range of 10 to 25 miles.

SRAM. An airborne short-range attack missile scheduled to be deployed in FY 1970.

SS-9. A large Soviet liquid-fueled ICBM. About two hundred and thirty have already been deployed and more are being deployed. It can carry a warhead with a yield estimated to run as high as 25 megatons.

SS-11. The liquid-fueled missile that comprises more than half of the Soviet ICBM force. Its warhead is in the megaton range, comparable to Minuteman.

SS-13. The latest Russian ICBM and the first to employ solid fuel. In range, payload and accuracy, it is considered roughly equivalent to the American Minuteman I.

SSN. Nuclear powered submarine.

STRATEGIC ALERT. A status of heightened readiness for a strategic attack, prompted by international political developments.

STRATEGIC FORCES. Includes offensive forces capable of delivering nuclear weapons against industrial or population targets, and defensive forces designed to defend against such attacks. Strategic forces include long-range bombers, ICBMs, missile-launching submarines and the defenses against these delivery systems.

SUBROC. Submarine rocket: U.S.-developed nuclear or conventional warhead rocket-torpedoes for use against subsurface targets.

TACMAR. An advanced multifunction radar which might be deployed as part of an ABM system.

TALLINN. A defensive system deployed by the Soviet Union, and given that designation because some of the facilities were located near Tallinn, Estonia. The Tallinn system is an antiaircraft system with no significant antiballistic defense capability in the generally shared view. However, some years ago it was believed that the Tallinn was primarily an ABM system.

TERMINAL DEFENSES. Defenses designed to intercept a missile during the final part of its trajectory. The missiles are deployed to defend one point and cannot defend other points some distance away. It is also called a "hard-point defense."

TITAN II. A liquid-fueled U.S. ICBM carrying a warhead of several megatons.

UHF. Ultrahigh frequency: the range of radio wavelengths from 10 to 100 centimeters. The PAR and MSR radar wavelengths are probably near the top and bottom of this range, respectively.

ULMS. Underwater Long-range Missile System: a possible future U.S. missile system which would provide U.S.

nuclear submarines with long-range (ICBM) missiles, supplementing or replacing the present medium-range (IRBM) POLARIS and the projected POSEIDON missiles.

WS 120. Weapons system number 120: the post-MINUTEMAN series of land-based offensive weapons, which would have greater range, accuracy and payload. Also called the ICM.

X-RAY KILL. The mechanism by which X-rays from an ABM nuclear explosion destroy or neutralize RVs at great distances.

YIELD. The total effective energy produced in a nuclear explosion. Usually expressed as an equivalent tonnage of TNT.

# CHRONOLOGY OF U.S. ABM DEPLOYMENT DECISIONS 1955–1969

(*Adapted from* Congressional Digest, *November, 1968, and the* New York Times Index)

## 1955

In February, the Army contracted with Bell Telephone Laboratories to undertake feasibility studies of a Nike-Zeus-type ABM system, with research and development focused on defending against the intercontinental ballistic missile (ICBM).

At about the same time, the Air Force contracted with General Dynamics to study its proposed Wizard ABM system.

## 1957

In January, the Army authorized full system development of the Nike-Zeus ABM system, based on the findings of the Bell feasibility study.

In April, the Atomic Energy Commission began a feasibility study on the Nike-Zeus missile warhead. The study was completed in September.

## 1958

In January, Defense Secretary McElroy selected Zeus over Wizard, and ordered the Air Force to discontinue all development work on Wizard. He pressed ABM development as a matter of urgency because of Sputnik and other indications of Soviet ICBM capabilities.

### 1959

President Eisenhower decided against Nike-Zeus deployment, while continuing research and development.

In June, the AEC began development engineering for a Zeus missile warhead.

In August, the first Zeus missile was fired at the White Sands, New Mexico, Missile Range.

### 1961

Work began on Ascension Island, Kwajalein Island, and Pt. Mugu, California, on ABM radar systems.

In December, a Zeus missile successfully intercepted a Nike-Hercules surface-to-air missile.

### 1962

In July, a missile fired from Kwajalein successfully intercepted an Atlas warhead fired from Vandenberg Air Force Base in California.

During the next two years, ten out of fourteen ICBMs fired from Vandenberg were reported to be successfully intercepted.

The contract for development of the Sprint missile was awarded to the Martin Co.

### 1963

In January, the Army reoriented the ABM system, and renamed it the Nike-X.

As reoriented, Nike-X took on some of the characteristics of the defunct Air Force Wizard ABM: area defense, multipurpose radars and SLBM capabilities.

The Senate Armed Services Committee moved to add $196 million to the Fiscal 1964 Department of Defense authorization bill for ABM parts procurement, but the move was opposed by the Administration and rejected by the full Senate. The Senate debated the question of U.S. defense against enemy missiles in the first secret session since World War II.

The U.S.S.R. announced it had designed an effective antimissile missile.

The Nuclear Test Ban Treaty was signed, prohibiting

nuclear testing in the atmosphere. The treaty thus limits the testing of ABM components and concepts.

## 1964

In January, President Johnson ordered a cutback in manufacturing of fissionable materials and arms as a step toward "eventual abolition of arms." He requested the U.S.S.R. to do the same.

In July, the MAR (multiple array radar) system, a substantially improved radar system to be incorporated into Nike-X, was tested at the White Sands Missile Range.

In October, it was reported that China detonated its first atomic bomb—a low-yield fissionable device.

## 1965

In May, it was reported that China detonated a second bomb—this one of low-intermediate yield.

In October, the Army presented its Nike-X deployment study to the Department of Defense.

In November, the first successful flight of the Sprint missile was conducted.

## 1966

Development proceeded on warheads for both the Sprint and the Spartan missiles.

In May, it was reported that China had exploded a hydrogen (thermonuclear) device. A second such device was reported detonated in December.

Meanwhile, Congress approved $167.9 million for ABM procurement; the Secretary of Defense had not requested these funds and did not obligate them.

In November, Secretary McNamara announced that the U.S.S.R. had begun to deploy an ABM system around Moscow. (Galosh had previously been characterized only as a missile, not a system.)

## 1967

In January, President Johnson communicated to the U.S.S.R. his desire for arms control negotiations (to include the discussion of defensive missile systems), and announced that no U.S. ABM deployment would be made until the completion of these negotiations. Secretary McNamara submitted a Posture Statement to the Congress which argued in detail against deployment of a thick, Soviet-oriented ABM system. General Wheeler, Chairman of the Joint Chiefs of Staff, subsequently made known that he disagreed with McNamara's position and supported a "measure of defense" for the country.

In February, the Soviets announced they had begun to deploy an effective ABM system.

In June, the House Appropriations Committee report accompanying the Department of Defense Appropriations Bill for Fiscal 1968 stated that a thin ABM system might be a useful first step in a larger missile defense.

China was reported to have detonated another hydrogen bomb.

President Johnson and Premier Kosygin met at Glassboro, New Jersey, and Johnson informed Kosygin that the United States wanted to negotiate to limit the development of strategic nuclear weapons, including antimissile defense.

During June and July, both houses of Congress debated the military budget, and voted to appropriate to the Department of Defense for Fiscal 1968 a total of $782.9 million for ballistic missile defenses. The President had requested $375 million for the Sentinel system, which had not yet been officially approved for deployment. Still, Congress pared $9 million off this request, and earmarked $366 of the $782.9 million for Sentinel.

The Congressional debate over appropriations also included a heated controversy over the question of deployment, which was not resolved when the First Session adjourned.

On September 18, Secretary McNamara announced the decision to deploy a thin antimissile system to guard against a future threat by Chinese ICBMs, expected to be deployed within the next few years. (See Appendix for text of this announcement.) Secretary McNamara rejected as "futile" the demands for an ABM system against Soviet ICBMs. He warned, however, that if the U.S.S.R. expanded its ABM system, the U.S. would increase its offensive forces. But he urged negotiations to halt or reverse the arms race, stating that the U.S. and U.S.S.R. now possess more ICBMs than either needs to deter nuclear war. Further, McNamara stated that current intelligence rendered it unlikely that either could secretly build up first-strike capability.

In October, the Military Applications Subcommittee of the Joint Atomic Energy Committee opened hearings on whether the U.S. should seek parity with the U.S.S.R. rather than superiority in nuclear warheads, and whether the U.S. should build a thick ABM system against the U.S.S.R. or should seek agreement with the U.S.S.R. to limit protection against a third power.

In November, Secretary McNamara reported that the U.S.S.R. was developing a FOBS system. He stated that U.S. over-the-horizon radar would negate the FOBS advantages.

The Nike-Zeus was renamed Sentinel, and Lieutenant General Alfred Starbird became head of the program.

The House Republican Committee on the Western Alliance warned that U.S. deployment of a thin system might drive European allies into "positions of defensive neutrality" and urged the study of a community defensive system.

The Administration postponed its decision whether to expand Sentinel to a thicker system, stating that the delay was necessary to keep the door open to East-West disarmament talks.

In December, Defense Department Research Director John Foster reported the development of MIRVs, intended to counter the U.S.S.R. development of more ICBMs. Foster stated the MIRVs would not orbit or fractionally orbit.

U.S. sources reported that China had installed launchers for nuclear-armed missiles on two submarines.

## 1968

In January, President Johnson asked $1.2 billion for Fiscal Year 1969 for manufacturing and deploying Sentinel. An additional $269 million was requested for further research into improved missile defense.

Secretary McNamara reported to Congress on the increase in Soviet missile strength and defenses, and asserted that talks to limit the arms race were more compelling than ever. (See Appendix for excerpts from Secretary McNamara's statement.) In the same Annual Posture Statement to Congress, Defense Department Research Director Foster said that the U.S. did not expect China to launch its first ICBM as soon as expected.

U.S. intelligence reported that the U.S.S.R. was nearing parity with the U.S. in land-based ICBMs: the U.S.S.R. had recently fired the first of its solid-fueled ICBMs and was believed to have begun deployment.

In March, the Defense Department studied a series of

improvements in Sentinel to thwart refinements in future Chinese ICBMs; the studies were linked to the charge by Professors Bethe and Garwin in *Scientific American* (an updated version is included, see page 130) that China could use a combination of offensive missiles and cheap penetration devices to thwart the Sentinel system.

The Non-Proliferation Treaty (NPT) draft was submitted to the U.N. Assembly by the United States, the U.S.S.R. and Britain. Ambassadors Goldberg and Kuznetsov pledged that if there were wide endorsement of the treaty, the United States and the U.S.S.R. would push forward with negotiations to further limit the arms race.

In April, the Senate Preparedness Subcommittee began an inquiry into U.S. strategic posture aimed at determining the U.S. response to recent increases in U.S.S.R. ICBM strength.

U.S. experts were confused at China's delay in deploying nuclear missiles, which it believed China had produced in modest numbers. China had also failed to test a booster thought large enough for use as an ICBM. She was expected to deploy ten to twenty medium-range missiles shortly, about a year later than U.S. estimates.

In June, the NPT draft was revised to promise more urgent efforts by the big powers to end the arms race. It was approved as revised by the U.N. Assembly.

Debate on Sentinel continued: a bipartisan group of Senators sought to postpone deployment for at least one year. A motion to postpone deployment was defeated by the Senate 34 to 52.

The Senate voted the $277 million asked by the Administration for beginning the $5.5 billion system. The Administration began to justify Sentinel as a defense against the U.S.S.R. as well as China. (Defense Construction Authorization bill.)

In July, the United States, the U.S.S.R., Britain and fifty-eight other nations signed the NPT. President Johnson, at the White House ceremony, announced that the U.S. and the U.S.S.R. had agreed to open talks aimed at limiting and reducing both offensive and defensive missile systems.

In July, President Johnson sent the NPT to the Senate, and urged its swift ratification.

France successfully tested a sea-to-ground and ground-to-ground ICBM.

Progress on the arms talks continued: the United States was completing preliminary studies outlining major differences.

In August, the Senate rejected a move to cut $277 million for Sentinel from the appropriations bill. (Defense Construction Appropriation bill.)

Protests against continued development of MIRVs and Poseidon and Minuteman III missiles prior to the arms talks were lodged within and outside of Congress, but the missiles were tested.

The U.S.S.R. invaded Czechoslovakia and the U.S. interest in arms talks cooled, although the Administration stated that it was determined to pursue the talks despite the invasion.

In September, Defense Secretary Clifford ordered Sentinel exempted from the budget cuts required by Congress. Clifford said he hoped talks with the Soviets would take place at the "appropriate time," indicating delay.

The Senate Foreign Relations Committee, 13 to 13, approved the NPT.

In October, notwithstanding renewed arguments against the ABM, the entire amount requested by the Administration for Sentinel—$963.6 million—was authorized and appropriated by the Ninetieth Congress prior to its October adjournment. (Defense Procurement Appropriation bill.)

The Soviet Union asserted in the U.N. that it was still interested in arms control talks with the United States. Secretary Clifford said that the United States remained hopeful of holding talks with the Soviets on controls, but urged moving with caution. Clifford conceded that the U.S.S.R. had markedly narrowed the U.S. nuclear missile lead, but he insisted that the United States maintained nuclear superiority.

In November, France reported test-firing an ICBM from a submerged submarine.

Protests were lodged against the building of an ABM base near Chicago. Demonstrations followed in Boston and elsewhere.

In December, Secretary Clifford urged that missile control talks begin as soon as possible on whatever level the two nations could agree on.

The U.N. Assembly Committee, 97 to 0, approved a resolution calling on the United States and the U.S.S.R. to start talks "at an early date" on limiting missile systems.

## 1969

In January, President Johnson's fiscal 1970 budget message contained request for over $2 billion to provide multiple warheads for Minuteman 3 and Poseidon, and $1.8 billion for deployment of Sentinel.

In his analysis to Congress of the Johnson Administration's final defense budget, Defense Secretary Clifford expressed "increasing concern" about rapid growth of the U.S.S.R.'s ICBM force, which had nearly quadrupled in two years and was expected to exceed that of the United States by 1970. (See page 251 for excerpts from Secretary Clifford's statement.)

The new Secretary of Defense, Melvin Laird, backed Sentinel system deployment; he saw it strengthening the U.S. bargaining position in possible talks with the U.S.S.R. on arms control.

In February, Senator Edward M. Kennedy asked Secretary Laird to freeze ABM deployment, pending completion of strategic weapons system review. House Armed Services Committee Chairman Mendel Rivers indicated that his Committee would not approve the metropolitan ABM sites in Illinois and Washington.

Opposition to ABM deployment rose in the Senate. Senate critics urged postponement of construction pending full review of cost, safety and diplomatic factors. The renewal of debate was linked in part to protests in Boston, Chicago and other cities designated as missile sites.

On February 6, Secretary Laird ordered a temporary halt in Sentinel deployment pending a one-month review of all major weapons systems. President Nixon, at a news conference, stressed that Sentinel was not designed simply as a defense against Chinese ICBMs but also to bolster "over-all defense capability."

U.S. intelligence sources indicated that the U.S.S.R. Galosh ABM around Moscow was about 70 percent complete, but had slowed in recent months to improve radar. Briefings by high Defense Department officials reported that the system even when completed will not alter the U.S.-U.S.S.R. balance of power or undermine U.S. ability to destroy the U.S.S.R. in retaliatory strike.

Senate Foreign Relations Committee began hearings on ABM deployment. Secretary Laird and other Administration officials appeared on numerous occasions in February and March.

In March, President Nixon, in Paris, termed arms talks with the Soviets an urgent duty. (*New York Times,* March 2, 1969, p. 1, col. 5.)

M.I.T. Chairman James Killian, testifying before the Senate Foreign Relations Committee, urged the appointment of an independent commission to study the ABM.

Pressure mounted for the President to postpone his decision pending continued research and development.

On March 14, 1969, President Nixon announced his revised proposals for the Sentinel ABM Program. (Text of this announcement and Defense Department elaborations of it are included in Basic Documents. . . .)

# BASIC DOCUMENTS
# IN THE DEBATE

*Excerpts from a speech by Secretary of Defense Robert S. Mc-Namara, on September 18, 1967, in San Francisco, California, before United Press International Editors and Publishers. In this speech, Secretary McNamara announced the Administration's decision to recommend deployment of the Sentinel ABM system.*

What is essential to understand here is that the Soviet Union and the United States mutually influence one another's strategic plans.

Whatever be their intentions, whatever be our intentions, actions—or even realistically potential actions—on either side relating to the build-up of nuclear forces, be they either offensive or defensive weapons, necessarily trigger reactions on the other side.

It is precisely this action-reaction phenomenon that fuels an arms race.

Now, in strategic nuclear weaponry, the arms race involves a particular irony. Unlike any other era in military history, today a substantial numerical superiority of weapons does not effectively translate into political control, or diplomatic leverage.

While thermonuclear power is almost inconceivably awesome, and represents virtually unlimited potential destructiveness, it has proven to be a limited diplomatic instrument. Its uniqueness lies in the fact that it is at one and the same time an all-powerful weapon—and a very inadequate weapon.

The fact that the Soviet Union and the United States can mutually destroy one another—regardless of who strikes first

—narrows the range of Soviet aggression which our nuclear forces can effectively deter.

Even with our nuclear monopoly in the early postwar period, we were unable to deter the Soviet pressures against Berlin, or their support of aggression in Korea.

Today, our nuclear superiority does not deter all forms of Soviet support of Communist insurgency in Southeast Asia.

It would not be sensible for either side to launch a maximum effort to achieve a first-strike capability. It would not be sensible because the intelligence-gathering capability of each side being what it is, and the realities of lead time from technological breakthrough to operational readiness being what they are, neither of us would be able to acquire a first-strike capability in secret.

Now, let me take a specific case in point.

The Soviets are now deploying an antiballistic missile system. If we react to this deployment intelligently, we have no reason for alarm.

The system does not impose any threat to our ability to penetrate and inflict massive and unacceptable damage on the Soviet Union. In other words, it does not presently affect in any significant manner our assured destruction capability.

It does not impose such a threat because we have already taken the steps necessary to assure that our land-based Minuteman missiles, our nuclear submarine-launched new Poseidon missiles, and our strategic bomber forces have the requisite penetration aids—and, in the sum, constitute a force of such magnitude that they guarantee us a force strong enough to survive a Soviet attack and penetrate the Soviet ABM deployment.

Now let me come to the issue that has received so much attention recently: the question of whether or not we should deploy an ABM system against the Soviet nuclear threat.

To begin with, this is not in any sense a new issue. We have had both the technical possibility and the strategic desirability of an American ABM deployment under constant review since the late 1950s.

While we have substantially improved our technology in the field, it is important to understand that none of the systems at the present or foreseeable state-of-the-art would provide an impenetrable shield over the United States. Were such a shield possible, we would certainly want it—and we would certainly build it.

And at this point let me dispose of an objection that is totally irrelevant to this issue.

It has been alleged that we are opposed to deploying a large-scale ABM system because it would carry the heavy price tag of $40 billion.

Let me make it very clear that the $40 billion is not the issue.

If we could build and deploy a genuinely impenetrable shield over the United States, we would be willing to spend not $40 billion, but any reasonable multiple of that amount that was necessary.

The money in itself is not the problem: the penetrability of the proposed shield is the problem.

There is clearly no point, however, in spending $40 billion if it is not going to buy us a significant improvement in our security. If it is not, then we should use the substantial resources it represents on something that will.

Every ABM system that is now feasible involves firing defensive missiles at incoming offensive warheads in an effort to destroy them.

But what many commentators on this issue overlook is that any such system can rather obviously be defeated by an enemy simply sending more offensive warheads, or dummy warheads, than there are defensive missiles capable of disposing of them.

And this is the whole crux of the nuclear action-reaction phenomenon.

Were we to deploy a heavy ABM system throughout the United States, the Soviets would clearly be strongly motivated to so increase their offensive capability as to cancel out our defensive advantage.

It is futile for each of us to spend $4 billion, $40 billion or $400 billion—and at the end of all the spending, and at the end of all the deployment, and at the end of all the effort, to be relatively at the same point of balance on the security scale that we are now.

In point of fact, we have already initiated offensive weapons programs costing several billions in order to offset the small present Soviet ABM deployment, and the possibly more extensive future Soviet ABM deployments.

That is money well spent; and it is necessary.

But we should bear in mind that it is money spent because of the action-reaction phenomenon.

If we in turn opt for heavy ABM deployment—at whatever price—we can be certain that the Soviets will react to offset the advantage we would hope to gain.

It is precisely because of this certainty of a corresponding Soviet reaction that the four prominent scientists—men who have served with distinction as the Science Advisers to Presidents Eisenhower, Kennedy and Johnson, and the three outstanding men who have served as Directors of Research and Engineering to three Secretaries of Defense—have unanimously recommended against the deployment of an ABM system designed to protect our population against a Soviet attack.

These men are Doctors Killian, Kistiakowsky, Wiesner, Hornig, York, Brown and Foster.

The plain fact of the matter is that we are now facing a situation analogous to the one we faced in 1961: we are uncertain of the Soviets' intentions.

At that time we were concerned about their potential offensive capabilities; now we are concerned about their potential defensive capabilities.

But the dynamics of the concern are the same.

We must continue to be cautious and conservative in our estimates—leaving no room in our calculations for unnecessary risk. And at the same time, we must measure our own response in such a manner that it does not trigger a senseless spiral upward of nuclear arms.

Now, as I have emphasized, we have already taken the necessary steps to guarantee that our offensive strategic weapons will be able to penetrate future, more advanced, Soviet defenses.

Keeping in mind the careful clockwork of lead time, we will be forced to continue that effort over the next few years if the evidence is that the Soviets intend to turn what is now a light and modest ABM deployment into a massive one.

Should they elect to do so, we have both the lead time and the technology available to so increase both the quality and quantity of our offensive strategic forces—with particular attention to highly reliable penetration aids—that their expensive defensive efforts will give them no edge in the nuclear balance whatever.

But we would prefer not to have to do that. For it is a profitless waste of resources, provided we and the Soviets can come to a realistic strategic arms-limitation agreement.

As you know, we have proposed U.S.-Soviet talks on this matter. Should these talks fail, we are fully prepared to take the appropriate measures that such a failure would make necessary.

The point for us to keep in mind is that should the talks fail—and the Soviets decide to expand their present modest ABM deployment into a massive one—our response must be realistic. There is no point whatever in our responding by going to a massive ABM deployment to protect our population, when such a system would be ineffective against a sophisticated Soviet offense.

Instead, realism dictates that if the Soviets elect to deploy a heavy ABM system, we must further expand our sophisticated offensive forces, and thus preserve our overwhelming assured destruction capability.

But the intractable fact is that should the talks fail, both the Soviets and ourselves would be forced to continue on a foolish and feckless course.

It would be foolish and feckless because—in the end—it would provide neither the Soviets nor us with any greater relative nuclear capability.

The time has come for us both to realize that, and to act reasonably. It is clearly in our own mutual interest to do so.

Having said that, it is important to distinguish between an ABM system designed to protect against a Soviet attack on our cities, and ABM systems which have other objectives.

One of the other uses of an ABM system which we should seriously consider is the greater protection of our strategic offensive forces.

Another is in relation to the emerging nuclear capability of Communist China.

There is evidence that the Chinese are devoting very substantial resources to the development of both nuclear warheads and missile delivery systems. As stated last January, indications are that they will have medium-range ballistic missiles within a year or so, an initial intercontinental ballistic missile capability in the early 1970s and a modest force in the mid-seventies.

Up to now, the lead-time factor has allowed us to postpone a decision on whether or not a light ABM deployment might be advantageous as a countermeasure to Communist China's nuclear development.

But the time will shortly be right for us to initiate production if we desire such a system.

China at the moment is caught up in internal strife, but it seems likely that her basic motivation in developing a strategic nuclear capability is an attempt to provide a basis for threatening her neighbors, and to clothe herself with the dubious prestige that the world pays to nuclear weaponry.

We deplore her development of these weapons, just as we deplore it in other countries. We oppose nuclear proliferation because we believe that in the end it only increases the risk of a common and cataclysmic holocaust.

President Johnson has made it clear that the United States will oppose any efforts of China to employ nuclear blackmail against her neighbors.

We possess now, and will continue to possess for as far ahead as we can foresee, an overwhelming first-strike capability with respect to China. And despite the shrill and raucous propaganda directed at her own people that "the atomic bomb is a paper tiger," there is ample evidence that China well appreciates the destructive power of nuclear weapons.

China has been cautious to avoid any action that might end in a nuclear clash with the United States—however wild her words—and understandably so. We have the power not only to destroy completely her entire nuclear offensive forces, but to devastate her society as well.

Is there any possibility, then, that by the mid-1970s China might become so incautious as to attempt a nuclear attack on the United States or our allies?

It would be insane and suicidal for her to do so, but one can conceive conditions under which China might miscalculate. We wish to reduce such possibilities to a minimum.

And since, as I have noted, our strategic planning must always be conservative, and take into consideration even the possible irrational behavior of potential adversaries, there are marginal grounds for concluding that a light deployment of U.S. ABMs against this possibility is prudent.

The system would be relatively inexpensive—preliminary estimates place the cost at about $5 billion—and would have a much higher degree of reliability against a Chinese attack than the much more massive and complicated system that some have recommended against a possible Soviet attack.

Moreover, such an ABM deployment designed against a possible Chinese attack would have a number of other advantages. It would provide an additional indication to Asians that we intend to deter China from nuclear blackmail, and thus would contribute toward our goal of discouraging nuclear weapon proliferation among the present nonnuclear countries.

Further, the Chinese-oriented ABM deployment would enable us to add—as a concurrent benefit—a further defense of our Minuteman sites against Soviet attack, which means that at modest cost we would in fact be adding even greater effectiveness to our offensive missile force and avoiding a much more costly expansion of that force.

Finally, such a reasonably reliable ABM system would add protection of our population against the improbable but possible accidental launch of an intercontinental missile by any one of the nuclear powers.

After a detailed review of all these considerations, we have decided to go forward with this Chinese-oriented ABM deployment, and we will begin actual production of such a system at the end of this year.

In reaching this decision, I want to emphasize that it contains two possible dangers—and we should guard carefully against each.

The first danger is that we may psychologically lapse into the old oversimplification about the adequacy of nuclear power. The simple truth is that nuclear weapons can serve to deter only a narrow range of threats. This ABM deployment will strengthen our defensive posture—and will enhance the effectiveness of our land-based ICBM offensive forces. But the independent nations of Asia must realize that these benefits are no substitute for their maintaining, and where necessary strengthening, their own conventional forces in order to deal with the more likely threats to the security of the region.

The second danger is also psychological. There is a kind of mad momentum intrinsic to the development of all new nuclear weaponry. If a weapon system works—and works well—there is strong pressure from many directions to procure and deploy the weapon out of all proportion to the prudent level required.

The danger in deploying this relatively light and reliable Chinese-oriented ABM system is going to be that pressures will develop to expand it into a heavy Soviet-oriented ABM system.

We must resist that temptation firmly—not because we can for a moment afford to relax our vigilance against a possible Soviet first strike—but precisely because our greatest deterrent against such a strike is not a massive, costly, but highly penetrable ABM shield, but rather a fully credible offensive assured destruction capability.

The so-called heavy ABM shield—at the present state of technology—would in effect be no adequate shield at all against a Soviet attack, but rather a strong inducement for the Soviets to vastly increase their own offensive forces. That, as I have pointed out, would make it necessary for us to respond in turn—and so the arms race would rush hopelessly on to no sensible purpose on either side.

Let me emphasize—and I cannot do so too strongly—that our decision to go ahead with a *limited* ABM deployment in no way indicates that we feel an agreement with the Soviet Union on the limitation of strategic nuclear offensive and defensive forces is any the less urgent or desirable.

The road leading from the stone ax to the ICBM—though it may have been more than a million years in the building—seems to have run in a single direction.

If one is inclined to be cynical, one might conclude that man's history seems to be characterized not so much by consistent periods of peace, occasionally punctuated by warfare; but rather by persistent outbreaks of warfare, wearily put aside from time to time by periods of exhaustion and recovery —that parade under the name of peace.

I do not view man's history with that degree of cynicism, but I do believe that man's wisdom in avoiding war is often surpassed by his folly in promoting it.

However foolish unlimited war may have been in the past, it is now no longer merely foolish, but suicidal as well.

It is said that nothing can prevent a man from suicide if he is sufficiently determined to commit it.

The question is: What is our determination in an era when unlimited war will mean the death of hundreds of millions— and the possible genetic impairment of a million generations to follow?

Man is clearly a compound of folly and wisdom—and history is clearly a consequence of the admixture of those two contradictory traits.

History has placed our particular lives in an era when the consequences of human folly are waxing more and more catastrophic in the matters of war and peace.

In the end, the root of man's security does not lie in his weaponry.

In the end, the root of man's security lies in his mind.

What the world requires in its twenty-second year of the Atomic Age is not a new race toward armament.

What the world requires in its twenty-second year of the Atomic Age is a new race toward reasonableness.

We had better all run that race.

Not merely we the administrators, but we the people.

Thank you, and good afternoon.

•   •   •

*Excerpt from the Defense Posture Statement of Secretary of Defense Robert S. McNamara, prepared January 22, 1968.*

Each year in presenting our projections of the strategic nuclear threat to the United States, I have cautioned that while we have reasonably high confidence in our estimates for the closer-in period, our estimates for the most distant years are subject to considerable uncertainty. This is still the case with regard to our current projections. The estimates through 1969 are reasonably firm. Beyond that point they become progressively less firm, especially where they deal with the period beyond the production and deployment lead times of the weapons systems involved.

## 1. The Soviet Strategic Offensive-Defensive Forces

### a. Intercontinental Ballistic Missiles

Over the past year, the Soviets have continued their build-up of hardened and dispersed land-based missiles. We estimate that as of October 1, 1967, they had a total of 720 ICBM launchers operational compared to 340 a year earlier. We believe that Soviet ICBM force will continue to grow over the next few years, but at a considerably slower rate than in the recent past.

As you may recall, I announced last November that the Soviets were intensively testing what we believe to be a Fractional Orbital Bombardment System (FOBS). Such a system—which is really an ICBM of different trajectory—could be launched on a very low trajectory across the northern approaches of the United States, thus reducing the possibility of timely detection by the Ballistic Missile Early Warning System (BMEWS); or, alternatively, around the southern approaches which are not covered by BMEWS. In either event, the weapon would not have a very high order of accuracy and would have to pay a heavy penalty in payload. It would, therefore, be useful primarily against soft targets. Although years ago we considered and rejected such a system for our own use, the Soviets may believe it to be useful in a surprise nuclear strike against our bomber bases or as a penetration tactic against ABM systems.

### b. Antiballistic Missile Defense

Last year I noted that in addition to the Galosh system around Moscow, the Soviets were deploying another type of defensive system elsewhere in the Soviet Union. I cautioned, however, that the weight of the evidence at the time suggested that this system was not intended primarily for antiballistic missile defense. Now I can tell you that the majority of our intelligence community no longer believes that this so-called "Tallinn" system (which is being deployed across the northwestern approaches to the Soviet Union and in several other places) has any significant ABM capability. This system is apparently designed for use within the atmosphere, most likely against an aerodynamic rather than a ballistic missile threat.

Although construction of the Galosh ABM system around Moscow is proceeding at a moderate pace, no effort has been made during the last year to expand that system or extend it to other cities. It is the consensus of the intelligence community that this system could provide a limited defense of the Moscow area but that it could be seriously degraded by sophisticated penetration aids. Nevertheless, knowing what we do about past Soviet predilections for defensive systems, we must, for the time being, plan our forces on the assumption that they will have deployed some sort of an ABM system around their major cities by the early 1970s.

### 2. Red Chinese Nuclear Threat

Our current estimates of the Red Chinese nuclear threat are essentially the same as those I presented here last year. The Chinese have the technical and industrial capabilities required for the deployment of ballistic missiles, and we believe that they are making an intensive effort to develop a medium-range missile. We estimate that the first of these missiles could be deployed as early as 1967–68 and that by the mid-seventies they could have a modest force operational.

With regard to ICBMs, we continue to believe that the Chinese nuclear weapons and ballistic missile development programs are being pursued with a high priority. However, it is now clear that they failed to conduct either a space or a long-range ballistic missile launching before the end of 1967, as we thought possible last year. We still believe such a launching could be made on relatively short notice. In any event, our estimate last year that it appeared unlikely the Chinese could achieve an IOC with an ICBM before the early 1970s, or deploy a significant number of operational ICBMs before the mid-seventies, still holds. And, of course, those ICBMs would not have a very high degree of reliability, speed of response or protection against attack.

The Red Chinese also have several types of aircraft which could carry nuclear weapons, but most of them have a limited operational radius and none have an intercontinental radius. It is highly unlikely on the basis of cost alone that they would undertake the development, production and deployment of an intercontinental bomber force. If they chose to do so, it would take them a decade or more before they could deploy such a force.

There are two major issues this year in the damage limitation portion of the strategic forces program. The first concerns the deployment of an antiballistic missile defense.

## 1. Antiballistic Missile Defense

Last year I presented to you in considerable detail our analysis of the antiballistic missile defense issue. I described the three major purposes for which we might want to deploy an ABM system, the kinds of radars and missiles which would be involved, the technical uncertainties which still remained to be resolved, and the costs and benefits of some of the alternative deployments. With regard to the three purposes, I concluded that:

1. The deployment of an ABM defense for Minuteman might offer a partial substitute for the further expansion of our offensive forces in the event the greater-than-expected Soviet threat began to emerge.

2. The deployment of an austere ABM defense against a Red Chinese ICBM threat might offer a high degree of protection to the entire nation, at least through the 1970s.

3. The deployment of an ABM defense for the protection of our cities against the kind of heavy, sophisticated, missile

attack the Soviets could launch in the 1970s would almost surely cause them to react by increasing the capabilities of their offensive forces, thus leaving us in essentially the same position we were before.

Further study of this issue during the last year has served to confirm these conclusions. Since I have already touched on the first purpose in connection with the analysis of our assured destruction capabilities against the greater-than-expected Soviet threat, I will limit my discussion at this point to the other two purposes.

### a. Defense against the Red Chinese nuclear threat

As I noted earlier, there is mounting evidence that the Red Chinese are devoting very substantial resources to the development of both nuclear warheads and missile delivery systems. Within a period of thirty-nine months, they detonated seven nuclear devices. The first, in October, 1964, was an all U-235 fission test with a low yield; the second, in May, 1965, was a similar test with a low-intermediate yield. In May, 1966, they detonated their first device involving thermonuclear material. Then, in October, 1966, they tested their first missile-delivered device with a low-yield fission warhead, thus demonstrating sufficient engineering skill to conduct a missile-warhead systems test. In December, 1966, they detonated their second device involving thermonuclear material. In June, 1967, they detonated a device with a yield of a few megatons dropped from an airplane. Finally, last December, they detonated another device, but this test was apparently a partial failure.

These seven nuclear tests, taken together with their continuing work on surface-to-surface missiles, lead us to believe that they are moving ahead with the development of an ICBM. Indeed, if their programs proceed at the present pace, they could have a modest force of ICBMs by the mid-1970s.

In the light of this progress in nuclear weapons and missile delivery systems, it seemed both prudent and feasible to us last September to initiate the deployment of an austere Chinese-oriented ABM defense. We knew from our continuing study of this system that it could be deployed at an investment cost of about $5 billion, and could be highly effective against the kind of threat a Chinese force might pose in the 1970s.

As presently defined, the Sentinel ABM system, that is, the

system specifically designed against the Chinese threat, would consist of perimeter acquisition radars (PARs), missile site radars (MSRs), long-range Spartan area-defense missiles and, later, some Sprint local-defense missiles for certain special purposes. The effectiveness of this deployment in reducing U.S. fatalities from a Red Chinese attack in the 1970s is shown in Table 1.

Table 1. U.S. Fatalities from a Chinese First Strike, 1970s

| | NUMBER OF CHINESE ICBMs | | |
|---|---|---|---|
| U.S. fatalities (in millions): | X | 2.5X | 7.5X |
| Without Sentinel | 7 | 11 | 15 |
| With Sentinel | ($^1$) | ($^1$) | 1 |

[1] Fewer than 1,000,000 U.S. dead, with some probability of no deaths.

It is apparent from the foregoing table that the Sentinel system, facing a relatively "primitive" attack, could probably hold U.S. fatalities below one million. Obviously, if and when the Chinese ICBM force grows, quantitatively and qualitatively, beyond the levels shown in the foregoing table, additions and improvements would probably have to be made in the Sentinel system. We believe, however, that for relatively modest additional outlays the system could be improved so as to limit the Chinese damage potential to low levels into the mid-1980s. The Sentinel system would also have a number of other advantages. It would provide an additional indication to the people of Asia that we intend to support them against nuclear blackmail from China, and thus help to convince the nonnuclear countries that acquisition of their own nuclear weapons is not required for their security. Furthermore, this initial deployment would serve as a foundation to which we could add a defense for our Minuteman force if that later becomes desirable. Finally, it could protect our population against the improbable, but possible, accidental launch of a few ICBMs by any one of the nuclear powers.

*b. Deployment of Nike-X for defense of our cities against Soviet attack*

Nothing has occurred during the last year to change my

conviction that the deployment of the Nike-X system for the defense of our cities against a Soviet attack would, under present circumstances, be a futile waste of our resources. I believe it is clear from my earlier discussion of the trends in the nature of the threat, as evaluated by our intelligence community, that the Soviets are determined to maintain a nuclear deterrent against the United States. If this is true, as I believe it is, any attempt on our part to reduce their assured destruction capability below what they might consider necessary to deter us would simply cause them to respond with an offsetting increase in their offensive forces. It is precisely this process of action and reaction upon which the arms race feeds, at great cost to both sides and benefit to neither. This point is illustrated in Table 2, page 250, which is based on nuclear strike capabilities as they might be viewed by the potential adversaries.

"Posture A" is a light defense against a Soviet missile attack on our cities. It consists of an area defense of the entire continental United States, providing redundant (overlapping) coverage of key target areas, and, in addition, a relatively low-density Sprint defense of 25 cities to provide some protection against those warheads which get through the area defense. "Posture B" is a heavier defense with the same area coverage, but with much greater sophistication in its electronics and a higher-density Sprint defense for 52 cities.

Postures A and B would also require some improvement in our defense against manned-bomber attack in order to preclude the Soviets from undercutting the ABM defense; we would also want to expand and improve our antisubmarine-warfare forces to help defend against Soviet missile-launching submarines. The "current" estimates of the investment cost of the total "damage-limiting" package are at least $13 billion for posture A and at least $22 billion for posture B. On the basis of past experience, however, actual costs would more likely be $40 billion by the time the system had been completed.

Cost, however, is not the problem. If we could actually build and deploy a genuinely impenetrable shield over the United States, we would be willing to spend $40 billion. But, if after spending these tens of billions of dollars, we could still expect to find ourselves in a position where a Soviet attack could inflict unacceptable damage on our population because of their response to our defensive efforts, I do not see how we

## Table 2. Numbers of Fatalities in an All-Out Strategic Exchange, Mid-1970s[1]
### (in millions)

| U.S. program | Soviet response | Soviets strike 1st against military and city targets, United States retaliates against cities | | United States strikes 1st at military targets, Soviets retaliate against U.S. cities, United States retaliates against Soviet cities | |
|---|---|---|---|---|---|
| | | U.S. fatalities | Soviet fatalities | U.S. fatalities | Soviet fatalities |
| No ABM | None[1] | 120 | 120 | 120 | 80 |
| Sentinel | None | 100 | 120 | 90 | 80 |
| | Pen-Aids | 120 | 120 | 110 | 80 |
| Posture A | None | 40 | 120 | 10 | 80 |
| | MIRV, Pen-Aids | 110 | 120 | 60 | 80 |
| | Plus mobile ICBMs | 110 | 120 | 90 | 80 |
| Posture B | None | 20 | 120 | 10 | 80 |
| | MIRV, Pen-Aids | 70 | 120 | 40 | 80 |
| | Plus 550 mobile ICBMs | 100 | 120 | 90 | 80 |

[1] At fatality levels approximating 100,000,000 or more, differences of 10 to 20,000,000 in the calculated results are less than the margin of error in the estimates.

would have really improved our security or freedom of action. And neither can I see how the Soviets will have improved their security and freedom of action if after all their additional expenditures for offensive and defensive systems, we can still inflict unacceptable damage on them, even after absorbing their first strike. For this reason we have come to the conclusion that both sides would be far better off if we can reach an agreement on the limitation of all strategic nuclear forces, including ABMs.

In any event, there is no point whatever in our responding to a massive ABM deployment on their part with a massive ABM deployment of our own. Instead, we should act realistically and further strengthen our offensive forces, if and when necessary, to preserve our "assured destruction" capability.

• • •

*Excerpt from the Defense Posture Statement, relating to the ABM, of Secretary of Defense Clark M. Clifford, prepared January 15, 1969.*

In the Soviet strategic posture, the large increase in deployments of hardened, land-based ICBMs has been the most significant development of the past year; we project that by the end of 1969 they will have deployed over 1,000 intercontinental ballistic missiles. This advance represents the coming to fruition of a long-term program, however, and by itself probably does not represent any shift in over-all policy. Soviet strategic aircraft and strategic missile-firing submarine capabilities continue to lag considerably behind ours. It is also noteworthy that during 1968 work on the only positively identified Soviet ABM complex, that at Moscow, slowed down—apparently because of technical difficulties, rising costs and system inefficiencies. However, ABM research and development is still at a high level of activity.

It is quite apparent from the foregoing review of the threat that the Soviet Union is moving vigorously to catch up with the United States at least in *numbers* of strategic missiles— both land-based and sea-based. But it is also apparent that they are still well behind us in advanced missile technology— accuracy, MIRVs and penetration aids. Indeed, their new solid-fuel ICBM appears to be no better than our earliest

Minuteman missiles, first deployed in FY 1963. Their new ballistic missile submarine is probably most comparable to our earliest Polaris submarines, which first became operational about a decade ago. Their Galosh ABM system resembles in certain important respects the Nike-Zeus system, which we abandoned years ago because of its limited effectiveness. Their Bison and Bear long-range bombers are distinctly inferior to our B–52s, and we have long since eliminated from our forces the B–47s, which were clearly superior to their Badger medium bombers.

Accordingly, it is reasonable to conclude that even if the Soviets attempt to match us in numbers of strategic missiles we shall continue to have, as far into the future as we can now discern, a very substantial qualitative lead and a distinct superiority in the numbers of deliverable weapons and the over-all combat effectiveness of our strategic offensive forces.

We remain convinced, however, that insofar as the Soviet threat is concerned we should continue to give first priority in the allocation of available resources to the primary objective of our strategic forces, namely, "assured destruction." Until technology progresses to the point where an effective ABM defense against the Soviet threat becomes feasible, our major hope for limiting damage if a nuclear war occurs is that it can be stopped short of an all-out attack on our cities. We try to bring this about by providing our forces with characteristics that will permit them to be used effectively in a limited and controlled retaliation as well as for "assured destruction," thereby being prepared for any type of Soviet attack.

We also remain convinced that we must explore with the utmost diligence every avenue of negotiation which might lead to a meaningful and verifiable agreement on the limitation of strategic forces—both offensive and defensive. We stand on the eve of a new round in the armaments race with the Soviet Union, a race which will contribute nothing to the real security of either side while increasing substantially the already great defense burdens of both. Conversely, an appropriately designed and safeguarded limitation agreement can maintain our deterrent posture at present levels and enhance the stability of the strategic balance. The Soviet incursion into Czechoslovakia made the opening of talks on this matter inappropriate last year. It is our hope that the Soviet leaders will re-establish an atmosphere in which talks can begin.

For active defense we are deploying the Sentinel system. This system, as noted earlier, is specifically oriented to the potential Chinese Communist ICBM threat. It is being deployed in such a manner as to provide a thin defense over the entire nation, including Hawaii and Alaska. The system approved for deployment is essentially the same as that presented to the Congress last year.

The program is moving forward on schedule, except for some small delays which will be made up before the planned full operational date. Such relatively minor modifications in the schedule must be expected in a system as widespread and complex as the Sentinel. Delays in the acquisition of sites, development difficulties and production problems will inevitably require adjustments in the deployment schedule as we move forward with the program. But we believe the final deployment completion date can be met.

The development of all five major components making up the Sentinel system is proceeding on schedule. The PAR, which is used for long-range surveillance, acquisition and tracking, is a state-of-the-art, low-frequency, phased-array radar and no development prototype is deemed necessary. Since its performance can be simulated by a radar already on Kwajalein, where the full systems tests will be conducted, the first one will be built directly at an operational site. The radar is still in the design stage.

The first MSR, which is used both for tracking the target and the defending missile, has completed factory tests and is now being tested at Kwajalein.

The Sprint missile, which is designed to attack incoming warheads after the atmosphere has helped to separate out the accompanying decoys, chaff, etc., is in the test-firing state. By and large, this test program is proceeding satisfactorily. Indeed, a very high proportion of the last several flights were successful.

The Spartan missile, which will be used for area defense, is in the flight test stage at Kwajalein, and these tests, too, are proceeding satisfactorily.

The fifth major component, the data-processing system, is being installed at the contractor's plant and is partially operational. A second system is being installed at Kwajalein for use in the full systems tests.

For the Sentinel system, alone, we have included in the FY

1970 Budget a total of about $1,788 million: $335 million for Research and Development; $736 million for Procurement; $647 million for Construction; and $70 million for Operations. The FY 1969 Budget provides a total of $962 million— $311 million for Research and Development; $346 million for Procurement; $266 million for Construction; and $39 million for Operations. (Funds for ABM warhead development and production are included in the AEC budget.)

• • •

*Text of President Nixon's announcement concerning the Sentinel antiballistic missile system, issued in advance of his White House press conference on March 14, 1969. In this announcement President Nixon indicated a modification of the Johnson Administration's ABM system.*

Immediately after assuming office, I requested the Secretary of Defense to review the program initiated by the last Administration to deploy the Sentinel ballistic missile defense system.

The Department of Defense presented a full statement of the alternatives at the last two meetings of the National Security Council.

These alternatives were reviewed there in the light of the security requirements of the United States, and of their probable impact on East-West relations, with particular reference to the prospects for strategic arms negotiations.

After carefully considering the alternatives, I have reached the following conclusions:

1. The concept on which the Sentinel program of the previous Administration was based should be substantially modified.

2. The safety of our country requires that we should proceed now with the development and construction of the new system in a carefully phased program.

3. This program will be reviewed annually from the point of view of (a) technical developments, (b) the threat, (c) the diplomatic context including any talks on arms limitation.

The modified system has been designed so that its defensive intent is unmistakable. It will be implemented not according to some fixed, theoretical schedule, but in a manner clearly related to our periodic analysis of the threat.

The first deployment covers two missile sites; the first of these will not be completed before 1973. Any further delay would set this date back by at least two additional years.

The program for fiscal year 1970 is the minimum necessary to maintain the security of our nation.

This measured deployment is designed to fulfill three objectives:

1. Protection of our land-based retaliatory forces against a direct attack by the Soviet Union.

2. Defense of the American people against the kind of nuclear attack which Communist China is likely to be able to mount within the decade.

3. Protection against the possibility of accidental attacks from any source.

In the review leading up to this decision, we considered three possible options in addition to this program:

• A deployment which would attempt to defend U.S. cities against an attempt by the Soviet Union.

• A continuation of the Sentinel program approved by the previous Administration.

• An indefinite postponement of deployment while continuing research and development.

I rejected these options for the following reasons:

Although every instinct motivates me to provide the American people with complete protection against a major nuclear attack, it is not now within our power to do so.

The heaviest defense system we considered, one designed to protect our major cities, still could not prevent a catastrophic level of U.S. fatalities from a deliberate all-out Soviet attack. And it might look to an opponent like the prelude to an offensive strategy threatening the Soviet deterrent.

The Sentinel system approved by the previous Administration provided more capabilities for the defense of cities than the program I am recommending, but it did not provide protection against some threats to our retaliatory forces which have developed subsequently.

Also, the Sentinel system had the disadvantage that it could be misinterpreted as the first step toward the construction of a heavy system.

Giving up all construction of missile defense poses too many risks. Research and development does not supply the answer to many technical issues that only operational experience can provide.

The Soviet Union has engaged in a build-up of its strategic forces larger than envisaged in 1967 when the decision to deploy Sentinel was made. The following is illustrative of recent Soviet activity:

1. The Soviets have already deployed an ABM system which protects to some degree a wide area centered around Moscow. We will not have a comparable capability for over four years.

We believe the Soviet Union is continuing their ABM development, directed either toward improving this initial system, or more likely, making substantially better second-generation ABM components.

2. The Soviet Union is continuing the deployment of very large missiles with warheads capable of destroying our hardened Minuteman forces.

3. The Soviet Union has also been substantially increasing the size of their submarine-launched ballistic missile force.

4. The Soviets appear to be developing a semiorbital nuclear weapon system.

In addition to these developments, the Chinese threat against our population, as well as the danger of an accidental attack, cannot be ignored.

By approving this system, it is possible to reduce U.S. fatalities to a minimal level in the event of a Chinese nuclear attack in the 1970s, or in an accidental attack from any source. No President with the responsibility for the lives and security for the American people could fail to provide this protection.

The gravest responsibility which I bear as President of the United States is for the security of the nation. Our nuclear forces defend not only ourselves but our allies as well.

The imperative that our nuclear deterrent remain secure beyond any possible doubt requires that the U.S. must take steps now to insure that our strategic retaliatory forces will not become vulnerable to a Soviet attack.

Modern technology provides several choices in seeking to insure the survival of our retaliatory forces.

First, we could increase the number of sea- and land-based missiles and bombers. I have ruled out this course because it provides only marginal improvement of our deterrent, while it could be misinterpreted by Soviets as an attempt to threaten their deterrent. It would therefore stimulate an arms race.

A second option is to harden further our ballistic missile forces by putting them in more strongly reinforced underground silos. But our studies show that hardening by itself is not adequate protection against foreseeable advances in the accuracy of Soviet offensive forces.

The third option was to begin a measured construction on an active defense of our retaliatory forces.

I have chosen the third option.

The system will use components previously developed for the Sentinel system. However, the deployment will be changed to reflect the new concept.

We will provide for local defense of selected Minuteman missile sites and an area defense designed to protect our bomber bases and our command-and-control authorities.

In addition, this new system will provide a defense of the continental United States against an accidental attack and will provide substantial protection against the kind of attack which the Chinese Communists may be capable of launching throughout the 1970s.

This deployment will not require us to place missile and radar sites close to our major cities.

The present estimate is that the total cost of installing this system will be $6–$7 billion.

However, because of the deliberate pace of the deployment, budgetary requests for the coming year can be substantially less—by about one half—than those asked for by the previous Administration for the Sentinel system.

In making this decision, I have been mindful of my pledge to make every effort to move from an era of confrontation to an era of negotiation.

The program I am recommending is based on a careful assessment of the developing Soviet and Chinese threats. I have directed the President's Foreign Intelligence Advisory Board—a nonpartisan group of distinguished private citizens—to make a yearly assessment of the threat which will supplement our regular intelligence assessment.

Each phase of the deployment will be reviewed to ensure that we are doing as much as necessary but no more than that required by the threat existing at that time.

Moreover, we will take maximum advantage of the information gathered from the initial deployment in designing the later phases of the program.

Since our deployment is to be closely related to the threat, it is subject to modification as the threat changes, either through negotiations or through unilateral actions by the Soviet Union or Communist China.

The program is not provocative. The Soviet retaliatory capability is not affected by our decision. The capability for surprise attack against our strategic forces is reduced.

In other words, our program provides an incentive for a responsible Soviet weapons policy and for the avoidance of spiraling U.S. and Soviet strategic arms budgets.

I have taken cognizance of the view that beginning construction of a U.S. ballistic missile defense would complicate an agreement on strategic arms with the Soviet Union.

I do not believe that the evidence of the recent past bears out this contention. The Soviet interest in strategic talks was not deterred by the decision of the previous Administration to deploy the Sentinel ABM system—in fact, it was formally announced shortly afterward.

I believe that the modifications we have made in the previous program will give the Soviet Union even less reason to view our defense effort as an obstacle to talks.

Moreover, I wish to emphasize that in any arms limitation talks with the Soviet Union the United States will be fully prepared to discuss limitation on defensive as well as offensive weapons systems.

The question of ABM involves a complex combination of many factors:

· Numerous, highly technical, often conflicting judgments.
· The costs.
· The relationship to prospects for reaching an agreement on limiting nuclear arms.
· The moral implications the deployment of a ballistic missile defense system has for many Americans.
· The impact of the decision on the security of the United States in this perilous age of nuclear arms.

I have weighed all these factors. I am deeply sympathetic to the concerns of private citizens and members of Congress that we do only that which is necessary for national security.

This is why I am recommending a minimum program

essential for our security. It is my duty as President to make certain that we do no less.

•   •   •

*Excerpt from the Defense Posture Report of Secretary of Defense Melvin R. Laird, relating to the ABM, delivered to the Senate Committee on Armed Services, March 19, 1969.*

President Nixon last Friday explained the reasons why we have reached the conclusion that we must go ahead with the development and deployment of a ballistic missile defense system. He pointed out that the system now being proposed is based on a different concept than the Sentinel system approved by the preceding Administration. The modified ABM system has been designed so that its defensive intent is unmistakable. Moreover, it will be deployed in a manner clearly related to the emerging threat, rather than on the basis of some fixed schedule based on theoretical assumptions.

In reviewing this program, we examined all the major alternatives:

1. A deployment which would defend U.S. cities against a Soviet attack.
2. No deployment at all, but a continuation of research and development.
3. The continuation of the Sentinel program approved by the preceding Administration.
4. The deployment of a modified system which would fulfill three objectives:

   a. Defense of our land-based strategic offensive forces against a first strike by the Soviet Union.
   b. Protection of the American people against the kind of nuclear attack which Communist China is likely to be able to mount within the decade.
   c. Defense of the nation against an accidental or small attack from any source.

*Alternative 1*

We rejected the first alternative, not because we do not want to provide complete protection for the American people against a major Soviet attack, but rather because it is not now in our power to do so. The heaviest defense system we considered in our review, one designed to protect our major cities, could still not prevent a catastrophic level of U.S. fatalities in the event of a deliberate all-out Soviet attack. And such a deployment might look like the prelude to an offensive strategy designed to undercut the Soviet deterrent.

## Alternative 2

We rejected the second alternative (no deployment) because it left us with no option to provide defense for our deterrent on the schedule that might be required by the Soviet threat if we do not reach an agreement with the Soviets on limiting strategic forces. The Soviet Union is increasing its offensive forces at a considerably faster rate than was envisaged in 1967 when the decision to deploy Sentinel was made.

As you will recall, former Secretary Clark Clifford, in his Posture Statement in January, pointed out that in a period of a little more than two years the Soviets had increased their number of operational ICBM launchers more than threefold, from 250 in mid-1966 to 896 by September 1, 1968. As of today, the Soviets have in being and under construction more ICBM launchers than the 1,048 possessed by the United States.

Moreover, the Chinese threat against our population, as well as the danger of an accidental or small attack from some other source, cannot be ignored. Since it is within our power to reduce U.S. fatalities to a minimum level or to prevent them altogether in the event of Chinese attacks or small attacks from other nations, we must act to do so.

## Alternative 3

We rejected the third alternative (deployment of the Sentinel system approved by the preceding Administration) because it would not provide sufficient protection against the emerging Soviet threat to our strategic offensive forces. (These emerging threats include the rapid build-up in the Soviet submarine-launched ballistic missile force, their development of a Fractional Orbital Bombardment System (FOBS), and their likely deployment of large ICBMs with multiple warheads. Also, the original Sentinel plan could be misinterpreted as—and could in fact have been—a first step toward the construction of a heavy system for the defense of our cities.

## Alternative 4

I believe we can all agree that our nuclear deterrent must be made as secure as is technically and economically feasible. Our nuclear forces defend not only ourselves but our allies. Accordingly, we must take whatever steps are practicable to ensure that our strategic retaliatory forces can survive a Soviet attack.

After examining the available alternatives, we have concluded that a combination of approaches provides the most realistic means of safeguarding our retaliatory capability.

This combination consists of beginning a measured deployment of an active defense of our retaliatory forces, structured to expand as circumstances may dictate, and preserving the option, if we later find it necessary, to harden further our land-based missiles. The combination is necessary because our studies show that hardening alone would not provide adequate protection against foreseeable advances in the accuracy of Soviet missiles.

The ABM defense system we now propose to deploy will use components previously developed for Sentinel. However, these components will be deployed in such a way as to provide:

1. A local defense of the Minuteman missile silos.

2. Early-warning and area defense of our bomber bases and command-and-control system.

3. A defense of the continental United States against the kind of attack which the Chinese Communists may be able to launch in the mid-1970s.

4. Protection against an accidental or small attack from any source.

This system will not require the emplacement of missiles or radars in or near our major cities, except for the protection of the National Command Authority in Washington, D.C.

Mr. Packard will discuss in greater detail the options for full deployment of the system.

Our current plan includes a total of fourteen sites, compared with seventeen sites in the previous plan. Twelve of the sites are in the continental United States. The other two, Alaska and Hawaii, have been included as an option. The Chicago, New York and Salt Lake City sites have been eliminated. Thus far only the first two sites—Grand Forks Air Force Base and Malmstrom Air Force Base—have been approved for deployment, each with one four-face Missile Site Radar (MSR), one one-face Perimeter Acquisition Radar (PAR), standard Spartans and Sprints. The schedule on which the remaining sites will be deployed will be determined year by year in step with the emergence of the threat.

The new system, if fully deployed (not including the option for Alaska and Hawaii), would provide 12 MSRs with 48 faces instead of 17 MSRs with 38 faces; and 7 PARs with 11 faces instead of 6 PARs with 6 faces. The increase in PAR capability is required to provide all-round radar coverage of the U.S., including the seaward approaches. The latter is particularly important for the defense of our deterrent forces against the Soviet SLBM threat. Our present early-warning systems do not provide adequate coverage of the seaward approaches, and our alert bombers may be caught on their bases by a surprise SLBM attack. Furthermore, the Soviets may configure their SLBMs for depressed-trajectory launch. In that case, the total time to target might be considerably less than the fifteen minutes required for a normal high-trajectory launch. Since our alert bomber forces require fifteen minutes from warning to get off their bases, we must also be able to intercept at least the first salvo of SLBMs, and this the proposed new system is designed to do.

An improved, longer-range Spartan is now under development. If we later find that this missile promises sufficient advantage to warrant proceeding further, we will substitute some improved Spartans for the standard Spartan. The longer-range Spartan would give us better coverage of the entire continental United States.

All the ABM sites would be equipped with some Sprints. The four sites to be located in the Minuteman fields (Grand Forks, Malmstrom, Whiteman and Warren) would have a considerably larger number than the others.

In summary, the proposed system would work as follows:

1. The Spartan batteries at each of the twelve locations would provide area protection against the early Chinese Communist ICBM threat.

2. The PARs would provide surveillance and tracking against ICBMs, FOBS and SLBMs.

3. The PARs and MSRs would give extra warning, and the Spartans and Sprints some extra protection, to the alert bomber force.

4. The system as a whole would protect the ABM sites themselves, and some of the bomber bases, against an FOBS attack.

5. The four ABM sites located in the Minuteman fields would provide some initial protection (and the option for additional protection) to a portion of our Minuteman force.

6. The site at Washington, D.C., would give protection to the National Command Authority against a moderately heavy attack.

The investment cost (procurement and construction) of the new system, if fully deployed, would range from $6 billion to a little over $7 billion, depending on the options that are exercised. This is somewhat more than the cost estimates of the Sentinel system proposed by the preceding Administration. The modified system, however, provides additional capabilities. Because the new system would be deployed at a much more deliberate pace, budgetary requirements in FY 1970 will be about one-half that proposed in the original budget—about $900 million compared with about $1.8 billion.

•    •    •

*Excerpt from the statement of Secretary of Defense Melvin R. Laird on the ABM to the Senate Committee on Armed Services, delivered March 20, 1969.*

The antimissile defense question is certainly one of the most important decisions we have faced in modern times because it affects the safety and security of the American people.

Peace is not only our goal, Mr. Chairman. It is our solemn responsibility. The Safeguard system which President Nixon announced last week is designed to contribute toward peace.

It is not an escalation of the arms race.

It is not a stumbling block to arms limitation talks.

Safeguard is a building block for peace.

The purpose of my remarks is to explain why we hold these views and why we urge the Congress to support the President's decision. Deputy Secretary David Packard will discuss the Safeguard program and the nature of the threat in greater detail upon the conclusion of my remarks.

*Safeguard—Not an Escalation of the Arms Race*

The modified ABM system has been designed so that its defensive intent is unmistakable. It is not an escalation of the arms race. The original Sentinel plan could have been interpreted as a first step toward the construction of a heavy system toward the defense of our cities. Indeed, it could have been used for that purpose.

The Safeguard system—both in fact and in appearance—is a protection for our retaliatory forces. It is an essential safeguard for United States interests because of the nature of the threat we face from the Soviet Union and Red China.

The potential threat from the Soviet Union lies in the growing force of missiles which could destroy a portion of our own deterrent, or retaliatory, forces. We cannot stop a massive Soviet attack on our cities; technically we just don't know how. We must rely on deterrence to insure that nuclear war doesn't start in the first place. In order to deter an attack we must be positive—and the Soviet Government must be positive—that a substantial number of our long-range missiles and bombers will survive any attack and then destroy the attacker as a modern society. The Soviet Union today is building at a rapid rate the kinds of weapons which could be used to erode our essential deterrent force.

They are installing many SS-9 intercontinental ballistic missiles (ICBMs)—a large and accurate weapon. With improvements in accuracy and a continued increase in numbers, the Soviet missile force could gain real effectiveness against our Minuteman. The Soviets also can build at a rate of one per month nuclear submarines which could come close to our shores and attack at short range many of our missiles and bomber bases. They are also working hard on FOBS, a Fractional Orbital Bombardment System, also designed to reduce the warning time to our bombers so that they will not have sufficient time to become airborne.

Communist China is another potential threat to us. It cannot threaten our retaliatory weapons systems for many years, but by the mid-1970s China could pose a threat to our people and our property. The government of Communist China is devoting an astonishing portion of its limited national resources to the development of nuclear weapons and ICBMs.

The Safeguard system proposed by President Nixon is carefully designed to meet these threats adequately without overreacting.

Continuing research and development without any initial deployment would leave us with no option to provide defense for our deterrent on the schedule that might be required by the Soviet threat if we do not reach an agreement with the Soviets on limiting strategic forces.

Under the new concept of phased and measured installation, we give added insurance that our ballistic missile defense will be adequate but not wasteful. If further threats do not develop, we can stop the installation with the two sites that will be constructed under Phase 1 of our program. If either the Soviet or Chinese threat continues to grow, we can meet the threat with added installations.

Our obviously thin protection of cities and the added protection of our deterrent forces will require no reaction at all from the Soviet Union—providing the Soviet Union has a responsible, *deterrent* nuclear war policy, as we do.

## Safeguard—Not a Stumbling Block to Arms-Limiting Talks

Mr. Chairman, the Safeguard system is not a stumbling block to arms-limiting talks with the Soviet Union. On the contrary; under the type of deployment we have chosen the Soviet Union is given an added incentive to negotiate a meaningful agreement on limitation of both offensive and defensive weapons. First, the modified ABM program would show the Soviets that we are quite serious about protecting our deterrent forces—about assuring all enemies that they cannot achieve an effective, low-risk first strike against the United States. Second, it would show the Soviets that we are not preparing for a low-risk attack on them and that it is worthwhile to negotiate limits on strategic arms.

Under the proposed Safeguard program even the first two installations will not be operating before 1973. This gives ample time for the two countries to negotiate agreements on these and other weapons. Thus the modified ABM opens the door wider to mutual arms control.

But if the Soviets should slam the door on an agreement,

the modified ABM would permit us to continue steps toward protection of our retaliatory forces. This option would be more important than ever before, because we would have to assume that a Soviet rejection of meaningful negotiations would demonstrate a Soviet determination to continue to build toward a low-risk first-strike force.

The public Soviet reaction to the President's announcement of a week ago is encouraging, however. The Soviet press indicates that the Soviet Government correctly views the modified ABM as a purely defensive weapon.

### Safeguard—A Building Block for Peace

Mr. Chairman, the system we are proposing is the best kind of people protection because it strengthens our ability to deter nuclear war. To the extent that it does that, it can truly be called a building block for peace.

Our studies showed that while we could not defend our cities effectively against a massive attack—only a small one— we could defend our Minuteman missiles and bombers to a significant degree against any size of threat. The problems here are different. In defending cities, our minimum objective must be to intercept all incoming warheads. If one gets through, the city and most of its people are destroyed. But in the case of our Minuteman missiles and our alert bombers we do not have to preserve every one of them. We must preserve only a certain number—the minimum essential number— enough to guarantee immense destruction in the aggressor's own country.

This, the Safeguard antiballistic missile system has the capability to provide—both for the immediate threat and for whatever threat emerges in the decade of the 1970s.

In providing a safeguard for our retaliatory forces under the program we have recommended, we provide ourselves with the option of protecting our people against the Communist Chinese ICBM threat, should it materialize.

The Safeguard system is a building block for peace because it meets the following requirements:

1. It clearly rejects a provocative expansion into a heavy defense of our cities against a Soviet attack.
2. It offers more protection, as needed, to our deterrent forces.

3. It offers protection, as needed, of the entire country, from a small attack.

4. It offers the Soviet Union added incentive for productive arms control talks.

5. It provides the protection needed for the safety and security of our country—but *only the protection needed*.

In summary I want to say that my technical advisers are convinced and have convinced me that this limited ballistic missile defense is feasible. Mr. Packard, the Service Secretaries, the Joint Chiefs of Staff and I agree, unanimously, that the recommended program will be adequate, will be timely and will be the appropriate counter to the threat. We recommended the Safeguard program to the President and we recommend it unanimously to you.

# SOME EFFECTS OF
# NUCLEAR WEAPONS

IN THE DETONATION of a conventional explosive such as TNT there is a sudden liberation of energy that creates hot compressed gases. These gases initiate a shock wave in the surrounding medium—air, water or earth—and it is this shock wave that causes the damage.

Nuclear explosions can cause destruction by shock (also called "blast," in some circumstances), but they also produce several other important effects. For one, they release a large portion of their energy in the form of electromagnetic radiation, manifesting itself as heat, light and X-rays. This energy, as we shall see, can start fires and cause serious skin burns at great distances when multimegaton nuclear weapons are exploded in the upper atmosphere. Nuclear explosions also yield an initial nuclear radiation that can heat materials greatly, destroy living things, incapacitate electronic equipment and intensely ionize the gases of the surrounding atmosphere.

When a nuclear weapon explodes, its residues and the nearby air attain extremely high temperatures—of the order of several tens of millions of degrees. These extremely hot materials radiate large amounts of energy, leading to the formation of a hot, brilliant, rapidly expanding sphere of air known as the fireball. Accompanying the explosion and the gaseous ionization is an extremely strong electromagnetic pulse which could damage or immobilize electronic and electrical equipment and possibly create false signals in computers and in control and communication systems.[1]

But this is not all. The materials remaining after a nuclear explosion are radioactive, and they emit radiation for a long

[1] Much of this description is taken from "The Effects of Nuclear Weapons," United States Atomic Energy Commission, 1962.

time. When this mixes with material thrown up by a nuclear explosion on the earth's surface, radioactive clouds form and create a fallout hazard for people who happen to be downwind.

Because of the many effects that accompany nuclear explosions, there is widespread confusion regarding the use of nuclear weapons. This confusion is particularly acute when one hopes to use them to defend against enemy missiles and must simultaneously consider factors such as weapons effects, yield, the amount of fission products and the distribution of the explosive energy between X-rays, neutrons, and so on. The problem is further complicated by the fact that it is possible to design a nuclear weapon so as to create a desired effect, such as the creation of shock waves, the production of radioactive fallout, the output of thermal energy or of neutrons.

Our objective here is to consider primarily the effects of nuclear attacks upon soft, unprotected targets such as urban areas, bomber bases or radar equipment, though we shall also examine briefly the requirements for destroying hardened targets such as the Minuteman silos.

## Soft Targets: Attacks Upon Cities

Cities are vulnerable to nuclear weapons in several ways. Their structures can be destroyed or damaged by blast, fire or a combination of the two. Their inhabitants may experience blast, burns, radiation and suffocation due to the effects of fires. Fire, which appears to be a major hazard—possibly the biggest danger—is rarely treated adequately in analyses of the effects of nuclear weapons. For example, the question seems to have been ignored in the preparation of Secretary McNamara's much quoted 1968 Posture Statement before the Senate Armed Services Committee, in which he claimed that a Sentinel ABM system with extra terminal defense would reduce U.S. fatalities—from 120 down to 40 million—in the event the U.S.S.R. struck first. We will see that against high-altitude attacks using very large weapons, the Sentinel system (and its current descendants) will most likely provide no protection whatsoever.

The Soviet Union is estimated to have deployed a large number (approximately 230 by 1969) of SS-9 missiles.

Secretary Laird has stated that an SS-9 can deliver a 20–25 megaton weapon, or several 5-megaton weapons, against an unprotected target like a city. For large, soft targets, one 10-megaton weapon is roughly comparable in destructive effects to six 1-megaton weapons.

There is no really solid information on the payload of the Chinese ICBM; in fact, the best guess is that a Chinese ICBM probably doesn't exist, even in a test model. However, it would be almost as easy for the Chinese to develop and build a large missile capable of carrying multimegaton weapons as to build one with a lesser payload capacity. Thus, until we learn to the contrary, we should assume that Chinese ICBMs will be capable of delivering large payloads, either in the form of large weapons or as a mixture of weapons and penetration aids.

In an attack upon a soft, dispersed target, maximum total destruction is achieved when the nuclear weapon is detonated some distance above the target in an airburst; the airburst's range of destruction is substantially greater than if the weapon were exploded on the ground. The best altitude for the explosion will depend primarily upon the yield of the nuclear weapon and the characteristics of the target; the larger the weapon, the higher will be the best height for an airburst. For a given weapon, as the height of the explosion is increased, the blast overpressure and the heat on the ground will vary, getting less intense directly below the explosion but extending over a larger area. The optimum altitude will be reached when the largest possible area is exposed to the minimum blast and thermal conditions required to destroy the targets within it. An airburst at optimum altitude produces much less radioactive fallout than would result from a ground-level explosion of the same weapon. Some effects of large nuclear weapons are given in Table 1.

The AEC publication "Effects of Nuclear Explosions" states that overpressures of six pounds per square inch (psi) in the shock wave will totally destroy ordinary structures, and overpressures from 10–25 psi will completely destroy reinforced concrete structures. Four psi overpressure is adequate to destroy aircraft parked in the open.

### The Faulty Shield: Foiling the ABM

ABM systems such as the Sentinel use a Sprint-type close-in defense to cope with heavy attacks on cities. An attacker trying to penetrate such a system could use a combination of heavy decoys and multiple warheads to saturate and overwhelm the system, for there is clearly an attack level at which such a strategy will work. The advocates of the Sentinel system have said that the system will be 90 to 95 percent effective. If this is correct, then one incoming object in 10 or 20 would get through to the target, which means that it would take only a modest number of SS-9 missiles carrying multiple warheads and heavy decoys to penetrate such a defense. Two hundred SS-9 missiles could carry several thousand low-megaton weapons and heavy decoys so that even if the system worked, several hundred warheads would probably penetrate the defense in a massive Soviet attack.

Even so, a Soviet military planner who is trying to get at American cities defended by a Sentinel/Safeguard–type of ABM has an option: He can bypass it. He can either make his weapons hit outside the defended area and depend upon the resulting radioactive fallout to produce casualties, or, if he has very large nuclear weapons, he can explode them above the maximum altitude at which the ABM is effective. Schreiber and Mason[2] have studied these modes of attack and concluded that for weapons of the size useful against city targets, the fire effect is much larger than the blast effect or the fallout effect. The larger the bomb, the greater the fire effect is, and when very large weapons (20 to 30 megatons) are exploded above the Sentinel's reach, the fire and blast can be much more disastrous than the fallout. For a 30-megaton bomb, the blast effects become unimportant if the explosion occurs above approximately 10 miles, but the incinerated area continues to increase with increasing height of burst up to approximately 20 miles and remains a serious problem up to altitudes of 40 to 50 miles. The success of fire attacks depends on the weather, but the weather is usually good enough for such attacks.

Thermal radiation of the order of 12 calories/$cm^2$ will cause third-degree burns on exposed skin and ignite a very large number of fires in exposed urban areas. At this or somewhat higher levels of thermal radiation the fires could be expected to be so numerous that the conflagration, combined with some blast damage, would make it extremely difficult for people to flee the city. Thus, there would be few survivors.

[2] Samuel J. Mason and William F. Schreiber, "Fire and Fallout: The Effects of Clean Nuclear Weapons," statement before the House Armed Services Committee, June 24, 1963.

# Table 1. Comparative Effects of Large Nuclear Weapons

| Blast Effects | Fire Effects (on a clear day) |
|---|---|

## A 10-megaton groundburst would

| | |
|---|---|
| 1. Dig a crater 500 feet deep and almost ¾ mile wide (2,100 feet, not including the crater lip). | 1. Cause second-degree (blistering) burns out to 23½ miles from the explosion. |
| 2. Completely destroy ordinary structures, such as homes, out to a distance of 6 miles from the explosions and cause minor damage, such as window breaking, out to 15½ miles. | 2. Cause most fabrics and paper (such as cotton and newspaper) to burst into flame out to 14½ miles. |
| 3 Create winds sufficient to hurl objects through the air at speeds endangering life 9 miles out. At this distance, people in the open could be hurled through the air at lethal speeds. | 3. Ignite dry leaves out to 24 miles. |

## A 10-megaton airburst, exploded at a height to achieve maximum destruction, would

| | |
|---|---|
| Extend the area of complete destruction of brick houses to 8 miles, of minor damage to 26½ miles and of dangerously high winds to 14 miles. | Cause second-degree burns out to 26½ miles, ignite most fabrics and paper out to 17½ miles and ignite dry leaves out to 28 miles. |

## A 1-megaton groundburst would

1. Dig a crater 230 feet deep and 950 feet wide (not including the crater lip).
2. Completely destroy ordinary structures out to 2.7 miles from the explosion and cause minor damage out to 7.2 miles.
3. Create winds sufficient to hurl objects (and even people) through the air at lethal speeds out to 4 miles.

1. Cause second-degree burns out to 9.4 miles.
2. Cause most fabrics and paper to burst into flame out to 5.6 miles.
3. Ignite dry leaves out to 9½ miles.

## A 1-megaton airburst, exploded at a height to achieve maximum destruction, would

Cause complete destruction of brick houses out to 3½ miles, minor damage out to 13 miles and dangerously high winds out to 6½ miles.

Cause second-degree burns out to 11 miles, ignite most fabrics and paper out to 6 miles and ignite dry leaves out to 11½ miles.

—from AEC, *Effects of Nuclear Weapons* (1964)

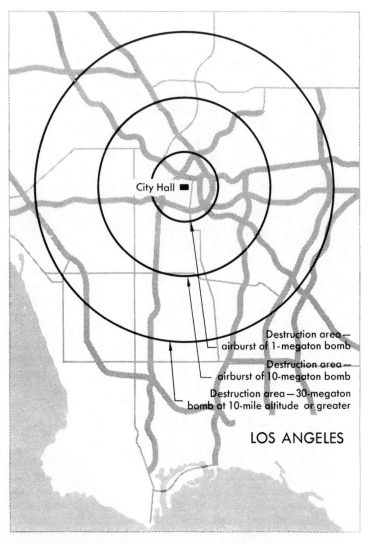

City Hall ■

Destruction area —
airburst of 1-megaton bomb

Destruction area —
airburst of 10-megaton bomb

Destruction area — 30-megaton
bomb at 10-mile altitude or greater

LOS ANGELES

The circles superimposed on a map of Los Angeles show the potential damage from an airburst attack using 1-megaton and 10-megaton nuclear weapons and the destruction from a 30-megaton warhead exploded at a very high altitude. (Courtesy *Scientific American*)

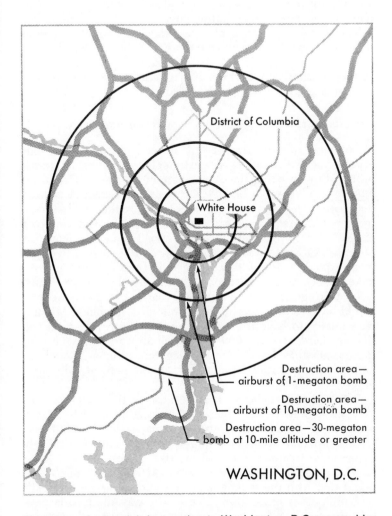

The areas of potential destruction to Washington, D.C., caused by the airburst of 1-megaton and 10-megaton nuclear weapons and by the very high altitude explosion of a 30-megaton warhead are shown by the circles superimposed on a map of the capital. (Courtesy *Scientific American*)

Experience in World War II in both atomic and fire bomb attacks indicates a negligible survival rate among persons who remain in areas which are burned over.

The preceding maps of Los Angeles and Washington show the circle within which there will be serious damage from optimum-altitude airburst attacks using 1-megaton and 10-megaton weapons and the effective radius of a 30-megaton weapon exploded at very high altitude.

### Attacks on Hardened Targets: Accuracy Required

Minutemen missiles are stored in concrete-and-steel silos capable of withstanding an extremely severe shock transmitted through either the atmosphere or the earth. The siloed missiles are known to be able to take shock waves of at least 300 pounds per square inch, which means they will survive the shock created by a large nuclear weapon unless the point of explosion is relatively near the silo. Deputy Secretary of Defense Packard has testified that a 20-megaton weapon must explode within 0.6–0.8 of a mile from a Minuteman to have an 80 percent chance of destroying the missile. Thus, using this figure, one can calculate that a 1-megaton weapon would have to hit within 0.2–0.3 mile of a hardened Minuteman missile to have the same chance of destroying it. If the silo was hardened to 1,000 psi, which appears to be feasible, the permissible error for a 1-megaton weapon would be approximately 0.15–0.2 miles for an 80 percent kill probability.

It is generally believed that because of the extreme accuracy needed to destroy hardened missile sites with MIRVs using 1- or 2-megaton weapons, a major development and testing program would be required before a nation could rely upon such weapons for a first-strike attack. In analyzing attacks on such hard targets using MIRVs and SS-9s, we found that with the same guidance accuracy the resulting kill probability was quite insensitive to the way the missile payload was used. A few large weapons or many small weapons have roughly the same effectiveness over the range explored.

### Achilles' Heel: The Vulnerable Radars

The ABM depends on radar, and this raises the question of how its radar will survive attack by nuclear weapons. Among the many deficiencies of the Nike-Zeus system was the extreme softness of its radars. They could have been knocked out by a 2 psi overpressure. This meant that as part of a hardpoint defense, that radar system would be much more vulnerable than the target it was attempting to defend, a somewhat absurd situation. In the design of the Sentinel/Safeguard system, the radars that scanned the skies mechanically—with exposed antennae—were replaced by radars that scan electronically and have no exposed moving parts. The resistance of these new radars to nuclear blast and thermal effects depends on the hardness of their protective cover. But this cover must be transparent to electromagnetic waves, and so there are severe limitations on the degree to which these radars can be made blast resistant. While the exact hardness of the Sentinel/Safeguard system has not been made public, it is known that heavy concrete structures will be damaged by 20–30 psi overpressure, and it is reasonable to assume that the radars are at least this vulnerable. This means that in the case of a Minuteman defense, radars able to withstand 20 psi overpressure, or possibly less, are vital elements of a system protecting targets able to withstand overpressures of 300 psi or greater. Thus the radar again becomes the most attractive target in the complex.

# TECHNICAL NOTES

## 1. Some Useful Numbers

1 kiloton of TNT $\equiv 10^{12}$ calories $\equiv$ energy released by complete fission of 56 grams of fissionable material

1 nautical mile = 1.1516 miles = 1.853 km

Velocity of satellite in low circular orbit $= v_0 = 4.26$ nautical miles/sec

Radius of earth: R = 3,440 nautical miles

The density of the atmosphere drops a factor $e = 2.718$ for every 4 nautical miles altitude up to 80 n.m.

## 2. Ballistic Missile Trajectories

Consider missile in empty space; neglect earth's rotation and oblateness.

### General Ballistic Orbits

Define:

$\quad$ d $\equiv$ distance along earth's surface from launch to target

$\quad$ s $\equiv$ distance along earth's surface from launch to point under missile

$\quad$ e $\equiv$ eccentricity of elliptical missile orbit (ratio of minor to major axis)

$\quad$ R $\equiv$ radius of earth $\equiv$ 3,440 nautical miles

$$\phi \equiv (s - \frac{d}{2})/R \qquad \phi_0 \equiv \frac{d}{2R} \qquad \text{(radians)}$$

$\quad v_0 \equiv$ velocity of earth satellites in low orbits (FOBS)
$\quad\quad = 4.26$ nautical miles/sec

Then missile altitude is:

$$h(\phi) = eR\left(\frac{\cos \phi - \cos \phi_0}{1 - e \cos \phi}\right)$$

Time elapsed after mid-course:

$$t(\phi) = \left(\frac{R}{v_0}\right)(1 - e \cos \phi_0)^{3/2}$$

$$\left\{\frac{e \sin \phi}{(1 - e^2)(1 - e \cos \phi)} + \frac{2 \tan^{-1}\left[\frac{(1 + e)}{\sqrt{1 - e^2}} \tan\left(\frac{\phi}{2}\right)\right]}{(1 - e^2)^{3/2}}\right\}$$

[Before mid-course, $\phi$ and $t(\phi)$ are negative.]

Total time from launch to target:

$$T = 2t(\phi_0)$$

Time left before impact:

$$t^*(\phi) = \frac{T}{2} - t(\phi)$$

Horizontal and vertical components of missile velocity are:

$$v_H(\phi) = v_0 (1 - e \cos \phi_0)^{-\frac{1}{2}} (1 - e \cos \phi)$$

$$v_V(\phi) = -e v_0 (1 - e \cos \phi_0)^{-\frac{1}{2}} \sin \phi$$

Missile speed is:

$$v(\phi) \equiv (v_H^2 + v_V^2)^{\frac{1}{2}} = v_0 \left(\frac{1 + e^2 - 2 e \cos \phi}{1 - e \cos \phi_0}\right)^{\frac{1}{2}}$$

NB: At mid-course set $\phi = 0$, at launch set $\phi = -\phi_0$, at target set $\phi = +\phi_0$

## PAR Acquisition

Assume a PAR is at target, and acquires missile when it rises over horizon. At acquisition $\phi$ is:

$$\phi_A = \phi_0 - 2 \tan^{-1} (e \sin \phi_0)$$

Set $\phi = \phi_A$ in above formulas for altitude, time, velocity, etc. Distance along ground from acquisition to impact is:

$$R(\phi_o - \phi_A) = 2R \tan^{-1} (e \sin \phi_o)$$

*Minimum Energy Trajectory*

Missile speed at launch is:

$$v(\phi_o) = v_o \left( \frac{1 + e^2 - 2 e \cos \phi_o}{1 - e \cos \phi_o} \right)^{\frac{1}{2}}$$

For fixed d and $\phi_o$, this is *minimum* for:

$$e = \frac{1 - \sin \phi_o}{\cos \phi_o}$$

NB:  angle between missile trajectory and ground at impact is:

$$\tan^{-1} \left( \frac{-v_V(\phi_o)}{v_H(\phi_o)} \right) = \tan^{-1} e = 45° - \frac{\phi}{2}$$

*FOBS trajectory*

A FOBS missile travels in circle ($e = 0$) at constant altitude h with constant velocity:

$$v(h) = v_o \left( 1 + \frac{h}{R} \right)^{-\frac{1}{2}}$$

PAR acquires when distance along ground from point under missile to PAR is:

$$s^*(h) = R \cos^{-1} \left( \frac{R}{R + h} \right)$$

Time from acquisition to arrival at PAR is

$$t^*(h) = \left( \frac{R}{v_o} \right) \left( 1 + \frac{h}{R} \right)^{3/2} \cos^{-1} \left( \frac{R}{R + h} \right)$$

## 3. Payload Ratios

Consider missile undergoing rapid acceleration; neglect air resistance. Ignore weight of vehicle except for fuel and payload. Define:

$v_E \equiv$ effective exhaust velocity ("specific impulse" times 32 ft/sec$^2$)

$v_M \equiv$ velocity of missile after end of acceleration

Then payload ratio (ratio of payload weight to fuel plus payload weight) is:

$$P = e^{-v_M/v_E}$$

If $v_E = 1$ nautical mile/sec, then $P = 0.014$ for FOBS, $P = 0.020$ for 6,000 nautical-mile minimum-energy trajectory.

## 4. Nuclear Weapons Scaling Laws

*Blast:* For a nuclear weapon of yield Y exploding in air with uniform ambient pressure $P_A$ and density $\rho_A$, define units of length and time as:

$$a_0 \equiv Y^{1/3} P_A^{-1/3} \qquad t_0 \equiv P_A^{-5/6} \rho_A^{1/2} Y^{1/3}$$

Then the overpressure (expressed in units of $P_A$) is a universal function of time (in units of $t_0$) and positions (in units of $a_0$).

*Thermal Power:* Rate of emission of thermal energy = function of $t/Y^{1/2}$ times $Y^{1/2}$. (Total thermal energy proportional to Y.)

## 5. Hard-Point Kill Probabilities

Let d be the distance at which a 1 MT explosion will destroy a particular hard-point target. Then the probability it will be destroyed by a missile with given C.E.P. and yield Y MT is:

$$P = 1 - 2^{-d^2/a^2}$$

with

$$a = \text{C.E.P.}/Y^{1/3}$$

# ACKNOWLEDGMENTS

We owe many individuals large debts of gratitude for their work in helping us assemble this report. Chief among them, of course, are those who contributed the actual papers that make up part of the report, and did so freely, on almost impossibly short notice. We thank them for the light they shed on the ABM debate, and for adding the weight of their knowledge and experience to the final document.

Two additional individuals made substantial contributions. K. Dun Gifford, Legislative Assistant to Senator Kennedy, helped us assemble the necessary background materials and kept us apprised of the contours of the ABM debate in the Congress. John Jay Iselin of Harper & Row was a constructive critic and willing hand as we translated the papers and overview into a report.

A number of our colleagues lent their invaluable expertise and advice. These include Joel Orlen, Professor George Kistiakowsky, Professor Paul Doty, Professor I. I. Rabi and Professor Irwin Shapiro. James Egleson of *Scientific American* deserves our thanks for assembling the various charts and diagrams.

Finally, we must pay tribute to the skills of those who maintained order amidst seeming disorder: Jane Lakes, Ann Tevepaugh, Loretta Cubberley, Clair Charles, Linda McGrew, Lesley Krauss, Barbara Wollan, Frances Lindley and Peter Mollman.

THE EDITORS